EAT UP
SLIM DOWN

ANNUAL
RECIPES
2008

In all Rodale cookbooks, our mission is to provide delicious and nutritious recipes. Our recipes also meet the standards of the Rodale Test Kitchen for dependability, ease, practicality, and, most of all, great taste. To give us your comments, call (800) 848-4735.

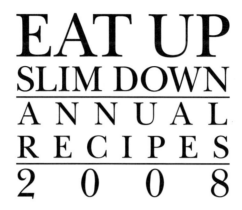

EAT UP
SLIM DOWN
ANNUAL
RECIPES
2 0 0 8

**150 Simply Delicious Recipes
for Permanent Weight Loss**

RODALE

© 2007 by Rodale Inc.

Printed in the United States of America
Rodale Inc. makes every effort to use acid-free ∞, recycled paper ♻.

Book design by Kristen Morgan Downey
Interior and cover photography credits are on page 349.
Front cover photo: Chocolate Cupcakes with Butterscotch Frosting (page 258)

ISBN-13 978–1–59486–751–4
ISBN-10 1–59486–751–8

2 4 6 8 10 9 7 5 3 1 hardcover

We inspire and enable people to improve their lives and the world around them
For more of our products visit **rodalestore.com** or call 800-848-4735

Contents

Special Thanks

In grateful appreciation to all the supporters and sponsors of the *Eat Up Slim Down Recipe* Sweepstakes, we would like to thank . . .

The companies that so generously provided the terrific prizes for the sweepstakes:
Capresso, William Bounds, Component Design Northwest (CDN), Hearthware Home Products, and Frieling.

The product representatives who were so generous with their time and talents:
ACH Food Companies, FIFTY 50 Foods, Frieda's, General Mills, Glory Foods, Gnu Foods, Goya Food, Kettle Foods, Kraft Foods, McCormick & Company, OXO International, R.A.B. Food Group, Weber-Stephen Products Company.

And sincere, heartfelt thanks . . .
. . . to all the readers of www.eatupslimdown.com and www.prevention.com who were kind enough to share their delicious recipes, clever tips, and inspiring stories of weight-loss success for this book. We salute you and wish you continued success.

. . . to the six weight-loss winners who shared their stories of success with us in personal profiles: Barbara Dolan, Marni Halasa, Sharon Hildebrandt, Michele James-Williams, Terri Stewart, and Janet Utz.

Acknowledgments

A very special thank you to everyone who had a hand in creating *Eat Up Slim Down Annual Recipes 2008*.

Carol Angstadt
JoAnn Brader
Chris Detris
Kristen Morgan Downey
Marilyn Hauptly
Jan Latshaw
Mitch Mandel
Joan Parkin
Stacy Petrovich
Sharon Sanders
Pam Simpson
Julia VanTine-Reichardt
Diane Vezza
Lauren Zehnder
Shea Zukowski

Contributors

This book is a compilation of the delicious and creative recipes sent to us by weight-loss winners across the United States and even beyond. The number of recipes we received was so great, it was a difficult task choosing 150. But after a careful selection process, we managed to whittle it down. Here are this year's recipe contributors. We salute their innovative efforts in the kitchen and hope you'll enjoy eating up and slimming down with their recipes!

Introduction

The wait is over! The seventh edition of *Eat Up Slim Down*, the weight-loss cookbook created by you, the readers, is here.

We're really excited to share this year's compendium—the biggest ever, at 347 pages! Throughout the years, as our readers have lost pounds, they've gained a community of like-minded friends who support them in their weight loss and, even more important, assist them in maintaining the healthy weight they have achieved.

As always, this year's *Eat Up Slim Down* serves up a sampler of essential information, recipes, tips, strategies, photographs—all the tools you need to transform yourself in the months ahead. You'll find . . .

- Summaries of the latest scientific findings in the field of diet research

- More than 150 fabulous recipes from *Eat Up Slim Down* contributors across the United States and Canada

- Recipe analyses listing calories, protein, carbohydrate, fat, cholesterol, sodium, fiber, Diet Exchanges, and Carb Choices so that you, along with your physician or nutritionist, can decide on the most balanced nutrient intake for your personal weight loss program

- Delectable full-color photographs of the recipes, which look as good as they taste

- Dozens of weight-loss tips and strategies

- Inspirational "It Worked for Me!" profiles—with "before" and "after" photographs of successful dieters

- A "Shopping Savvy Guide" that's a must-read before you enter the supermarket

- New healthy weight-loss food products that you'll want to stock in your pantry

- An authoritative 58-page "Calorie and Nutrients Chart of Common Foods" that you'll refer to again and again

- "Menus for Special Times" because dieting does *not* have to mean deprivation

So, if you're already a member of the *Eat Up Slim Down* community, welcome back. We've kept your seat at the table. If you're new to the group, pull up a chair. We've set a place for you, too.

Countdown to a New, Slimmer You

This is the year you finally lose those extra pounds, and you have it all figured out. You will consume nothing but boiled eggs, cottage cheese, and apples. You will walk on the treadmill 1 hour a day, 6 days a week. And as God is your witness, chocolate—be it in the form of a cake, bar, or kiss—will never pass your lips again.

Sounds like a plan, all right—for failure. Any diet that severely restricts the variety of whole foods you can eat is not a diet that develops long-term healthy eating habits. Likewise, any commitment to exercise has to fit in realistically with the rest of your daily activities for lifetime success. And, finally, if chocolate is your preferred indulgence, not only is it highly unlikely you will

be able to give it up completely, you shouldn't have to!

Take heart. By counting—literally—on the weight-loss strategy that follows, you will not only lose weight but know how to keep the weight off for the rest of your life.

To help you make the small but significant changes that lead to lasting weight loss, we've created a simple—yet powerful—10-step strategy. Each step is backed by sound science, and, in combination, they can add up to lasting weight loss.

But do yourself a favor and take baby steps. "Start with the easiest step. Once you master it, move on," says John Jakicic, PhD, director of weight management at the University of Pittsburgh.

1. Step on the scale 1 time per day.

Why to try it: Weekly weigh-ins are a staple of many popular diet programs, but studies now show that daily weighing is the key to lasting loss. When researchers at the University of Minnesota monitored the scale habits of 1,800 dieting adults, they found that those who stepped on the scale every day lost an average of 12 pounds over 2 years (weekly scale watchers lost only 6) and were less likely to regain lost weight. The reason: "The more often you monitor your results, the quicker you can catch the behavioral slip that causes weight gain," says Dr. Jakicic.

Who counted on it: Heidi Hurst of Los Angeles. "I was in denial about my size, so I never used a scale. When I started weighing daily, I lost 7 pounds in 2 weeks. I loved the immediate gratification and eventually lost 77 pounds."

Count yourself in: Step on the scale first thing every morning, when you weigh the least. Expect small day-to-day fluctuations because of bloating or dehydration, but if your weight creeps up by 2 percent (that's just 3 pounds if you weigh 150), it's time to pass up the second helpings.

2. Channel-surf no more than 2 hours a day.

Why to try it: TV junkies miss out on calorie-burning activities like backyard tag with the kids; instead, they become sitting ducks for junk-food commercials. One recent study found that adults who watch more than 2 hours of TV per day take in 7 percent more calories and consume more sugary snacks than those who watch less than an hour a day.

Who counted on it: Christy Taylor of Sylacauga, Alabama. "TV was one reason I weighed 220 pounds. I watched it constantly. My blood pressure skyrocketed during pregnancy, and when it didn't come down after my son was born, I decided to try to limit myself to one show a day. That was 10 months ago, and I've since lost 32 pounds."

Count yourself in: Wean yourself off the tube by introducing other activities into your life. Eliminate the temptation to watch between-show filler by recording your must-see programs so you can fast-forward through the ads. Or subscribe to a mail-order DVD service for commercial-free entertainment.

3. Connect with a friend 3 times per week.

Why to try it: "Long-term weight loss requires support," says Marion Franz, RD, a nutrition consultant in Minneapolis. Her study review found that people who meet regularly with a dietitian or attend groups like Weight Watchers are more likely to maintain their losses than those who don't.

GIVE YOUR DIET A WINTER VACATION

New Year's Eve has come and gone, but those holiday pounds are still hanging around—and you're panicking. The best advice: Give yourself a break, eat healthfully—and wait out winter weight.

The issue: Your brain isn't ready to emerge from hibernation just yet. That's because serotonin, a feel-good brain chemical that acts as a brake on hunger, is at a low point during the winter, says Howard Steiger, PhD, director of the Douglas Eating Disorders Program at McGill University in Montreal. "Dieting midwinter is like holding your breath," says Dr. Steiger. "You can do it for a short time; then you overcompensate." And for bingers, whose serotonin levels are already subpar, winter months are a double whammy.

Dr. Steiger suggests a saner approach: Give yourself permission to experience seasonal weight changes. Here's how to get a handle on them.

- Return to preholiday healthy eating, instead of making drastic changes that guarantee failure.

- Don't ban entire food groups such as carbohydrates. That can create major nutrient shortages—and you're bound to binge. Instead, focus on whole grain carb choices whenever possible.

- Be alert to self-talk that may trigger overeating. Examples: "I starve all week, so I'm entitled to eat what I really want on the weekend." Or "I want a slice of pizza, but I'll force myself to eat a salad instead."

Who counted on it: Maggie Ramos of Houston. "When I plateaued for months, my friend Nancy stepped in and cheered me on until I lost it all."

Count yourself in: If you can't attend group meetings, announce your weight-loss intentions so friends can support you, says Franz. And add a dieter pal to your regular call or e-mail list, too.

4. Eat 4 grams of fiber in every meal or snack.

Why to try it: A diet that's high in fiber—the indigestible cellulose in plant foods—can lower your caloric intake and make you feel fuller for longer. In a recent Tufts University study, women who ate 13 grams of fiber or less per day were five times as

BE A GI JANE: THE SKINNY ON THE GLYCEMIC INDEX

When Jessica Seaberg of Minneapolis eliminated white bread and other refined carbohydrates from her diet, she lost 65 pounds. "Now, I stick to whole grain bread, slow-cooking brown rice, and whole wheat pasta," she says.

That's the power of eating low on the glycemic index—GI, for short. The GI assigns foods that contain carbohydrates a number based on how these foods affect blood sugar after they're eaten. Foods with a GI less than 55 cause only a blip in blood sugar; those in the 55-to-70 range raise it a bit higher; and carbs with GIs higher than 70 cause blood sugar to soar. Studies have found that low-GI carbs are healthy, while high-GI carbs, eaten to excess, are not.

What's more, research suggests that a diet rich in low-GI carbs, which includes healthy fats like olive oil, almonds, and fish but few foods made with white flour and sugar, may encourage weight loss and help keep metabolism revving.

In a study conducted at Children's Hospital Boston and Brigham and Women's Hospital in Boston, researchers tracked 39 dieters ages 18 to 40 until they'd lost 20 pounds each. The dieters followed either a low-GI or a low-fat plan, but both allowed 1,500 calories a day. The low-GI group lost the weight slightly faster than the low-fat group. However, the low-GI dieters burned about 80 more calories daily.

To "go low," swap white foods—white bread, white potatoes, white pasta—for Crayola-hued fruits and veggies. Healthy swaps include a baked sweet potato (48 on the GI) instead of a russet potato (94); grapes (49) instead of dates (103); brown rice (55) instead of short-grain white rice (91); dried apricots (31) instead of jelly beans (80). And skip the liquid glucose known as juice.

likely to be overweight as those who ate more fiber. Experts see a number of mechanisms through which fiber promotes weight loss: It may slow down eating because it requires more chewing; it speeds the passage of food through the digestive tract; and, finally, it boosts satiety hormones.

Who counted on it: Monique Hester of North Richland Hills, Texas. "I started a diet that had me consuming more than 25 grams of fiber daily, and before I knew it,

I'd lost 23 pounds. I don't even like white bread anymore. I want something I can crunch and chew."

Count yourself in: To get 25 grams of fiber a day, make sure you eat six meals or snacks, each of which contains about 4 grams of fiber. For instance, Hester started her day with grapes (1 cup = 1.4 grams of fiber) and cracked wheat toast (2 slices = 6 grams) or oatmeal (1 cup = 4 grams). She often had black bean soup for lunch (1 cup = 4.4 grams) with a slice of cracked wheat bread (1 slice = 3 grams). One good trick: For to-go snacks, buy fruit; it's handier than vegetables, so it's an enjoyable way to up your fiber intake. For instance, one large apple has just as much fiber (5 grams) as 1 cup of raw broccoli.

5. Take 5 (thousand) extra steps a day.

Why to try it: A typical person takes about 5,000 steps per day by going to work, running errands, and doing chores around the house. Doubling that number can have significant health benefits: higher "good" HDL cholesterol levels, lower blood pressure, improved glucose control, and, yes, a lower number on the scale. Walking more steps per day also leads to a lower percentage of body fat and slimmer waists and hips, reports a recent University of Tennessee study of 80 women. An earlier University of South Carolina study of 109 people showed that those who took fewer than 5,000 steps per day were, on average, heavier than people who took more than 9,000.

Who counted on it: Joanna Webb of Queen Creek, Arizona. "I started walking when my daughter was 2 months old. I couldn't even make it around the block without stopping. I kept at it until I could walk 6 nights a week with my husband, our 5-year-old, and the baby. Now I've lost 35 pounds."

Count yourself in: Wear a pedometer to actually *see* the accomplishment of logging your 5,000 extra steps, or aim for about 50 extra minutes of walking (2½ miles) per day. In the Tennessee study, "some of the women walked with friends; others increased their steps by taking the stairs and parking farther away," says lead researcher Dixie Thompson, PhD.

CAN FAKE SUGAR MAKE YOU FAT?

The weight-conscious among us want to have our cake and eat it, too. And with the flood of products made with nonsugar sweeteners on the market, we are. Americans spent an estimated $8.8 billion on low-sugar products in 2005, many of them sweetened with additives such as sucralose (Splenda), aspartame (NutraSweet and Equal), or saccharin (Sweet'n Low). How sweet it is!

Not so fast. Preliminary research into nonsugar sweeteners suggests that they may actually ramp up your appetite, especially if consumed in beverages. A 2004 Purdue University study found that rats that drank liquids artificially sweetened with saccharin ate more food than those that had been fed sugar-sweetened liquids. Humans who chug sodas with these sweeteners may react by overeating, too: Your risk of being overweight rises 65 percent for every diet soda you down each day, according to a study presented in June 2005 at the American Diabetes Association meeting.

If you like cakes and cookies, Splenda—the additive that's best at retaining its sweetness during baking—makes it possible to create reduced-calorie desserts. "I use a mix of sugar and Splenda when I bake—I don't notice a difference at all," says Leigh-Anne Kent, a financial analyst in Denver.

If you have too much of a sweet tooth, however, you're better off limiting these products—or avoiding them completely. "Dieters turn to artificial sweeteners as a way to stem their sugar cravings, but they just make things worse," says Ann Zulze, MD, a physician in Charleston, South Carolina, and author of *Dr. Ann's 10-Step Diet.* "They drink a Diet Coke, and minutes later they're craving cookies. Once they cut out sugar substitutes, those yearnings drop."

Bottom line? You're better off dumping 1 teaspoon of sugar (only 16 calories) rather than a sugar substitute into your coffee. Why? Artificial sweeteners may make you feel extra hungry and fool your body into thinking sweet foods have fewer calories, so you unconsciously munch on more of them, says Sharon Fowler, MPH, a faculty associate in the division of clinical epidemiology at the University of Texas Health Science Center at San Antonio. So go ahead, have the real thing. Just have a little—and enjoy it a lot.

6. Jot down every morsel 6 days per week.

Why to try it: "Monitoring your eating and exercise every day will let you know if you're reaching the 500-calorie daily deficit you need to lose about a pound a week," says Robert Carels, PhD, a psychology professor at Bowling Green State University. His study of 40 obese adults found that those who recorded their food and exercise over 6 months lost more than 20 pounds. That was nearly twice the amount shed by less consistent note takers.

Who counted on it: Julie Fugett of Lawrence, Kansas. "Journaling was an important part of my program. I chronicled food intake using the Weight Watchers POINTS system and also printed out a monthly calendar to schedule workouts in advance. I'd mark each successful day of exercise with a purple smiley face, and eventually those stick-on grins added up to a 25-pound weight loss that I've maintained for over 2 years."

Count yourself in: Carry a small notebook or PDA to record what you eat, and use a pedometer to estimate the calories you burn. Although you should try to keep a daily log, it's realistic to give yourself a break 1 day a week and allow time off for holidays and houseguests. "Then get back on track," says Dr. Carels.

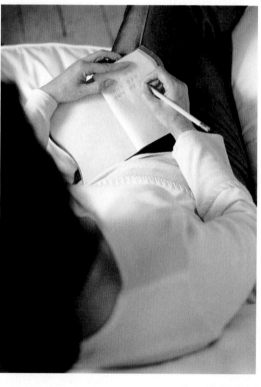

7. Get at least 7 hours of pillow time a night.

Why to try it: A University of Chicago study found that people deprived of z's had lower levels of the hormones that control appetite. "The research suggested that short sleep durations could be a risk factor for obesity," says James Gangwisch, PhD, an epidemiologist from Columbia University Medical Center. Sure enough, his follow-up study of 9,588 Americans found that women who slept 4 hours or less per night were 234 percent more likely to be obese.

Who counted on it: Julia Havey of St. Louis. "I used to stay up late watching movies and eating ice cream. I'd have to wake up at 6:00 a.m., so I always felt exhausted and bloated. Now I make it a point to be in bed by 11:00 p.m. The extra sleep makes it easier for me to stick to my diet and exercise routine because I have more energy and fewer cravings."

Count yourself in: The key number for most people is 7 hours or more a night, says Dr. Gangwisch, so get a comfy down pillow and some soft new sheets. Soon, you'll be tucking yourself in early every night.

8. Down 8 glasses of water per day.

Why to try it: Water is not just a thirst quencher—it actually speeds the body's metabolism. Researchers in Germany found that drinking two 8-ounce glasses of cold water increased their subjects' metabolic rate by 30 percent, and the effect persisted for 90 minutes. One-third of the boost came from the body's efforts to warm the water, but the rest was due to the work the body did to

absorb it. "When drinking water, no calories are ingested, but calories are used, unlike when drinking sodas, where additional calories are ingested and possibly stored," explains lead researcher Michael Boschmann, MD, of University Medicine Berlin.

Who counted on it: Paige Tomas of Corpus Christi, Texas. "I used to have a five-can-a-day Dr Pepper addiction. To stop, I'd make myself drink a whole glass of water before allowing myself a soda, and now I'm down to just two Diet Dr Peppers a day."

Count yourself in: Increasing water consumption to eight glasses per day may help you lose about 8 pounds in a year, says Dr. Boschmann, so try drinking a glass before meals and snacks and before consuming sweetened drinks or juices.

9. Work no more than 9 hours (including lunch), then head for home.

Why to try it: A University of Helsinki study of 7,000 adults found that those who'd packed on pounds in the previous year were more likely to have logged overtime hours. Lack of time for diet and exercise is most likely the cause, but it's also possible that work stress has a direct effect on weight gain through changes in hormones like cortisol.

Who counted on it: Nicole Bruni of Milwaukee. "I gained about 35 pounds in my first year at my law firm, so I started making it a point to wrap up the day in time for a 6:00 p.m. Spinning class, and I've since lost 40 pounds."

Count yourself in: Set firm limits on your workday so that when you're done, you still have the oomph to take a bike ride and

DIVINE DIETS

Suspect it'll take a miracle to help you drop a few? Your prayers have been answered—sort of. Several religion-based diet books offer plans based on foods mentioned in the Bible or meals Jesus would have eaten. But are the plans healthy—and do they work? Here's the skinny on these weight-spirational programs, "reviewed" by nutrition expert Christine Gerbstadt, MD, RD, a spokesperson for the American Dietetic Association.

- *The Maker's Diet*, by Jordan S. Rubin, PhD, puts you on a 40-day plan based on unprocessed foods such as fruits, vegetables, and raw nuts. While Dr. Gerbstadt liked the variety of meals, she wasn't a fan of the partial fast every week. That could be dangerous for people with diabetes or those with heart risk—and makes binges more likely.

- *Divine Health*, edited by Don Colbert, MD, and his wife, Mary, uses New Testament passages to illustrate healthy eating, and it's peppered with sound nutrition tips and advice. Though it makes for a good Bible study, there are few recipes and no menus.

- Also by Colbert, *What Would Jesus Eat?* offers an approach similar to the Mediterranean diet—whole grains, lean meat, olive oil, and fresh fruits and vegetables. Although the recipes are appealing and the nutritional advice sound, you could quibble about historical accuracy: It recommends foods such as edamame, pineapple, and bok choy that Colbert insists Jesus would have liked. Still, Gerbstadt says, it's the soundest plan of the bunch.

broil fish for dinner. To help you stay productive enough to finish on time, set an hourly alarm; when it goes off, deal with your most pressing duties.

10. Count to 10 before you eat.

Why to try it: Because this time-honored tactic actually works. Ticking off the primary numbers before you open the

refrigerator or root through the pantry can give you the time you need to differentiate "need to eat" (which signals hunger) from "want to eat" (which can mask anger, sadness, or boredom). If you discover that you're not physically hungry, you can choose to do something else—whip out your knitting needles, take out the garbage, read five pages of the novel by your bed.

Who counted on it: Joanne Pekrul. When she was diagnosed with diabetes, she knew she had to lose weight. "I learned that a lot of times when I thought I was hungry, I was really eating for emotional reasons, for comfort," says Pekrul, who lost 17 pounds in a 12-week weight-management program. "I learned to recognize and respond appropriately to my emotions."

Count yourself in: Try Pekrul's trick: She follows a points system to help her identify when it's time to have something to eat. Her points scale goes from zero (famished) to 10 (completely stuffed). The goal is to stay between 3 and 7 at all times: 3 represents reasonable hunger and a good time to eat; 7 means comfortably full but not stuffed.

1 Day to a Faster Metabolism

If you're like most people, you know enough about metabolism to curse it when your jeans grow tight. That is, you know metabolism and body weight are connected. But what *is* metabolism exactly? And how does it influence the number on the scale?

In a nutshell, metabolism—which, in Greek, means "transformation"—is the process by which the body "transforms" food into energy. During this biochemical conversion, units of energy (calories) from every morsel you eat—grilled chicken or chocolate cake, sweet potato or pizza—combine with oxygen to release the vital energy your body needs to function.

Only problem is that when you consistently take in more calories than you require, your body goes into thrifting mode and tucks away the extras in convenient storage lockers called fat cells. That's when the needle on the scale climbs up, up, up. Although we'd all like to believe otherwise, weight gain is rarely caused by a faulty metabolism or an underactive thyroid.

Another culprit: aging. As you age, your body becomes less effective at burning calories, mostly because of a gradual decrease in activity and resulting loss of muscle. Your metabolism can dip as much as 25 to 30 percent over your adult life, says Miriam Nelson, PhD, director of the John Hancock Center for Physical Activity and Nutrition at Tufts University. As a result, your system tends to store excess calories in the form

METABOLISM 101

Your basal metabolic rate, or BMR, is the number of calories you expend to sustain life. In other words, the energy spent to keep the heart beating, the lungs expanding, or the body humming along at a toasty 98.6°F. You also expend energy when you move—walk, take a meeting at the office, ride your bike, dig in your garden—as well as when you sleep.

Both the conversion of food to energy and your body's use of that energy—your metabolism—play a key role in weight control. Extra calories in all forms—protein, fat, carbohydrates, and alcohol—add up to weight gain.

If your body has an excess of calories from any source, it rearranges them into stores of fat and carbohydrates, to be drawn upon between meals and overnight in between fuel deliveries. If you take in more energy than you burn, you gain weight as body fat.

But don't even think of skipping a meal in a bid to reduce calories. When you do, your metabolic thermostat shuts down to conserve energy, hurting rather than helping your weight-loss efforts.

of—you guessed it—body fat, and that extra weight only slows you down more.

You don't, however, have to resign yourself to a frumpy future. For most women, strength training can help boost metabolism by as much as 10 percent in 12 weeks by rebuilding muscle. You can increase it further by making small but targeted lifestyle changes. "Anything that energizes you—a good night's sleep, fresh air, sunlight, a healthy diet, regular exercise—ultimately helps drive metabolism," explains Dr. Nelson.

To revitalize your body's ability to burn as many as 200 to 300 more calories a day, we've created the All-Day Metabolism Makeover. By boosting efficiency and maximizing calorie burn, your metabolism will convert from meek to sleek. Start with even a few of these steps to experience your very own makeover in progress.

The All-Day Metabolism Makeover

Morning

Eat a 300- to 400-calorie breakfast. In the morning, your energy stores are depleted by as much as 80 percent from the night before. Without food, your body shifts into starvation mode, which means it begins to conserve energy and burn fewer calories. (In other words: Your metabolic rate takes a nosedive.) That may be why, in one study, breakfast skippers were $4\frac{1}{2}$ times more likely to be obese than breakfast eaters. For the benefits of weight loss and more sustained energy, include whole grain complex carbohydrates like oatmeal.

SWAP SNACKS FOR MEALS—AND LIGHTEN UP

Battling a midafternoon slump, you raid the vending machine for chips. An hour later, you pay it another visit, this time for cookies. Tomorrow, opt for foods that you associate with meals, such as a hard-cooked egg or a turkey-and-cheese roll-up. You may feel full longer, say scientists from the State University of New York at Buffalo.

Their study found that undergrads who called midafternoon treats "snacks" ate 87 percent more at dinner than those who ate the same foods but classified them as "meals." If you choose items that you think of as meals—real food rather than treats—they'll more likely satisfy your appetite, says lead researcher Elizabeth D. Capaldi, PhD.

Kathy McManus, RD, director of the nutrition department at Brigham and Women's Hospital in Boston, developed the healthy meal-for-snack swaps below at two calorie levels. If you normally eat three substantial meals and two snacks every day, choose a 150-calorie minimeal. If you typically spread your daily calories over 5 or 6 small meals, select one of the 250-calorie options.

150 calories	250 calories
Instead of this snack: 6 ounces fruited fat-free yogurt	Instead of this snack: energy or breakfast bar
Eat this "meal": ½ small whole wheat pita, 2 thin slices turkey breast, sliced tomato, mustard	Eat this "meal": 1 slice whole wheat toast, 1 scrambled egg, 2 slices turkey bacon
Instead of this snack: 1 ounce pretzels, ½ cup grapes	Instead of this snack: trail mix with chocolate chips, cashews, dried fruit
Eat this "meal": ½ whole wheat English muffin, 1 ounce reduced-fat mozzarella cheese, green bell pepper, tomato slices	Eat this "meal": whole wheat tortilla, slice of avocado, 2 slices chicken breast, tomato, lettuce, 1 tablespoon salsa

Add a cup of halved strawberries. Research suggests that getting enough vitamin C—75 milligrams a day—may be essential for optimal fat burning. The strawberries provide 90 milligrams.

Pop your multi. Antioxidant nutrients help protect mitochondria, tiny structures found in every cell, from damage. They're the microscopic fat-burning furnaces that convert food into fuel.

(continued on page 16)

SPOON UP A SLIMMER MIDDLE

Research shows that people who regularly breakfast on ready-to-eat cereal with fruit weigh less than either breakfast skippers or those who fuel up on fatty fare like eggs and bacon or bagels. But which brands of cereal stick to your ribs while helping to trim your hips? Look no farther than the cereals listed here. Besides being low in

WE TEST IT: HEALTHY CEREAL

	BEST FOR KIDS **EnviroKidz Organic Peanut Butter Panda Puffs**	**BEST FLAKES** **Organic Weetabix Crispy Flakes & Fiber**
Description	Certified organic corn puffs are lightly sweetened with cane juice and flavored with all-natural peanut butter.	From the makers of the famed Weetabix biscuits comes a tasty, organic whole grain cereal with crunchy flakes and bran strands.
Comments	One tester's son loved these so much at breakfast, he demanded another bowl for lunch. Parents liked the low sugar but wanted more fiber.	Flake lovers applauded the serving size, which is larger than most. "Kept me full and satisfied—and never went soggy," said a fan. Adding banana slices made it the perfect bowl of flakes.
Nutritional Lowdown *Calories and other nutritional content are for cereal without milk*	Serving size: ¾ c; 130 cal, 3 g pro, 24 g carb, 2.5 g fat, 0 g sat fat, 0 mg chol, 2 g fiber, 140 mg sodium, 7 g sugar	Serving size: 1¼ c; 170 cal, 6 g pro, 44 g carb, 1.5 g fat, 0 g sat fat, 0 mg chol, 11 g fiber, 320 mg sodium, 10 g sugar
Price and Where to Buy	$4 per 10.6 oz box; grocery stores and natural food stores	$4.33 per 12 oz box; grocery stores and natural food stores

calories (200 or below per serving), they're also a good source of protein, a stick-to-your-ribs ingredient that, along with the cereal's fiber, helps you make it to lunch without scarfing a midmorning doughnut.

BEST HOT	BEST LOW-CALORIE
Arrowhead Mills Organic 4 Grain Plus Flax Hot Cereal	**South Beach Diet Whole Grain Crunch**
This hearty hot cereal, with a mix of cracked wheat, steel-cut oats, rye, and barley grits, also contains a boost of flax.	Whole grain flakes, ridged chips, puffed wheat, and almonds combine for a crunchy, nutty low-carb cereal.
Testers recommended getting creative with this simple oatmeal: Add blueberries or bananas, spice it up with nutmeg or cinnamon, or give it a nutty omega-3 blast with walnuts.	"Almonds add a rich, sweet flavor," said one South Beach cereal lover. Testers raved about the variety of textures that came in a low-cal bowlful.
Serving size: 1 packet (about 1/3 c dry); 140 cal, 5 g pro, 24 g carb, 3 g fat, 0.5 g fat, 0 mg chol, 4 g fiber, 70 mg sodium, 4 g sugar	Serving size: 3/4 c; 110 cal, 4 g pro, 21 g carb, 2.5 g fat, 0 g sat fat, 0 mg chol, 4 g fiber, 150 mg sodium, 4 g sugar
$3.29–$3.89 per 24 oz box; grocery stores; *www.arrowheadmills.com* (store locator)	$3.49 per 11.5 oz box; grocery stores and other major retailers (US only)

Sip a cup of coffee or tea. Caffeine is a central nervous system stimulant that moderately boosts metabolism, helping you burn about 20 extra calories.

Snack at midmorning. Good choices: a reduced-fat cheese stick or a cup of low-fat yogurt and a piece of fruit. Every time you eat, your body burns additional calories to digest the food. Take advantage of this automatic boost by eating something—even if it's very small—every 3 to 4 hours.

Afternoon

Eat a protein-packed lunch. You'll incinerate more calories digesting your midday meal because protein is more difficult to break down than carbohydrates or fat. Try:

- Roast turkey breast with sliced veggies and hummus wrapped in a whole wheat tortilla; add a piece of fruit
- Salmon salad (like tuna salad but with canned salmon) topped with lettuce and tomato on a whole wheat bun; carrot sticks and grapes on the side
- Chicken-vegetable soup with a whole wheat roll

Snack on nuts. As your sugar and energy levels hit the postlunch slump, your metabolism takes a dip. The protein and fiber in a handful of nuts (about 20) can help stave off hunger and keep you energized. "Nuts also contain monounsaturated fats, which have been found in studies to stimulate fat burning," says health and psychology researcher Robert K. Cooper, PhD, author of *Flip the Switch.*

Get a lunchtime metabolism boost. If you're looking to boost your calorie-burning into a bonfire, swap your typical lunchtime stroll for our 15-minute walk/sprint routine. The workout is based on a 1-to-10 scale of intensity, with 1 equivalent to sitting on the sofa and 10 equivalent to sprinting. For minutes 1 and 2, walk at intensity level 4 or 5, and gradually ramp up to 7. For minute 3, blast off for 30 seconds at intensity level 9 or 10, then taper down to 5 for 30 seconds. Alternate between the 2-minute midintensity walking and the 1-minute "bursts" until you've walked a total of 12 minutes. For the last 3 minutes, cool down at an intensity of 4 or 5.

Brew some green tea. Studies show that the polyphenol compounds in 2 to 4 cups may help raise metabolism by as much as 35 percent and encourage fat burning.

FORTIFY YOUR METABOLISM—WITH "IRON"

No doubt about it—diet can have a dramatic impact on metabolism. But if you're ready to kick your metabolism into super-high gear, get lots of iron—the kind you lift.

Strength training builds muscle, and building muscle keeps your metabolism revving at its fat-burning best. Every pound of muscle burns between 30 and 50 calories a day, even while you sleep. By comparison, every pound of fat burns a measly 2 to 5 calories.

Starting after age 35, women start losing metabolism-revving muscle—about a half pound a year after 35 and a pound annually by age 50. That's why women in their late thirties and forties often gain weight, even though they are not eating or exercising differently.

To stop midlife fat spread in its tracks, add a little muscle to your frame. Researchers at Tufts University in Boston found that people who strength trained for 12 weeks and increased their muscle mass by just 3 pounds could eat 15 percent more calories—about 300 calories a day for an average woman—without gaining an ounce. Even better, they also lost fat pounds in the process.

Over time, these muscle-metabolism gains can add up to major fat loss. Consider this: If you gain 3 pounds of muscle and burn 40 additional calories per pound, you'll burn 120 more calories per day, or 3,600 calories per month. At that rate, those 3 pounds of muscle will burn off 12 pounds over the course of a year.

Remain on the move. "Moving throughout the day—even if it's just walking to a colleague's office rather than sending an e-mail—keeps your metabolism higher than doing a workout and then remaining sedentary," says James O. Hill, PhD, director of the Center for Human Nutrition at the University of Colorado at Denver.

Evening

Have a light (500- to 700-calorie) dinner. A balanced meal—such as fish, chicken, lean meat, or soy with steamed or sautéed veggies and a side of beans and rice—will refuel you without slowing you down. "Pause 15 minutes before taking second helpings. A relaxed eating style will ensure you don't get overstuffed," suggests Dr. Cooper.

Consider a nighttime "lift." If you work out in the morning or during your lunch hour, consider scheduling your workout after 5:00 p.m. Body temperature inches upward as the day goes on, peaking around 5:00 p.m. (when it's about 1° to 2°F warmer than it is in the morning), priming your muscles for activity. Studies show that evening exercisers move faster, produce more power, and don't fade as fast—all while feeling less tired.

Drink warm milk. Some studies suggest that amino acids in dairy products help promote fat-burning. (Stick to low-fat or fat-free to keep calories in check.)

Snooze to lose. Skimp on shut-eye and you'll not only feel sluggish the next day—making activity less attractive—but you'll also be at greater risk of gaining weight. A new report from the Nurses' Health Study, which followed more than 68,000 women for 16 years, found that women who slept just 5 hours a night were 32 percent more likely to gain 30-plus pounds during adulthood than those who got 7 hours of shut-eye, even though the light sleepers typically ate less.

Eight "Fattening" Foods Every Dieter Needs

Are you dreaming of a tablespoon of peanut butter, enjoyed right off the spoon? A drizzle of pure virgin olive oil over a steaming plate of garlicky whole wheat pasta? Sweet, creamy wedges of avocado atop your dinner salad? Dig right in. You'll be glad to know that dietary fat does not lead to body fat—as long as you eat the right kinds in the right amounts.

You may know that we mean so-called healthy fats. They're found mainly in plants and fish: the monounsaturated fats in almonds and avocados, the polyunsaturated fats in soy and seeds, the omega-3 fatty acids in walnuts and fish, and the omega-6 fatty acids in nuts and seeds and their oils. These good-for-you fats are as different from those found in bacon cheeseburgers and French fries as classical music is from heavy metal.

"Not all fats are created equal," says Roberta Anding, RD, a clinical dietitian at Baylor College of Medicine. "Maybe a low-fat diet isn't the way we need to eat, but a right-fat diet is."

Small amounts of healthy fats don't just tantalize your palate. They may also help to rein in your appetite, according to research conducted at the University of California, Davis (UCD). This seems especially true for women, the study found. Fat signals your brain that you're full, and a bit may keep you from getting ravenous between meals. Research also shows that the right fats may lower your odds of a multitude of conditions,

19

including heart disease, cancer, Alzheimer's disease, and depression.

Moreover, just as regular physical activity helps fat-proof your hips, so can a dab of dietary fat in a postworkout meal. Researchers found that when women ate a meal containing monounsaturated fat, such as olive oil, and saturated fat 30 minutes after exercising, they burned off three times more of the monounsaturated fat than the saturated kind. "When dietary fat is burned off right away, it doesn't have a chance to be stored as excess fat tissue," says lead researcher Dale Schoeller, PhD. "This could be yet another reason to choose healthy plant fats such as olive oil over saturated animal fats such as beef burgers." Just remember to keep your fat calories to no more than 30 percent of total calories—that's roughly 57 grams of fat a day for women—and to consume most of your fat calories from healthy sources.

So go ahead, fatten up your diet with sensible portions of these very tummy-satisfying, good-fat foods. As you whittle your middle, you'll safeguard your health.

filling that study volunteers ate less at other times of the day without even realizing it. Crunchy peanuts also raised metabolism. Evidence suggests that consumption of walnuts, pecans, and almonds also has little impact on body weight, says study author Richard Mattes, PhD, RD. What's more, Pennsylvania State University research found that among more than 14,000 people, those who were regular peanut and peanut butter snackers actually had lower body mass indexes, a measure of obesity, and lower cholesterol intakes than those who didn't eat peanuts.

Your heart loves nuts as much as your hips. Five of the largest epidemiological studies in the United States found that eating nuts reduces the risk of heart disease. In the Nurses' Health Study at Harvard, eating at least 5 ounces of nuts a week lowered cardiovascular disease risk by 35 percent, probably because of their healthy fat.

We're not suggesting that you go hog wild on peanuts. Peanuts and peanut butter pack

Good Fat: Peanuts and Peanut Butter

Eat Them Because

An amazing Purdue University study found that people who snacked on 500 extra calories' worth of cocktail peanuts—which are technically legumes, not nuts—every day for 8 weeks didn't gain weight. So if you think you have to forgo your favorite fat-filled snack—nuts to that.

Researchers speculate that the healthy fats, fiber, and protein in peanuts are so

TRANS-FORM YOUR WAISTLINE

A calorie's a calorie, right? Not so fast. Wake Forest University School of Medicine researchers found that trans fat—the unhealthy fat formed when food manufacturers turn liquid oils into solid fats—releases more calories than other fats during digestion. Their test monkeys, which metabolize fats like humans, gained three times more weight on an 8 percent trans-fat diet than others fed the same number of calories but no trans fat. Although the average woman gets 3.9 grams of trans fat per day from partially hydrogenated oils, we found one stick margarine that contained 3.5 grams in a single tablespoon. Go trans-free by checking the labels on processed food products for the phrase "partially hydrogenated oils," especially in these major trans-fat sources.

- Cakes, pies, doughnuts, muffins, waffles

- Margarine

- Cookies, crackers

- French fries

- Potato and corn chips, popcorn

- Hot dogs, lunchmeat

- Salad dressing

- Ice cream

a lot of calories—170 per ounce of nuts, 94 for 1 tablespoon of peanut butter. Enjoy. Just don't go nuts.

Get More

Crush them and sprinkle a few tablespoons over coleslaw, rice dishes, shrimp or chicken salad, or a tropical fruit salad. Peanut butter isn't married to jelly. Spread 2 tablespoons of your favorite full-fat (the good stuff is in the fat) brand on whole wheat bread and add sliced apples, pears, or bananas. Mix ¼ cup of peanut butter with 1 tablespoon each of reduced-sodium chicken broth and soy sauce to create a rich, exotic sauce for grilled chicken, noodle dishes, or salad.

Nutrient profile of 28 peanuts (1 ounce): 14 g fat* (7 g monounsaturated, 4.5 g polyunsaturated, 2 g saturated), 166 calories; for 1 tablespoon peanut butter: 8.1 g fat (3.8 g monounsaturated, 2.2 g polyunsaturated, 1.7 g saturated), 94 calories

*Fat breakdowns are approximate.

Good Fat:
Olive Oil and Olives

Eat Them Because

Adding a luscious Mediterranean staple—flavorful full-fat olive oil—to your diet may help you control cravings, making it easier to slim down. In a Pennsylvania State University study led by Steve E. Specter, PhD, men who ate a lunch that included mashed potatoes prepared with monounsaturated oil such as olive oil stayed satisfied longer than when the potatoes contained polyunsaturated oil such as corn oil.

And Marshall Goldberg, MD, an endocrinologist at Thomas Jefferson University Medical College in Philadelphia, has found that a concentrated dose of olive oil—2 teaspoons on half a slice of bread, eaten 15 to 20 minutes before a meal—helps his patients, including people quitting smoking, control their cravings, too.

Researchers think olive oil may slow stomach contractions, which creates a sense of fullness, and it stimulates the release of cholecystokinin (CCK), a gut hormone that signals the brain to stop eating.

Olives and their oil may also protect your health. For starters, they are one of nature's most abundant sources of beneficial monos. They contain phytochemicals like polyphenols, protective compounds that may prevent both cardiovascular disease and cancer and reduce inflammation that can lead to chronic illness.

Get More

Scatter pitted olives among grilled shrimp, peppers, and onions, or stir chunks into spicy puttanesca sauce and serve over pasta or fish. Swap mayo for flavorful store-bought olive paste (called tapenade, and a teaspoon will do) on sandwiches or salads. Olive oil is an excellent butter substitute on steamed or grilled veggies: Drizzle 1 or 2 teaspoons over grilled asparagus or steamed broccoli, and lightly dust the veggies with grated cheese and a grind of black pepper. Choose flavorful extra-virgin olive oil—extracted from the first press of the olives—which contains the highest level of healthy phenolic compounds.

Nutrient profile of five large olives: 2.4 g fat (1.7 g monounsaturated, 0.2 g polyunsaturated, 0.3 g saturated), 25 calories; for 1 tablespoon oil: 13.5 g fat (9.9 g monounsaturated, 1.4 g polyunsaturated, 1.9 g saturated), 120 calories.

CURIOUSLY STRONG HUNGER-BLOCKER

Got an empty Altoids tin knocking around in a drawer? Put it to work helping you lose weight by filling it with almonds. An Altoids box holds just about 23 almonds—a 1-ounce serving (169 calories). That trick comes from Michelle Wien, DrPH, RD, whose 2004 study showed that almonds (in moderation) may help you stick to your diet.

Wien put 65 overweight and obese men and women on same-calorie diets that were either high in fat (39 percent of calories from 3 ounces of almonds) or low in fat (18 percent, with no almonds). After 24 weeks, the almond eaters lost 62 percent more weight and 56 percent more fat.

"We think that the fiber in the almonds may prevent some of the fat from being absorbed and used by the body as calories," says Dr. Wien. And nuts' healthy fats keep dieters satisfied longer, helping them stick to their resolve.

Good Fat: Almonds

Eat Them Because

These sweet, crunchy nuts help calm a hungry belly (see "Curiously Strong Hunger Blocker"). But they'll also do your heart good. In a UCD study, researchers substituted almonds and almond oil for half the fat in the diets of their volunteers: slightly more than 2½ ounces of almonds (about 48 nuts) and nearly 1½ ounces of almond oil daily. At the end of 6 weeks, the 22 men and women had lower total cholesterol (a drop of 4 percent), lower "bad" LDL levels (a drop of 6 percent), and significantly lower triglycerides (a 14 percent drop), while their "good" HDL levels went up by 6 percent.

Get More

Sprinkle a tablespoon or two of slivered almonds over whole wheat couscous or steamed jasmine rice with peas. Tuck them into beef or poultry dishes, or use them to top a curried vegetable stew or carrot soup. For a light summer dessert, sprinkle a tablespoon of crushed almonds over grilled figs, nectarines, or peaches drizzled with balsamic vinegar. For a twist on an old favorite, use almond butter on your PB&J.

Nutrient profile of 23 almonds (1 ounce): 14.4 g fat (9.1 g monounsaturated, 3.5 g polyunsaturated, 1.1 g saturated), 164 calories.

Good Fat: Walnuts

Eat Them Because

Even a small portion adds a pleasant crunch and tummy-satisfying fat to almost any dish—good to know when your stomach is clamoring to be filled. To stave off hunger, add 2 tablespoons of crushed walnuts to your morning cereal, or mix a teaspoon of chopped walnuts with six dried apricot halves for an on-the-go snack.

What's more, walnuts are one of the few plant sources of healthy omega-3 fats, which may protect against inflammation, heart disease, asthma, and arthritis and improve cognitive function. Just one small handful, or 14 walnut halves, supplies 2.6 grams of omega-3 fats, which surpasses the minimal daily amount recommended by the Institute of Medicine for optimal health.

Get More

These fragrant nuts lend themselves to both sweet and savory dishes. They're suited to crisp oatmeal cookies or a rich banana bread, but they also add spark and crunch to a butternut squash risotto, roasted Brussels sprouts, or mashed sweet potatoes.

Nutrient profile of 14 walnut halves (1 ounce): 18.5 g fat (2.5 g monounsaturated, 13.4 g polyunsaturated, 1.7 g saturated), 185 calories.

Good Fat: Avocados

Eat Them Because

They contain heart-healthy monounsaturated fats. Monos help lower total and LDL cholesterol. Some studies suggest that a high-mono diet may even protect against breast cancer. Recent research at Ohio State University found that when avocado was added to salads and salsa, it helped increase the absorption of specific carotenoids, chemicals linked to lower risk of heart disease and macular degeneration, a leading cause of blindness.

"Avocados are packed with other heart-protective compounds, such as soluble fiber, vitamin E, folate, and potassium," says Elizabeth Somer, RD, author of *10 Habits That Mess Up a Woman's Diet*.

Get More

Avocados aren't just for guacamole anymore. Start a summer meal with a refreshing bowl of chilled avocado soup (puree an avocado in a blender with 2 tablespoons of fat-free plain yogurt and a dash of lime juice and hot sauce, thinning the soup to taste with reduced-sodium chicken broth). Mash a quarter of an avocado (tightly wrap the remainder in plastic and freeze to retain color) to use in place of a tablespoon of mayonnaise on deli sandwiches of turkey or lean ham; you'll slash total fat (the avocado has 7 grams; full-fat mayo has 11 grams) and add beneficial monounsaturated fat, which you won't get by switching to fat-free mayo.

Nutrient profile of 1/5 avocado: 4.6 g fat (2.9 g monounsaturated, 0.6 g polyunsaturated, 0.6 g saturated), 50 calories.

ALL THE FISH IN THE SEA

Fish and shellfish are a waist-watcher's friend. Seafood is a great source of lean protein, it's relatively low in fat, and many species pack heart-protective omega-3 fats. But is it safe to eat?

It's true that much of the fish we eat is contaminated with mercury, a neurotoxin that can cause brain damage, and, to a lesser extent, polychlorinated biphenyls (PCBs), industrial pollutants linked to cancer. Children, women in their childbearing years, and those who are pregnant or nursing are considered high risk and need to restrict their intake of high-mercury fish because the heavy metal can interfere with youngsters' brain development.

But if you don't fall into a high-risk category, eating fish twice a week is good for you, experts contend. Their advice: Don't eat the same fish twice in 1 week, and restrict highly polluted species you love (like swordfish) to an occasional meal. "Having a variety means you're not going to miss any of the important nutrients, but you're not likely to get too much of something that's bad," says Walter Willett, MD, Fredrick John Stare professor of epidemiology and nutrition at Harvard School of Public Health and one of the leaders of the Nurses' Health Study.

If you are at risk, the EPA recommends that you pass up the fish that top its "most contaminated" list: shark, swordfish, tilefish, and king mackerel. Get your two servings a week (up to 12 ounces) by eating low-mercury seafood such as shrimp, canned light tuna, salmon, pollock, and catfish. (Albacore, or white, tuna has more mercury than light, so limit yourself to 6 ounces a week.) For types of PCB-contaminated fish to avoid, check state advisories at the EPA Web site, http://epa.gov/waterscience/fish/states.htm.

Good Fat: Sunflower Seeds

Eat Them Because

You need to get linoleic acid in your diet: Your body can't make it (as well as other essential fatty acids) and requires it to help synthesize other fats. Bonus: It's great for your heart. In the Nurses' Health Study at Harvard, women who had the highest intakes of linoleic acid had a 23 percent lower risk of heart disease than women who had the lowest intakes.

Get More

Add 2 or 3 tablespoons of these delicately flavored seeds to low-fat granola, trail mix, or hot cereal. Or lightly toast and sprinkle them, along with dried cherries, on top of a spinach salad dressed with a citrus vinaigrette. Use a tablespoon as a topping for an open-faced tuna, egg salad, or hummus sandwich on crusty pumpernickel bread. Storage tip: Sunflower seeds easily become

rancid, causing them to lose their nutritional benefits and develop off flavors, so store them in a tightly sealed container in the refrigerator.

Nutrient profile of ¼ cup sunflower seeds: 15.9 g fat (3 g monounsaturated, 10.5 g polyunsaturated, 1.7 g saturated), 10.5 g linoleic acid, 186 calories.

Good Fat: Edamame (soybeans)

Eat Them Because

Though recent studies have cast doubt on soy's ability to independently lower your risk of heart disease, it's a great substitute for meat in your diet, and that can help lower your cholesterol. A multicenter study, published in the March 2007 issue of the *American Journal of Clinical Nutrition*, found that a diet that substituted soy products for meat and contained specific kinds of fiber (such as that in oats), almonds, and plant-sterol-enriched margarine lowered cholesterol as much as statin drugs (more than 20 percent) for one-third of the participants.

Get More

Keep a bag of frozen, precooked edamame on hand, and add ¼ cup to stir-fries, vegetable stews, or whole wheat pasta dishes to boost polyunsaturated fat and protein. Toss them with some corn for an unusual succotash. Use them to replace meat in a stir-fry of broccoli, bok choy, and asparagus. Or substitute them for chickpeas in hummus.

Nutrient profile of 1 cup cooked edamame: 11.5 g fat (2.2 g monounsaturated, 5.4 g polyunsaturated, 1.3 g saturated), 254 calories.

THE DAIRY DEBATE

Do low-fat dairy products—reduced-fat cheese, fat-free milk, low-fat yogurt—really speed weight loss? Research shows mixed results. In a study at the University of Tennesee, Knoxville, researchers put 32 obese adults on one of three calorie-restricted diets: low calcium (400 milligrams daily from food), high calcium (an additional 800 milligrams from supplements), or high dairy (1,200 milligrams, all from food). After 6 months, the high-dairy group dropped 24 pounds—compared with 19 for the supplement group and 15 for those who got the least calcium.

However, when Mayo Clinic scientists put 72 overweight men on a low-calorie diet that delivered either 800 or 1,400 milligrams of calcium, both groups lost about 20 pounds in a year. A University of Vermont study of 54 overweight women found similar results: Although half received 500 milligrams of calcium a day from dairy and the rest got 1,200 to 1,400 milligrams, all lost an average of 22 pounds.

However, low-fat dairy will probably help you lose. Some scientists speculate that the calcium helps the body metabolize calories and burn fat faster. In the Mayo study, for example, even the "low-calcium" group got a relatively high amount—perhaps explaining why their weight loss was so dramatic. Because many dieters get as little as 200 milligrams of calcium a day, dairy could boost results.

Bottom line? There's no doubt that calcium protects your heart and bones, so whether or not you're dieting, aim for three servings a day of low-fat cheese, yogurt, or milk.

Good Fat: Flaxseed

Eat It Because

Flaxseed is famous for its omega-3s, but it's also an outstanding source of lignans, a type of fiber that acts like a weak form of estrogen in our bodies and may help fight some types of breast cancer. Researchers at the University of Toronto and Massachusetts General Hospital Cancer Center in Boston, who analyzed tumor tissue, found that tumor growth slowed significantly and cancer cell death increased by as much as 30 percent in recently diagnosed postmenopausal breast cancer patients who ate a muffin containing about 3 tablespoons of flaxseed daily for about a month before surgery.

Get More

Its nutty flavor makes flaxseed a natural addition to baked goods and breakfast foods. You must grind the hull from the seed to release all of flax's nutrients. Add ¼ cup of ground seeds to pancakes, muffins, cookies, and quick breads (but watch baking times—flaxseed can cause food to brown more quickly). Add a tablespoon or two to cereal, yogurt, soups, or fresh-fruit smoothies. Flax is best stored in the refrigerator, and ground flaxseed must be used promptly because it spoils more quickly than the whole seed.

Nutrient profile of 2 tablespoons ground flaxseed: 5.9 g fat (1.1 g monounsaturated, 4 g polyunsaturated, 0.5 g saturated), 75 calories.

Four Diet Options—
Which Ones
to Choose?

Walk into the local supermarket and you're deluged with diet foods: low carb, low fat, low sugar, low calorie . . . all promising great taste, convenience, and the ability to quickly squeeze you back into your skinny jeans. Meal-replacement shakes will "help control hunger for up to 4 hours." Low-carb ice cream allows you to "savor the sweet without the sacrifice."

Promises, Promises

Despite our ravenous consumption of these products, we're not slimming down. "Diet-food sales are growing, but so are our waistlines—rates of obesity in this country are increasing each year," says Dave Grotto, RD, a spokesperson for the American Dietetic Association, echoing the sentiment of most nutritionists. "Many of these foods can play a role in a healthy diet, but by themselves, they're not the magic bullet that can lead to permanent weight loss."

Before you throw up your hands in exasperation (and toss a bag of chips into your grocery cart), read on. We delved into the latest research—including new studies calling into question the long-term effectiveness of popular diets—and interviewed leading weight-loss specialists, nutritionists, and real dieters to zero in on the foods that really can help you lose. What follows: the science behind the products, who they're best for, and what not to waste your money on.

PUZZLING APPETITE SUPPRESSANT

Next time a food craving hits, counter it with a crossword puzzle, recommend British scientists. Their new study suggests that learning to divert your attention as soon as the urge strikes for an ice pop or that piece of pie in the fridge may help you regain your self-control.

The researchers gave 18 dieting coeds mental tasks and tempted them with three snacks: chocolate-covered sponge cake with orange filling, mini chocolate bars, and chips. The dieters ate less when distracted with tasks that engaged their complete attention, such as brainteasers like a Rubik's Cube. The distraction you choose must be totally absorbing, the scientists advise; hobbies like knitting won't do because they allow your mind to wander—maybe right back to that pie. And the more you practice, the better the method works. So choose a diversion you can use anywhere, like the travel version of Boggle or Sudoku books.

Entrées on Ice

Americans spent about $1.4 billion on low-cal frozen dinners (such as Lean Cuisine, Weight Watchers, and Healthy Choice) in 2004. These single-serving meals cost $3 to $5 each, pack up to 400 calories, and can be microwaved for lunch or dinner.

The Science

A 2004 University of Illinois study found that women who followed a 1,365-calorie diet in which they ate two packaged frozen entrées a day shed about 5 pounds more in 8 weeks than those who were instructed to follow a diet (with the same number of calories) based on the food pyramid.

Use 'Em

If you find it hard to guesstimate portions. "Frozen meals give your eyes and stomach a chance to readjust to what servings should be—I often advise patients to eat them for a week or two, and then keep the little trays and use them while making dinner as an easy way to eyeball portions," says Madelyn Fernstrom, PhD, director of the Weight Management Center at the University of Pittsburgh Medical Center. Frozen meals are also a sound option for busy dieters with no time (or desire) to cook and those who would otherwise grab fast food or order in pizza. "I've used them over the years whenever I've needed to lose weight because you can't beat the convenience: You just pop them into a microwave. And there's no way you can overeat," says Michelle Tennant, 36, a publicist in Asheville, North Carolina. "I try to pick the ones that have whole wheat or are mostly meat and vegeta-

bles, as I find they stick with me longer and I don't have a blood sugar crash."

Lose 'Em

If you're a foodie. "If you savor your meals, enjoy cooking, and really notice the different tastes, textures, and smells of food, these products won't offer enough stimulation for you," says Wahida Karmally, DrPH, RD, director of nutrition at the Irving Center for Clinical Research at Columbia University. The skimpy servings also may not provide enough calories if you're fairly active. "I used to take Lean Cuisine entrées to work and eat them for lunch because they're so convenient, but the portions were way too small to satisfy my appetite," says Sylvia Sklar, 60, a professor at McGill University in Montreal. "I was starving an hour later." One reason: Some of these dinners have less than 20 grams of protein per serving—not enough to keep many women, especially active ones, satisfied, says Kathy McManus, RD, director of the department of nutrition at Brigham and Women's Hospital in Boston. If that describes you, look for a product with at least 20 grams of protein, such as Kraft's line of South Beach Diet frozen entrées and Lean Cuisine's new Dinnertime Selects. One final caveat: Avoid this category if you have high blood pressure. Many entrées have 800 milligrams of

sodium or more, about one-third of the federal government's recommended upper limit for a day's intake.

Bottom Line

"Frozen entrées may make dieting easier because they remove the guesswork when it comes to figuring out portion sizes," explains Donald Hensrud, MD, an obesity specialist at the Mayo Clinic in Rochester, Minnesota. Just make sure to supplement your meal with hefty sides of fruits and veggies to ensure you get enough nutrients and stay full. "The fruit and vegetable portion in most of these meals is tiny. You need 7 to 10 servings of fruits and vegetables a day," says Karen Collins, RD, nutrition advisor to the American Institute for Cancer Research.

Liquid Lunches

Meal-replacement shakes, generally around 250 calories a serving, sub for one or two meals a day; you eat a snack and a third meal of about 700 calories on your own. Sales dropped 16 percent from 2002 to 2004, but this method is still popular with some dieters.

The Science

A 2003 Columbia University meta-analysis of six studies found that people who used a liquid meal replacement were likely to lose more weight (on average, 7 pounds) in a year than those who simply followed a reduced-calorie diet of about 1,200 calories per day. (No word on how the dieters fared after that.)

Use 'Em

If you tend to eat on the run. Liquid meal replacements are quick, easy, and

convenient. "Our program often recommends the shakes to executives who travel a lot—they can take them along instead of eating at an airport or ordering in room service," says Dr. Hensrud. "We sometimes even suggest they have one before a business dinner, so they eat a light meal of, say, a salad, instead of a high-fat, high-calorie entrée." Because the shakes are fairly low in calories, you'll want to add fruit or vegetables to provide more filling fiber. "I tell patients to mix the shakes in a blender with ice and fruit, which makes them thicker and whips up air to fill the stomach," says Scott Isaacs, MD, an endocrinologist at Emory University. These drinks can also be helpful for night eaters: "If one of your diet danger times is after dark, you can always use a shake to curb nighttime cravings for sweets," says McManus.

Lose 'Em

If you're an emotional eater. "The minute you get upset, you'll find a shake just won't cut it," says Christine Gerbstadt, MD, RD, a spokesperson for the American Dietetic Association. "I had one client who lost 100 pounds on a liquid diet plan but eventually gained it all back—during times of stress she just couldn't get over the urge to have food in her mouth." Liquid diets can also be hard to stick to for more than a few weeks. "I found it impossible to stay on," says Sara Dombroff, a 31-year-old lawyer in New York City. "I had to have shakes for breakfast and lunch, so I'd spend the whole day dreaming of real food." That may be because most people enjoy the satisfaction of chewing, says Ann Kulze, MD, a physician in Charleston, South Carolina, and author of *Dr. Ann's 10-Step Diet*. "In my experience, people who use diet shakes tend to complain of more hunger and less satisfaction than dieters who are on solid food. Besides, eating the same thing day in and day out is boring, and that makes it much more likely that you'll weaken and binge on doughnuts."

Bottom Line

They can be a quick and easy diet aid for the time-pressed. But experts warn that dieting on liquid meal replacements may not lead to lasting weight loss because they don't teach you how to eat "real" food. "I spent 5 years supervising a liquid-meal-replacement center, and I can tell you that while people in the program did a great job of losing weight, they did an even better job of gaining it back once they stopped because they never learned healthy eating habits," says Grotto. If you use shakes as grab-and-go meals or snacks, look for a product that has 220 to 300 calories and 12 to 15 grams of protein to fill you up. Some users report that

RENEW YOUR RESOLUTIONS

On December 31, you'd vowed to lose 15 pounds by spring. On March 21, nothing had changed except the weather. What happened? Don't beat yourself up. It's estimated that fewer than 30 percent of New Year's resolutions achieve success. No matter what the season, now's the perfect time to reignite your resolve—and, while you're at it, revamp your resolutions. The first step to success: Break your one and perhaps overwhelming goal—"to lose weight"—into several manageable mini-resolutions that meet these criteria.

- *They're doable.* Forgo grandiose pledges such as "I'll exercise an hour a day" for more modest goals you know you can keep. Consider this: Researchers at the University of Bristol assigned 78 people different goals, asking one group to take an extra 2,500 steps a day and another to walk a total of 10,000 steps a day. The 2,500-step group hit its goal twice as often as the 10,000-step group did.

- *They're short-term.* It's easy to nibble on cookies now if your resolution deadline is months away. Resolutions with a shorter time frame, like "I'll eat dessert just once a week," make what you do *today* more relevant.

- *They fit your life.* Log what you eat for 2 weekdays and 1 weekend day to identify the areas you need to work on. For instance, if your log reveals that you often pick up fast food because you're too tired to fix dinner, resolve to stock your fridge with precooked grilled chicken strips and bagged salad fixings for quick, healthy dinners.

more protein than that gives the shake a grainy, unpleasant taste.

Low-Carb Conveniences

About 6 years ago, low-carbohydrate bars, shakes, cereals, and ice cream flooded the market. But this trend has cooled: "We're seeing more and more of these products repositioned as 'low sugar' or 'low glycemic,' with companies claiming that they're digested more slowly and thus are less likely to affect blood sugar," says Tom Vierhile, an analyst for the market research group Datamonitor.

The Science

There is some evidence that low-carb diets—though not specific products—promote weight loss. But it's not the lack of carbs that's key: "It's the fact that people on low-carb diets tend to eat more protein, which is very satisfying and filling," explains Jonathan Waitman, MD, a clinical nutrition specialist in the Comprehensive Weight Control Program at Weill Cornell Medical Center in New York City. A recent University of Washington study found that people on a diet that was 30 percent protein ate fewer calories and reported less hunger than those who followed a meal plan that was 15 percent protein. (The diets had identical amounts of carbs, which suggests that protein really made the difference.)

Use 'Em

For an occasional snack or breakfast, especially if you tend to wake up ravenous or get hungry between meals. "I was always starving in the mornings until I switched from a regular shake to a high-protein one, which had about four times as much protein and kept me full until lunch," says dieter Dombroff, who didn't mind the latter's thick texture. New York City nutritionist Joy Bauer, RD, author of *The 90/10 Weight Loss Plan*, seconds the approach: "I often recommend low-carbohydrate bread to clients because some brands use oat or soy flour. That bumps up fiber and protein and thus really helps to control blood sugar, so they'll be less hungry later."

Lose 'Em

If you're not willing to cut portion size: They're often as high in fat and calories as the foods they're designed to replace. "I routinely have to explain to patients that these products are calorie traps; manufacturers are just replacing sugar with fat," says Kulze. Then there's the taste issue. "The cereals have the texture of cardboard, the ice cream has a slimy feel in your mouth, and the pancake mix isn't anything like the real thing," says Hilary Bruel, a 32-year-old graphic designer in Needham, Massachusetts. "The only product I liked was the Atkins Endulge Peanut Butter Cups, but with 320 calories and 26 grams of fat in a handful, they slowed down my weight loss." And that's not the only price you pay. "Some low-carb sweets replace regular sugar with large amounts of sugar alcohols like maltitol, which can have a laxative effect," says Dr. Hensrud.

Bottom Line

Staples such as bread and cereal make sense, but skip the snacks. "It's cheaper—and healthier—to have a snack like a banana with peanut butter for about the same amount of calories," says Dr. Gerbstadt.

Fat-Free Foodstuffs

Reduced-fat products have been around since the '80s and are still ultrapopular weight-loss foods. Sales topped $35 billion in 2005, dwarfing the performance of all other categories, such as low carb, says ACNielsen.

The Science

Research suggests that a low-fat diet may not do the trick when it comes to weight loss. A recent Harvard Medical School study found that those on a low-fat (20 percent of calories) diet actually gained 6 pounds, while those on a moderate-fat (35 percent) diet lost 9 over 18 months.

Use 'Em

If you're a big eater who needs voluminous portions to feel satisfied. "Because some

BLAST THOSE LAST 5 POUNDS

So you lost 25 pounds but keep losing and regaining the last 5. What should you do? According to *Prevention*'s weight-loss coach Michele Stanten, before you make another push to lose those last 5 pounds, ask yourself three questions.

- What will I gain by losing it? If you're at a healthy body mass index, or BMI (to find out, log on to www.prevention.com/ bmi), dropping 5 pounds won't make you healthier, and only you will notice. Even if you're still in the overweight category, additional health benefits will be minimal. Plus, studies suggest that yo-yoing 10 or more pounds is more harmful than maintaining a slightly heavier weight.

- Are you willing to give up dessert and log more hours at the gym? The smaller your body gets, the fewer calories it needs, which means that to lose more weight you need to either eat less or exercise more—or both.

- Are you giving the scale too much power? Body weight fluctuates throughout the day, week, and month, so don't let yourself get hung up on a magic number—instead, just focus on staying within a 5-pound range.

of the fat-free salad dressings, for example, are lower in calories, you can put a little on a huge amount of vegetables and eat a lot for very few calories," explains Bauer. "The same holds true for fat-free cheese—I encourage clients to go for a sharp Cheddar, which still has a strong taste." Dairy products such as milk and cheese are high in saturated fat, so 1 percent or fat-free versions are also a great way to get needed calcium and protein. The catch to this category:

Some fat-free salad dressings have added sugar, so check the label (2 tablespoons of fat-free Italian, for example, contain 15 calories, while 2 tablespoons of a honey Dijon have 50).

Lose 'Em

If you're diabetic or prediabetic or carry a lot of weight around your middle. All of these indicate that you may be prone to insulin resistance, and low-fat foods, which are likely to be loaded with sugar, could worsen the problem. "Most fat-free foods, with the exception of dairy products, tend to be refined carbohydrates, which will just drive up your blood sugars and overwork your pancreas, making you even more insulin resistant," says McManus. You should also steer clear of them if you have elevated triglyceride levels. "I've seen patients who think they are being superhealthy following a fat-free diet. They're shocked to learn they have insulin resistance or even high triglycerides—but as soon as they cut back on the refined carbohydrates and add in some healthy fat, the problem goes away," says Dr. Isaacs.

Bottom Line

Low fat usually doesn't equal low calorie, so go with a small portion of a regular version instead. "Most of these products have just as many—if not more—calories than the full-fat versions. The companies have simply cut out fat and poured in the sugar," says Dr. Fernstrom. One of the most common mistakes she sees is too much faith in low-fat peanut butter. "People assume that because it's reduced-fat, they can eat another tablespoon. But they're getting almost as many calories as with the regular variety, and it's actually more harmful to their health because they're losing 3 grams of heart-healthy fat and instead adding in extra carbohydrates and sugar," she says.

A Guide
to Savvy Shopping

Want to stay slim, get your fill of all the vital nutrients your body needs, protect yourself against diabetes and heart disease, plus delight your tastebuds—all on a busy schedule? Sounds like a tall order. But you can do it.

Like clothes shopping, grocery shopping can be either satisfying or bewildering. By following a few key guidelines, you can turn every visit to the supermarket into an opportunity to load your basket with the foods that dieters—or anyone who wants to be healthy—need most.

"Smart supermarket shopping strategies are the key to eating well at home," says Bonnie Tandy Leblang, RD, author of the nationally syndicated column "Supermarket Sampler" and six cookbooks, including *Grains, Rice and Beans.* "To eat healthy, you need to buy healthy."

For the latest, greatest healthy food products to assist you in losing weight, check out the Shopping Savvy sidebars scattered throughout the recipe chapters.

THE NUTRITIONAL TOP 40

To make trolling the produce aisle a breeze, consult the following shopping lists for vegetables and fruit. Selections are based on how well these foods satisfy the Daily Values (DVs) for key nutrients and fiber. (Unless otherwise noted, nutrient analysis for vegetables is based on a half-cup of cooked vegetables.)

Vegetables	Fiber (g)	Beta-Carotene	Vitamin C	Folate	Iron
Asparagus (4 spears)	1.26	✓	✓	✓	
Broccoli, raw	1.32	✓	✓✓		
Brussels sprouts	3.35	✓	✓✓	✓	
Cabbage, shredded	2.10		✓✓		
Carrot, raw	2.16	✓✓	✓		
Cauliflower	1.67		✓✓		
Collards, chopped	1.28	✓✓	✓		
Kale	1.30	✓✓	✓		
Kohlrabi	0.90		✓✓		
Peas, edible pods	2.24		✓✓		
Peas, green	4.40		✓	✓	
Peppers, bell, green, raw	0.90		✓✓		
Peppers, bell, red, raw	1.00	✓✓	✓✓		
Peppers, chile, raw	1.39		✓✓		
Potato, with skin	4.66		✓✓		✓✓
Rutabaga, cubed	1.53		✓✓		
Spinach	2.16	✓✓	✓	✓✓	✓
Squash, butternut, cubed	N/A	✓✓	✓✓		
Sweet potato	3.42	✓✓	✓✓		
Tomato, raw	1.35	✓	✓✓		

A single check mark (✓) indicates that a food provides 10 to 25 percent of the DV; a double check mark (✓✓) indicates that a food provides more than 25 percent of the DV.

Fruits	Fiber (g)	Beta-Carotene	Vitamin C	Folate	Potassium
Apricots (3)	2.54	✓✓	✓✓		
Banana	2.74		✓		✓
Blackberries (½ c)	3.60		✓✓		
Blueberries (½ c)	3.92		✓✓		
Cantaloupe (1 c cubed)	1.28	✓✓	✓✓		✓
Casaba (1 c cubed)	1.36		✓✓	N/A	✓
Cherries, sweet (1 c)	3.34		✓		
Grapefruit (½)	1.32		✓✓		
Grapes (1 c)	1.60		✓✓		
Honeydew (1 c cubed)	1.02	✓✓	N/A	✓	
Kiwifruit	2.58		✓✓	N/A	
Orange	3.14		✓✓		
Papaya	5.47	✓	✓✓	✓✓	✓
Pear	3.98		✓		
Pineapple (1 c diced)	1.86		✓✓		
Plum	0.99		✓		
Raspberries (1 c)	8.36		✓✓		
Strawberries (1 c)	3.43		✓✓		
Tangerine	1.93	✓	✓✓		
Watermelon (1 c diced)	0.80	✓	✓✓		

Drawing Your Nutritional Treasure Map

The average supermarket sells thousands of items, from fruit to Froot Loops, eggnog to eggplant, and fig bars to Dove Bars. "Some foods are good for you, some aren't, and some are in between," says David Schardt, associate nutritionist at the Center for Science in the Public Interest in Washington, DC, and author of *Eating Leaner and Lighter.* And the right choices aren't always obvious. "The key is knowing what to buy and what to pass up," he says.

Nutrition counselors we talked to shared the following practical strategies for filling a shopping cart with the absolute best in each major food category.

Study the layout. The better you know the territory, the faster you can make the right choices, says Densie Webb, RD, PhD, associate editor of the *Environmental Nutrition* newsletter and author of *The Complete Brand-Name Guide to Choosing the Lowest Fat, Calorie, Cholesterol and Sodium Foods.* "If you don't know your way around the supermarket very well, you'll have a hard time making healthy choices," says Dr. Webb. "Today's mega-supermarkets have everything; the choices are tremendous. If you familiarize yourself with what's available, you'll have more options."

It's a smart strategy to always shop at the same store, week after week. When you know where everything in the store is located, it's a lot easier to find the products you want.

List what you need, aisle by aisle. Experts say that preplanning your trip helps you stay focused, minimizing high-fat, high-calorie impulse buys and helping to ensure that you'll come home with what you were looking for, says Schardt.

Set up your shopping list by aisle. After years of going to the same place, you don't have to keep backtracking for something you've missed. You can zip right through.

Produce Tops the List

"The best place to start is in the produce department—it's usually the section closest to the entrance," says Judy E. Marshel, PhD, RD, a nutritional counselor in Great Neck, New York, and former senior nutritionist for Weight Watchers International, who conducts supermarket tours for health professionals and health-conscious consumers.

Think nine a day. Buy enough produce to provide at least nine servings of fruits and vegetables for each day's menu. Planning a meal around a vegetable that's in season is a great place to start.

Reach for green and gold. Dr. Marshel urges women to concentrate on dark green and deep yellow fruits and vegetables, the ones that are full of beta-carotene, the antioxidant that is "important because it protects against heart disease and certain types of cancer," she says. Her top picks are: kale, spinach, carrots, sweet potatoes, apricots, and cantaloupe.

Mix it up. It's crucial that you vary your selections from one shopping trip to the next, says Dr. Marshel, since some foods are higher in particular nutrients than others. Bananas, for example, provide plenty of potassium to help regulate high blood pressure, she says.

Save time—buy prewashed. Mindful of time constraints at home, nutritionists like Leblang are big fans of fresh, prewashed, bagged vegetables found in supermarkets. "This is a convenience that's worth the extra money," she says. Men and women alike should be eating many more fruits and vegetables to help maintain healthy weight and reduce the risk of heart disease and diabetes.

Don't shun the canned-goods aisle. Or the freezer case. If you shop every other week, back up your fresh purchases with canned fruit or frozen vegetables, say nutritionists. "Canned and frozen vegetables are acceptable alternatives," says Dr. Marshel. Although you lose some nutrients, it's better to eat frozen or canned vegetables than no vegetables at all, she says. "The loss of

nutrients is negligible in frozen vegetables but is significant in canned vegetables," adds Suzanne Havala Hobbs, MS, RD, a nutritionist in Charlotte, North Carolina, and author of *Get the Trans Fat Out: 601 Simple Ways to Cut the Trans Fat Out of Any Diet.* Nevertheless, they still count toward achieving your daily quota of five or more servings a day, says Dr. Marshel.

Bread, Cereal, and Bean Territory

Some experts say the healthiest choices are often found around the refrigerated periphery of the supermarket. And to some degree, that's true. The exceptions are legumes and grains—canned or dried beans, brown rice, whole grain breads and

(continued on page 44)

BEANS AND GRAINS: A SHOPPER'S CHECKLIST

In most supermarkets, you'll find beans and grains conveniently located in the same aisle or near each other. This handy guide will help you make your selections when planning meatless meals—high in fiber and key minerals and low in fat. (Unless otherwise noted, values are based on a half-cup of cooked beans, grains, or pasta.)

Beans	Calories	Fiber (g)	Folate	Magnesium	Iron	Zinc	Copper
Adzuki beans	147	N/A	✓✓	✓	✓	✓	✓
Black beans	114	7.48	✓✓	✓	✓		
Broad beans (fava beans)	94	4.59	✓				✓
Chickpeas (garbanzo beans)	134	N/A	✓✓		✓		✓
Cowpeas (black-eyed peas)	100	5.59	✓✓	✓	✓		✓
Cranberry beans	120	N/A	✓✓	✓	✓		✓
Great Northern beans	104	6.16	✓	✓	✓		✓
Kidney beans	112	6.51	✓✓		✓		✓
Lentils	115	7.82	✓✓		✓		✓
Lima beans	108	6.58	✓	✓	✓		✓
Mung beans	106	7.68	✓✓	✓			
Navy beans	129	N/A	✓✓	✓	✓		✓
Pink beans	125	4.45	✓✓	✓	✓		✓
Pinto beans	116	7.31	✓✓	✓	✓		✓
Small white beans	128	N/A	✓✓	✓	✓		
Soybeans	149	5.16	✓	✓	✓		✓
Split peas	116	8.13	✓				
White beans	125	5.67	✓	✓	✓		✓
Yellow beans	127	N/A	✓	✓	✓		

A single check mark (✓) indicates that a food provides 10 to 25 percent of the Daily Value (DV); a double check mark (✓✓) indicates that a food provides more than 25 percent of the DV.

Grains and Pastas	Calories	Fiber (g)	Folate	Magnesium	Iron	Zinc	Copper
Amaranth	367	14.90	✓	✓✓	✓✓	✓	✓✓
Barley, pearled	97	3.00					
Buckwheat groats	91	N/A		✓			
Bulgur	76	4.10					
Couscous	101	1.26					
Millet	143	1.56		✓			
Oat bran	44	N/A		✓			
Oats	303	N/A	✓	✓✓	✓	✓	✓
Quinoa	318	5.02	✓	✓✓	✓✓	✓	✓✓
Rice, brown, long-grain	109	1.76		✓			
Rice, white, enriched	100	0.35					
Triticale	323	N/A	✓	✓✓	✓	✓	✓
Wheat germ (¼ c)	104	3.83	✓	✓	✓	✓	✓
Wild rice	83	1.48					
Macaroni, enriched (2 oz)	99	0.91					
Spaghetti, enriched	99	1.19					

cereals, and whole wheat pasta, which are often found in interior aisles of most stores. They're a major source of fiber, of which we need 30 grams a day, according to the USDA Food Guide.

Follow the two-for-one rule. "When it comes to bread, look at fat and fiber content," says Janis Jibrin, RD, a nutrition consultant in Washington, DC, and author of *The Supermarket Diet.* "Otherwise, they don't vary significantly." Her nutrition rule of thumb: Buy bread (including English muffins) with about 2 grams of fiber and no more than 1 gram of fat per slice, with about 65 or 70 calories. Possible exceptions are mini-pita loaves and "lite" breads, some of which are as low as 40 calories per slice.

Opt for whole wheat over white. To boost your fiber intake, says Jibrin, "look for whole wheat flour as the first ingredient. Even if the package is marked 'wheat bread,' it may be made with white flour, not whole

wheat flour, or contain a small quantity of whole wheat flour." Oat-bran bread products are usually good nutritional choices, says Jibrin.

Put cereal on the list. Breakfast cereal is one of the best ways to meet your daily fiber quota and get your fair share of B vitamins, says Jibrin. "There are some super-high-fiber cereals, some with as many as 13 grams of fiber per serving," she says. "If you like the taste, go for the highest-fiber ones you can get—at minimum, one containing 4 grams of fiber per ounce."

Read before you buy. When it comes to cereal, you need to read labels carefully, says Jibrin. Traditionally packed with fat, granola cereals are now available in fat-free versions, for example. But many are loaded with sugar, making their calorie counts sky high, she says.

"Some consumers find the Nutrition Facts labels confusing because they count natural sugar, such as is found in fruit, in with added sugar as part of the total grams of sugar," says Dr. Marshel. "Read the label for raisin bran, for example, and it appears to be high in sugar. But raisins, not added sugar, account for the total. So you have to read the ingredients listed and note what order they're in. If sugar, fat, or sodium is high on the list, avoid that cereal."

For some people, says Jibrin, a little sugar is a worthwhile trade-off. "If the only high-fiber cereal you like is sweetened, then buy it, but count that toward your day's sugar allowance," says Jibrin. "Still, calories rise with the addition of sugar and fat," she adds. "Avoid cereals with a sugar content that's more than 25 percent of the total carbohydrates and more than 2 grams of fat per ounce."

Buy the king-size box of oatmeal. Don't ignore that perennial cold-weather favorite, oatmeal, which is low in fat and high in soluble fiber to help slash cholesterol.

Don't run out of rice. Like breads and cereals, whole grains like brown rice are high in fiber, says Jibrin. "So the more whole grains you buy—like brown rice and whole grain pasta—the better. To avoid getting bored, experiment with interesting varieties of rice, such as Texmati and Jasmati rice."

Pair up with beans. Nutritionally, beans and grains differ in their nutritional makeup: Beans contain a generous amount of protein and fiber. Grains (rice, pasta, bulgur, and the like) contain a generous amount of complex carbohydrates but less protein. Beans are high in fiber, and most contain little fat (except for soybeans). Together, beans and brown rice are a low-fat, high-fiber duo that experts say is nutritionally preferable to meat.

"If you have beans two or three times a week, you'll be doing a lot to increase your fiber level, and you'll also be getting an excellent source of vegetable protein," says Schardt.

Canned beans spell instant meals. Dried beans require long hours of soaking and cooking, and they tend to lose flavor and moisture in the process, so many cooks prefer to buy canned beans. Nutritionists like Dr. Marshel give canned beans their blessing: "If time is short, canned beans and lentils are pretty good. If you're worried

about the sodium content, purchase low-sodium beans or rinse them before eating; it reduces the sodium by about one-third." Conveniently, beans and grains are frequently shelved near each other in the supermarket.

If You Buy Meat, Go Lean

If meat is on your shopping list, you'll probably find the meat case along the refrigerated periphery of the store. While most of us will want to limit consumption of meat to control intake of saturated fat, "women of childbearing age need iron, and lean red meat is a rich source," says Dr. Webb.

MEAT-AND-POULTRY LOVER'S
GUIDE TO SELECTED CUTS

The following list will help you select cuts of meat and poultry that supply easily absorbable iron yet offer limited quantities of saturated fat. (Unless otherwise noted, values given are based on 3-ounce servings of trimmed meat or skinless poultry, cooked.)

Meat	Calories	Total Fat (g)	Saturated Fat (g)	% Saturated Fat (g)
Turkey breast	115	0.63	0.20	2
Chicken breast	142	3.07	0.87	6
Turkey wing	98	2.06	0.66	6
Beef, top round, select	144	3.15	1.08	7
Turkey (leg meat)	135	3.21	1.08	7
Veal leg	126	2.88	1.04	7
Chicken drumsticks (2)	151	4.98	1.30	8
Beef, eye of round, select	136	3.40	1.23	8
Pork tenderloin	139	4.09	1.41	9
Beef, bottom round, select	167	5.78	1.96	11

Note: Values based on US Department of Agriculture data.

Stick to lean cuts. This is Dr. Marshel's advice: "If you compare heavily marbled meats (like a Porterhouse steak or pork chop) with lean meat (like a top round of beef or boneless center pork loin), you'll see that when the fat is ingrained in the meat rather than around the edge, it's much harder to trim off, and you'll end up eating more fat."

For a list of meat and poultry cuts that are lowest in unwanted fat and calories, see the table above.

Fish: Choose Fresh, Frozen, or Canned

Ocean fish (like cod), seafood (like lobster), and lake fish (like pike) are low-calorie sources of cell-building protein, says Dr. Marshel. And the omega-3 fatty acids found in fish are thought to reduce triglycerides, inhibit growth of breast cancer, and prevent gallstones. For recommended choices, see "Fish Picks."

FISH PICKS

You can serve fish twice a week and not repeat a meal for weeks. To benefit from omega-3 fatty acids (which seem to reduce blood levels of triglycerides and bestow other possible health benefits) without going overboard on calorie intake, alternate between low-fat species (like haddock) and fattier choices (like salmon). (Unless otherwise noted, values given are for 3 ounces of fresh fish cooked with dry heat, such as broiling.)

Fish	Calories	Total Fat (g)	Saturated Fat (g)	Omega-3 Fatty Acids (g)
Bass, freshwater	124	4.02	0.85	0.65
Bluefish	135	4.62	1.00	0.84
Catfish	89	2.42	0.63	0.21
Crab, Alaskan king (moist heat)	82	1.31	0.11	0.35
Flounder or sole	99	1.30	0.31	0.43
Grouper	100	1.11	0.25	0.21
Haddock	95	0.79	0.14	0.20
Halibut	119	2.50	0.35	0.40
Herring, Atlantic	173	9.85	2.22	1.71
Mackerel, Atlantic	223	15.14	3.55	1.02
Perch	99	1.00	0.20	0.28
Pike	96	0.75	0.13	0.12
Salmon, Coho	118	3.66	0.90	0.90
Salmon, canned	118	5.14	1.30	1.41
Sardines, canned (2)	50	2.75	0.37	0.23
Snapper	109	1.46	0.31	0.27
Swordfish	132	4.37	1.20	0.70
Trout	128	4.95	1.38	0.84
Tuna, fresh	156	5.34	1.37	1.28
Tuna, light, canned in water	99	0.70	0.20	0.23
Tuna, white, canned	115	2.09	0.56	0.60
Whitefish	146	6.38	0.99	1.38

Splurge on salmon. Fattier fish are a bit higher in calories, but they're even richer in omega-3 fatty acids. So nutritionists say you may want to include these fish in your menu: 3 ounces of cooked Atlantic herring (173 calories and 1.7 grams of omega-3s), canned pink salmon (118 calories and 1.4 grams of omega-3s), or cooked Atlantic mackerel (223 calories and 1 gram of omega-3s). To get the benefit of fish oil, fresh or canned will do.

Pack in some tuna and sardines. Less glamorous but equally nutritious is canned or pouch tuna, a pantry staple. Low-sodium, water-packed albacore tuna is a terrific low-calorie source of protein. And 3 ounces of canned sardines with bones provide about the same amount of calcium as a cup of fat-free milk. Canned or pouch salmon is a close second. Throw it into your cart with a package of whole wheat crackers, some vegetables, and fresh fruit, and you have the makings of a perfect lunch.

Bone-Building Choices from the Dairy Case

"Women who need to stock up on good sources of calcium will find much of what they need in the dairy case," says Schardt. Choose from low-fat dairy products, fat-free or 1 percent milk, low-fat or nonfat cheese, fat-free ricotta, reduced-fat cheese, nonfat yogurt, and the like.

Count fat grams, not percents. As with buying cereal, reading milk labels is critical, says Dr. Marshel. "Whole milk has 8 grams of fat per cup. By comparison, 2 percent milk isn't low-fat—it has 5 grams of fat per cup. One percent milk is considered low-fat (although it contains 3 grams of fat per cup). Fat-free milk, on the other hand, has only a trace of fat. So if your goal is to get your calcium from foods lowest in fat, grab a carton of skim."

Pick up some cottage cheese. Apply the "grams, not percent" rule to cottage cheese. A tub of creamed cottage cheese contains 5 grams of fat per half-cup serving. In contrast, the same amount of 2 percent contains just over 2 grams of fat, and 1 percent has about 1 gram. With the two reduced-fat versions, you get about 70 milligrams of calcium with a fraction of the fat.

Take home a substitute. The dairy case

GUIDE TO LOW-FAT DAIRY FOODS

The table below can serve as a guide to the very best low-fat sources of calcium in the dairy case, to help you avoid osteoporosis without piling on too many calories. Values vary from brand to brand, so read labels when you make purchases.

A single check mark (✔) indicates that a food provides 10 to 25 percent of the Daily Value (DV); a double check mark (✔✔) indicates that a food provides more than 25 percent of the DV.

Cheese	Portion	Calories	% Fat	Calcium
American, singles, fat-free	1 slice	30	0	✔
Cheddar, fat-free	1 oz	45	0	✔
Cheddar, reduced-fat	1 oz	80	8	✔
Monterey Jack, reduced-fat	1 oz	80	8	✔
Mozzarella, fat-free	1 oz	45	0	✔
Mozzarella, light	1 oz	60	5	✔
Mozzarella, part-skim	1 oz	90	9	✔
Ricotta, fat-free	¼ c	60	0	✔✔
Ricotta, light	¼ c	75	6	✔
Milk				
Buttermilk	1 c	99	20	✔✔
Fat-free	1 c	100	6	✔✔
1%	1 c	119	22	✔✔
2%	1 c	137	32	✔✔
Yogurt				
Fat-free, fruit	8 oz	100	0	✔✔
Fat-free, plain	8 oz	127	3	✔✔
Low-fat, fruit	8 oz	225	10	✔✔
Low-fat, plain	8 oz	144	22	✔✔

TAKE THIS CODE SHEET TO THE SUPERMARKET

Nutrition Facts labels make it easy to compare various brands of supermarket items and make the right choices in terms of calories, fat, sodium, and key nutrients. But what about those other key words and phrases on labels? Just as authorities such as the Food and Drug Administration and the U.S. Department of Agriculture set strict guidelines for those Nutrition Facts labels, they also have set criteria for other labeling language. Here's how to decipher the label lingo.

Sugar-free: contains less than 0.5 gram of sugar per serving

Calorie-free: contains fewer than 5 calories per serving

Low-calorie: contains 40 calories or less per serving

Reduced-calorie: contains one-fourth fewer calories than the regular product

Fat-free: contains less than 0.5 gram of fat per serving

Low-fat: contains 3 grams of fat or less per serving

Reduced-fat: contains no more than 75 percent of the fat found in a comparable food

Low in saturated fat: contains 1 gram or less of saturated fat per serving and no more than 15 percent of the food's calories come from saturated fat

Reduced saturated fat: contains no more than 75 percent of the saturated fat found in a comparable food

Cholesterol-free: contains less than 2 milligrams of cholesterol per serving and 2 grams or less of saturated fat per serving

is also home to eggs and refrigerated cholesterol-free egg products. (Frozen egg substitutes are in the frozen foods section.) Egg substitute will save about half the calories and all of the cholesterol and fat you'd get in whole eggs, notes Dr. Marshel.

Swing By the Oil Section

Nutritionists advise steering clear of solid fats like butter, lard, and margarine found in the dairy case. Butter is two-thirds saturated fat, which seems to drive up blood levels of cholesterol. Lard is about 40 percent saturated fat. Margarine is a significant source of trans-fatty acids, which have been implicated as contributing to heart disease.

Seek out bottled vegetable oils. Instead of seeking out margarine and other spreads, says Dr. Marshel, wheel your shopping cart down the oil aisle and go for the cooking and salad oils that are highest in monounsaturated and polyunsaturated fats (olive, canola, and safflower, for

Low-cholesterol: contains 20 milligrams or less of cholesterol per serving, 2 grams or less of saturated fat per serving, and 13 grams or less of total fat per serving

Reduced-cholesterol: contains 75 percent or less of the cholesterol found in the regular food and 2 grams or less saturated fat

Sodium-free: contains less than 5 milligrams of sodium/salt per serving

Low-sodium: contains 140 milligrams or less of sodium per serving

Very low-sodium: contains less than 35 milligrams of sodium per serving

Reduced-sodium: contains no more than 75 percent of the sodium found in the regular food

High in . . . : provides 20 percent or more of the recommended Daily Value (DV) of this nutrient

Good source of . . . : provides 10 to 19 percent of the recommended DV in one serving

Light or "lite": contains one-third fewer calories or half the fat of the regular food; could also apply to a "low-calorie" or "low-fat" food that contains 50 percent less sodium than the regular food. In all other cases, the package must specify whether the word "light" refers to color, texture, or other qualities.

Fresh: food that is raw and has not been processed, frozen, or heated and contains no preservatives

Freshly: may be used with "baked" if the food has been made recently

instance). While they still contain about 120 calories and 14 grams of fat per tablespoon, liquid oils are lower in saturated fat and higher in monounsaturated and polyunsaturated fats, which are less harmful and may even protect against heart disease. Vegetable oils also supply vitamin E, one of the antioxidants that seem to protect against heart disease.

So although you want to keep your intake of fats and oils low to stay slim and keep your heart healthy, says Dr. Marshel,

the right types, when used judiciously, can have their place on your shopping list.

Buy an oil or two and make it last. Among oils most commonly sold in supermarkets, these are your best

choices, ranked from lowest levels of saturated fat to the highest.

1. Canola oil

2. Walnut oil

3. Safflower oil

4. Sunflower oil

5. Corn oil

6. Olive oil

7. Sesame oil

8. Soybean oil

9. Peanut oil

Healthy Choices in the Snack Aisle

Not all snacks are junk foods, say the pros. When chosen carefully, they can actually be a low-calorie, low-fat way of helping you get your nutrients.

Crackers count. Low-fat crackers, says Jibrin, will help you achieve the daily fiber quota recommended by experts. Jibrin recommends crackers that contain about 2 grams of fiber per half ounce, with zero to 4 grams of fat. "They're a really good

way to get a lot of fiber, especially if you can develop a taste for those Scandinavian or German-type brands such as Wasa and RyKrisp. Even some brands of whole wheat matzoh have 11 grams of fiber per half-ounce serving," she says.

Graham is good. Graham crackers are generally low in fat and provide some iron and riboflavin, earning them a spot on your shopping list.

Reach for the unsalted and fat-free nibbles. Dr. Marshel's top picks: unsalted whole grain pretzels, corn or rice cakes, and baked fat-free potato or tortilla chips.

"Some of these snacks are good sources of fiber, and you should use the same rule of thumb you would with crackers: Try for 2 grams of fiber per half ounce," says Jibrin.

Check for sugar. One caveat: Dr. Marshel reminds us not to be seduced by every label marked "low-fat" or "fat-free": "The first ingredient listed on a package of low-fat and fat-free cakes and cookies is usually sugar—which means it may be high in calories."

Try more than one brand. "Some of the fat-free baked chips taste rather bland, and some are not so bad, particularly with salsa, so you've got to experiment," says Jibrin.

Deli Ahead: Proceed with Caution

If you happen to head for the checkout counter without stopping at the deli, you'll probably save money, fat, and calories. Should you stop at the deli, proceed with caution, says Dr. Marshel. Few of the items you'll see here sport nutrition information, she says, so it's advisable to approach this tempting display of variety meats, cheeses, prepared salads, barbecued chicken, and other specialty items carefully. Here are some guidelines for buying the best and leaving the rest.

Be specific. Think about what you want and be very specific when you order, says Dr. Marshel. "If you're asking for turkey, for example, ask for 100 percent turkey rather than turkey roll, which is higher in sodium because it's been processed," she says.

Limit your choices to unprocessed foods. Some processed deli foods may have added sugar, says Dr. Marshel. And the prepared salads often contain too much mayonnaise, which means lots of fat. The more you stick to unprocessed foods, such as sliced turkey or chicken, the better off you'll be. If you're buying cold cuts at all, you might want to buy the low-fat packaged kinds found in the refrigerator case. "There you're able to read the labels, which you often can't do behind the deli counter. Many of those products are also high in sodium and sugar," notes Dr. Marshel.

Salads
and Soups

SALADS

SOUPS

Easy Tropical Fruit Salad

—Stephanie Patrick, Mill Creek, Washington

Getting nine servings of produce each day can be delightful when you're eating sweet, refreshing fruit dishes like this.

Prep time: 15 minutes
Chill time: 1 hour

½ **cup fresh or canned-in-juice pineapple chunks**
½ **cup sliced banana**
½ **cup orange sections**
½ **cup red or green grapes, halved**
½ **cup sliced kiwifruit (about 2 kiwis)**
½ **cup sliced strawberries**
½ **cup orange juice**
2 **teaspoons Grand Marnier (optional)**
2 **tablespoons sweetened flaked coconut**

In a large bowl, combine the pineapple, banana, orange, grapes, kiwifruit, strawberries, orange juice, and Grand Marnier, if using. Stir to mix well. Cover and refrigerate for 1 hour. Serve sprinkled with the coconut.

Makes 6 servings

Per serving: *73 calories, 1 g protein, 17 g carbohydrate, 1 g fat, 0 mg cholesterol, 6 mg sodium, 2 g fiber*

Diet Exchanges: *0 milk, 0 vegetable, 1 fruit, 0 bread, 0 meat, 0 fat*

1 Carb Choice

SHOPPING SAVVY

Making the Cut

Mangos are a sweet, juicy, and delicious treat whether you're on a diet or not. But as anyone who has ever tackled cutting this tropical fruit knows, the soft orange flesh clings to the big seed in the middle tighter than a poker player to his cards. Many a mango has ended up as a mangled mess in the hands of inexperienced cutters. To the rescue comes the **OXO Good Grips Mango Splitter.** One simple press removes the seed and cuts the fruit in half cleanly, leaving almost nothing behind on the seed. Soft, comfortable

grips cushion while you press, and the stainless steel blades are sharp and sturdy. The tool is dishwasher safe. Look for it wherever quality houseware tools are sold. OXO manufactures more than 500 innovative, ergonomically designed tools. Take a look at www.oxo.com.

176 Calories

Apple Yummie

—Carol Weber, French Village, Missouri

*Add a splash of lemon juice or a teaspoon of vanilla extract
for a pleasant flavor accent.*

Prep time: 10 minutes
Chill time: 30 minutes

  4 **apples, peeled and cubed**
⅓ **cup light mayonnaise**
½ **cup golden raisins**
½ **cup orange sections**
  1 **tablespoon orange juice**
  1 **teaspoon grated orange peel**
¼ **cup roasted, salted sunflower seeds**

In a large bowl, combine the apples, mayonnaise, raisins, orange, orange juice, and orange peel.

Stir gently to mix. Cover and refrigerate for about 30 minutes. Sprinkle the sunflower seeds on the mixture before serving.

Makes 6 servings

Per serving: *176 calories, 2 g protein, 28 g carbohydrate, 7 g fat, 5 mg cholesterol, 132 mg sodium, 3 g fiber*

Diet Exchanges: *0 milk, 0 vegetable, 2 fruit, 0 bread, 0 meat, 1½ fat*

2 Carb Choices

135 Calories

Citrus-Avocado Salad

—Veronica Callaghan, Glastonbury, Connecticut

"This salad provides lots of potassium and vitamin C while filling me up at lunchtime to help me lose weight."

Prep time: 10 minutes

S A L A D

- 8 **cups mixed salad greens**
- 2 **navel oranges, separated into segments and chopped**
- 1 **avocado, chopped**
- 1 **tablespoon chopped walnuts**

D R E S S I N G

- 2 **tablespoons lime juice**
- 2 **tablespoons extra-virgin olive oil**
- 1 **tablespoon finely chopped cilantro**
- ¼ **teaspoon salt**
- ⅛ **teaspoon ground red pepper**

To prepare the salad: In a large shallow salad bowl, arrange the greens. Top with the oranges and avocado. Sprinkle with the walnuts.

To prepare the dressing: In a small bowl, whisk together the lime juice, oil, cilantro, salt, and pepper. Drizzle over the salad. Toss gently.

Makes 6 servings

Per serving: 135 calories, 2 g protein, 11 g carbohydrate, 10 g fat, 0 mg cholesterol, 118 mg sodium, 5 g fiber

Diet Exchanges: *½ vegetable, ½ fruit, 2 fat*

1 Carb Choice

161 Calories

Apple Paradisio

—J. Johnson, Elizabethtown, Indiana

Adding fruit to your diet lessens the craving for processed sugary snacks.

Prep time: 10 minutes
Chill time: 1 hour

- 5 apples, cubed (about 6 cups)
- 2 cups (12 ounces) green seedless grapes
- ¾ cup (3 ounces) pecan halves
- 1 carton (6 ounces) low-fat lemon yogurt
- ¼ teaspoon ground cinnamon

In a mixing bowl, combine the apples, grapes, pecans, yogurt, and cinnamon. Stir gently to mix. Cover and refrigerate for 1 hour.

Makes 8 servings

Per serving: *161 calories, 2 g protein, 24 g carbohydrate, 8 g fat, 1 mg cholesterol, 16 mg sodium, 3 g fiber*

Diet Exchanges: *0 milk, 0 vegetable, 1 fruit, ½ bread, 0 meat, 1½ fat*

1½ Carb Choices

SECRETS OF WEIGHT-LOSS WINNERS

• I try to drink a glass of water before and during my meals to help fill me up.
—Cheryl Imayoshi, British Columbia, Canada

• Drink lots of water.
—Lisa Mallia, Toronto, Ontario, Canada

• I use a crystal water glass. I enjoy seeing its beautiful crystal design, and it helps to remind me to drink more water throughout the day.
—Mary Gonzales, Winter Garden, Florida

• Drink plenty of water and keep busy.
—Gloria Schulte, Edmond, Oklahoma

• I have bottles of water everywhere: in my car; at my desk; in my bedroom; while watching TV.
—Kirsten Kimball, Graham, Washington

• Drink eight glasses of water a day. Every morning I put eight pennies on the kitchen counter. When I drink a glass of water, I put a penny back in the drawer until all eight pennies are gone at the end of the day.
—Cindy Phillips, Saint Helens, Oregon

56 Calories

Simple Slaw

—Nancy Woolweber, Charlotte, North Carolina

"There's wonderful fiber in these veggies."

Prep time: 15 minutes

1 small head (2 pounds) green or red cabbage, thinly sliced (about 14 cups)
1 small red onion, thinly sliced
6 tablespoons red wine vinegar
3 tablespoons extra-virgin olive oil
½ teaspoon salt
   Freshly ground black pepper

In a large bowl, combine the cabbage and onion. In a cup, whisk together the vinegar, oil, salt, and pepper to taste. Drizzle the dressing over the salad. Toss to mix well.

Makes 12 servings

Per serving: *56 calories, 1 g protein, 5 g carbohydrate, 3½ g fat, 0 mg cholesterol, 115 mg sodium, 2 g fiber*

Diet Exchanges: *0 milk, 1 vegetable, 0 fruit, 0 bread, 0 meat, 1 fat*

½ **Carb Choice**

24 Calories

Broccoli Salad

—Karen Scott, Levering, Michigan

"This is an easy salad to make. It's always a hit, and you get your fresh raw veggies!"

Prep time: 5 minutes
Chill time: 1 hour

- 1 bag (8 ounces) fresh precut broccoli, cut into bite-size pieces
- 2 tablespoons chopped red onion
- ¼ cup light balsamic salad dressing
  Freshly ground black pepper
- 1 tablespoon grated Parmesan/Romano cheese blend

In a large bowl, combine the broccoli and onion. Drizzle the dressing on top. Season to taste with pepper. Toss to mix. Refrigerate for 1 hour to chill. Serve sprinkled with the cheese.

Makes 6 servings

Per serving: *24 calories, 2 g protein, 4 g carbohydrate, 1 g fat, 1 mg cholesterol, 154 mg sodium, 1 g fiber*

Diet Exchanges: *0 milk, ½ vegetable, 0 fruit, 0 bread, 0 meat, 0 fat*

0 Carb Choices

161 Calories

Green Bean Vegetable Salad

—Maria Diehl, Schenectady, New York

"This recipe is a great side dish that is low in calories and can be substituted for a green salad, which over time can get boring."

Prep time: 10 minutes
Microwave time: 1 minute
Chill time: 3 hours

- ¼ cup red or white wine vinegar
- 1 tablespoon water
- 2 teaspoons sugar or Splenda
- ⅛ teaspoon salt
- 3 tablespoons canola or olive oil
- 1 package (16 ounces) frozen French-style green beans, thawed
- 1 package (10 ounces) frozen baby peas, thawed
- 1 package (10 ounces) frozen white kernel corn, thawed
- ½ cup chopped onion
- ½ cup chopped celery
- 1 jar (4 ounces) pimientos, drained
- 2 slices turkey bacon, cooked and crumbled

In a microwaveable bowl, whisk together the vinegar, water, sugar or Splenda, and salt. Cover and microwave on high power for 1 minute or until the sugar or Splenda is dissolved. Set aside to cool to room temperature.

Pour the vinegar mixture into a large bowl. Add the oil and whisk to blend. Add the beans, peas, corn, onion, celery, and pimientos. Toss to mix.

Cover and refrigerate, stirring occasionally, for at least 3 hours. Top with the bacon bits before serving.

Makes 8 servings

Per serving: *161 calories, 6 g protein, 19 g carbohydrate, 8 g fat, 7 mg cholesterol, 276 mg sodium, 4 g fiber*

Diet Exchanges: *0 milk, 1 vegetable, 0 fruit, 1 bread, ½ meat, 1½ fat*

1 Carb Choice

Easy Summer Cucumber Salad

—Vicki Koch, Port St. Lucie, Florida

This is a tasty side dish with a grilled chicken breast or grilled salmon steak.

Prep time: 10 minutes

1 large English cucumber, halved lengthwise
1 cup cherry tomatoes, halved
½ cup thinly sliced red onion
⅓ cup reduced-fat sour cream
2 tablespoons white wine vinegar
2 teaspoons sugar or Splenda
2 tablespoons chopped olives
¼ teaspoon salt
  Freshly ground black pepper

Cut the cucumber halves into ¼" thick slices. Transfer to a large bowl. Add the tomatoes, onion, sour cream, vinegar, sugar or Splenda, olives, and salt. Toss to mix. Season to taste with pepper.

Makes 6 servings

Per serving: *41 calories, 1 g protein, 5 g carbohydrate, 2 g fat, 5 mg cholesterol, 129 mg sodium, 1 g fiber*

Diet Exchanges: *0 milk, ½ vegetable, 0 fruit, 0 bread, 0 meat, ½ fat*

½ **Carb Choice**

210 Calories

Corkscrew Pasta Vegetable Salad

—Patricia Albrecht, Ripon, Wisconsin

Boost nutrients by tossing crispy vegetables into pasta salad.

Prep time: 20 minutes
Microwave time: 2 minutes
Chill time: several hours

DRESSING

1 cup light mayonnaise or salad dressing
1 teaspoon minced garlic
1 tablespoon minced fresh dill
¼ teaspoon salt

SALAD

4 cups broccoli florets, cut into bite-size pieces
6 ounces corkscrew pasta, cooked, drained, and cooled (about 3 cups)
2 small carrots, chopped
1 cup cherry or grape tomatoes, halved
6 radishes, sliced
1 small red onion, chopped
2 tablespoons sliced black olives
  Ground black pepper

To prepare the dressing: In a large bowl, combine the mayonnaise or salad dressing, garlic, dill, and salt. Set aside.

To prepare the salad: Place the broccoli in a shallow microwaveable dish in a single layer. Add a few tablespoons of water. Cover and microwave for 2 minutes on high power. Remove and drain the water.

To the dressing in the bowl, add the pasta, carrots, tomatoes, radishes, onion, olives, and reserved broccoli. Season to taste with pepper. Toss to mix well. Cover and refrigerate for several hours to chill.

Makes 8 servings

Per serving: *210 calories, 4 g protein, 24 g carbohydrate, 11 g fat, 11 mg cholesterol, 357 mg sodium, 2 g fiber*

Diet Exchanges: *0 milk, 1 vegetable, 0 fruit, 1 bread, 0 meat, 2 fat*

1½ Carb Choices

177
Calories

Linguine Salad

—Katrina Meyer, Waukesha, Wisconsin

*This dish calls for truly ripe garden or farmers' market tomatoes,
which are juicy and bursting with flavor.*

Prep time: 15 minutes
Cook time: 10 minutes
Chill time: 1 hour

  8 ounces linguine
  3 tomatoes, quartered
½ cup loose-packed fresh basil leaves
  2 tablespoons grated Pecorino Romano
    cheese
  1 teaspoon minced garlic
¼ cup low-fat Italian salad dressing
    Pinch ground red pepper

Cook the linguine according to package
directions. Drain and set aside to cool.

In a large bowl, combine the linguine,
tomatoes, basil, cheese, garlic, and pepper.
Drizzle with the dressing. Toss to mix well.

Cover and refrigerate for 1 hour.

Makes 6 servings

Per serving: *177 calories, 7 g protein, 32 g
carbohydrate, 2 g fat, 3 mg cholesterol, 119 mg
sodium, 2 g fiber*

Diet Exchanges: *0 milk, ½ vegetable, 0 fruit,
2 bread, 0 meat, ½ fat*

2 Carb Choices

Black-Eyed Pea Salad

—Janine Lewis, St. Petersburg, Florida

This hearty dish makes a wonderful light meal.

Prep time: 10 minutes
Chill time: 1 hour

1 can (15½ ounces) black-eyed peas, rinsed and drained

1 medium seedless cucumber, peeled and cubed

2 tomatoes, chopped

½ cup chopped red onion

½ cup chopped green bell pepper

¼ cup balsamic vinaigrette dressing

⅛ teaspoon salt

   Freshly ground black pepper

2 tablespoons crumbled feta cheese

In a medium bowl, combine the peas, cucumber, tomatoes, onion, bell pepper, dressing, salt, and black pepper to taste. Toss to mix. Cover and refrigerate for 1 hour. Serve topped with the cheese.

Makes 4 servings

Per serving: *150 calories, 6 g protein, 20 g carbohydrate, 6 g fat, 4 mg cholesterol, 514 mg sodium, 4 g fiber*

Diet Exchanges: *0 milk, 1½ vegetable, 0 fruit, 1 bread, 0 meat, 1 fat*

1½ Carb Choices

Ted's Fresh Mozzarella Salad

—Ted Kranenberg, Cambridge, Minnesota

"It's very quick to make and filling. You can't beat fresh ingredients."

Prep time: 10 minutes
Chill time: 1 hour

- 12 ounces fresh mozzarella cheese, drained and sliced
- 6 ripe plum tomatoes, sliced
- 2 tablespoons extra-virgin olive oil
- ½ teaspoon dried oregano
- ⅛ teaspoon salt
  Freshly ground black pepper
- 6 fresh basil leaves, thinly sliced (optional)

In a large shallow dish, arrange the cheese and tomatoes. In a small bowl, combine the oil, oregano, and salt. Whisk to blend. Drizzle over the cheese and tomatoes. Cover and marinate for 1 hour.

Serve, seasoned to taste with pepper and drizzled with the marinating juices. Sprinkle the basil on top, if desired.

Makes 6 servings

Per serving: *217 calories, 11 g protein, 3 g carbohydrate, 17 g fat, 41 mg cholesterol, 224 mg sodium, 1 g fiber*

Diet Exchanges: *0 milk, ½ vegetable, 0 fruit, 0 bread, 0 meat, 1 fat*

0 Carb Choices

Chopped Quick Lunch Salad

—Laura Lubin, New York, New York

*"Since I'm not much of a salad eater, this was a great find for me.
The coleslaw, which I normally would not eat as a side dish, somehow flavors
the lettuces and works nicely with the spice element of the turkey, in addition to
adding a level of vegetables (the cabbage)."*

Prep time: 10 minutes

- ¼ cup delicatessen vinaigrette coleslaw
- 2 tablespoons light mayonnaise
- ¼ teaspoon ground black pepper
- ⅛ teaspoon salt
- 4 cups mixed baby salad greens
- 2 thick slices (2 ounces each) spicy pepper delicatessen turkey, cut into cubes
- 1 ounce low-fat Swiss cheese, cut into small pieces
- ½ cup frozen baby peas, thawed
- ¼ cup chopped baby carrots

In a large bowl, combine the coleslaw, mayonnaise, pepper, and salt. Stir to mix well. Add the greens, turkey, cheese, peas, and carrots. Toss to coat all the ingredients with the dressing.

Makes 4 servings

Per serving: *86 calories, 6 g protein, 6 g carbohydrate, 4.5 g fat, 14 mg cholesterol, 332 mg sodium, 2 g fiber*

Diet Exchanges: *0 milk, ½ vegetable, 0 fruit, 0 bread, 1 meat, ½ fat*

½ Carb Choice

Luscious Lime Shrimp Salad

—Cathy Cook, Cobbtown, Georgia

"It's low in calories and carbs, and it's a lovely salad to eat any day of the week."

Prep time: 10 minutes
Cook time: 3 minutes
Chill time: 30 minutes

1½ tablespoons lime juice, preferably
    freshly squeezed
1 tablespoon chopped cilantro
1 small scallion, white and green parts,
    chopped
½ tablespoon hoisin sauce
½ teaspoon extra-virgin olive oil
¼ teaspoon minced garlic
    Pinch of ground white pepper
8 ounces large shrimp, peeled, deveined,
    and rinsed
1 tablespoon chopped red bell pepper
    Bibb lettuce leaves

In a large bowl, combine the lime juice, cilantro, scallion, hoisin sauce, oil, garlic, and white pepper. Whisk to mix. Set aside.

In a large nonstick skillet over medium heat, warm 1 tablespoon of the reserved mixture. Add the shrimp. Cook, tossing, for 2 to 3 minutes, or until the shrimp are opaque. Pour the skillet contents into the reserved mixture. Add the bell pepper. Cover and refrigerate, tossing occasionally, for 30 minutes. Place two serving dishes in the refrigerator, if desired.

Line each chilled plate with the lettuce leaves. Spoon the shrimp and some of the marinade onto the lettuce.

Makes 2 servings

Per serving: *151 calories, 24 g protein, 5 g carbohydrate, 3.5 g fat, 173 mg cholesterol, 235 mg sodium, 1 g fiber*

Diet Exchanges: *0 milk, 0 vegetable, 0 fruit, 0 bread, 3 meat, ½ fat*

½ Carb Choice

Easy Chix Salad

—L. Peters, Edmonton, Alberta, Canada

"This is a great one for summer. It's high in protein and complex carbohydrates and low in fat. The salad greens help fill me up, and the other ingredients take a long time to be processed, so I'm not hungry in an hour or so."

Prep time: 10 minutes

2 boneless, skinless chicken breasts, cooked and cut into bite-size cubes

4 cups mixed baby salad greens

1 can (15 ounces) chickpeas, rinsed and drained

1 cup mashed avocado

½ cup fresh salsa

¼ cup sliced scallions

½ cup chopped fresh cilantro leaves (optional)

In a large bowl, combine the chicken, greens, chickpeas, avocado, scallions, salsa, and scallions. Toss to mix. Sprinkle each serving with the cilantro, if desired.

Makes 6 servings

Per serving: *163 calories, 13 g protein, 13 g carbohydrate, 7 g fat, 23 mg cholesterol, 208 mg sodium, 5 g fiber*

Diet Exchanges: *0 milk, ½ vegetable, 0 fruit, ½ bread, 1½ meat, 1 fat*

1 Carb Choice

SHOPPING SAVVY

Glorious Greens

Dark-green leafy vegetables are among the most nutritious vegetables on the planet. Just 3½ ounces of cooked kale, for instance, contain 228 milligrams of potassium, 28 milligrams of phosphorus, 18 milligrams of magnesium, and 817 micrograms of vitamin K, all for a paltry 28 calories! The only downside of preparing greens is the amount of water and time required to wash all the sand off the leaves. But now Glory Foods of Columbus, Ohio, is taking care of that task for us by cleaning and bagging a host of healthy leaves. The company, known for its trademark Southern-style foods and seasoning products, offers 16-ounce bags of mustard, collard, turnip, and kale greens. (Check out the fast and easy recipe on page 146 for an introduction to just how delicious good-for-you can taste!) And for more about Glory products, visit www.gloryfoods.com.

193 Calories

Buffalo Fiesta Salad with Fire-Roasted Salsa

—Tom Pooser, DeFuniak Springs, Florida

"I ate this hearty salad at least three times a week and lost over 70 pounds in 5 months."

Prep time: 4 minutes
Cook time: 8 minutes

  2 teaspoons olive or canola oil
  1 pound ground buffalo
  2 teaspoons chili powder
  2 teaspoons chipotle seasoning
  ¼ teaspoon salt
  8 ounces spring mix salad greens
1½ cups chopped cucumber
  ½ cup Fire-Roasted Salsa (page 78)

In a large nonstick skillet over medium-high heat, warm the oil. Crumble in the buffalo. Season with the chili powder, chipotle seasoning, and salt. Cook, stirring occasionally, for about 8 minutes, or until browned.

Divide the greens onto 4 plates. Spoon the buffalo mixture and cucumber over the greens. Top each serving with 12 tablespoons of salsa.

Makes 4 servings

Per serving: *193 calories, 25 g protein, 6 g carbohydrate, 7 g fat, 55 mg cholesterol, 220 mg sodium, 2 g fiber*

Diet Exchanges: *0 milk, 1 vegetable, 0 fruit, 0 bread, 3½ meat, 1 fat*

½ Carb Choice

4
Calories

Fire-Roasted Salsa

Prep time: 10 minutes
Grill time 10 to 12 minutes
Chill time: 1 hour

4 medium ripe fresh tomatoes

4 scallions

2 poblano chile peppers

1 jalapeño chile pepper (wear plastic gloves when handling)

1 tablespoon canola oil

1 cup chopped fresh cilantro

2 tablespoons apple cider vinegar

Preheat a grill. Coat the tomatoes, scallions, and chile peppers with the canola oil. Grill the vegetables over high heat, turning frequently, for 10 to 12 minutes, or until the tomato and pepper skins are lightly charred. Remove from the heat. Set aside until cool enough to handle.

Chop the roasted vegetables. Place in a large bowl. Add the cilantro and vinegar. Stir to mix. Cover and refrigerate for 1 hour.

Makes 40 servings; 2 tablespoons per serving (2½ cups)

Per serving: *4 calories, 0 g protein, 1 g carbohydrate, 0 g fat, 0 mg cholesterol, 2 mg sodium, 0 g fiber*

Diet Exchanges: *0 milk, 0 vegetable, 0 fruit, 0 bread, 0 meat, 0 fat*

0 Carb Choices

— *Kitchen Tip* —

Extra salsa may be refrigerated in a closed container for several weeks.

135 Calories

Chicken Caesar Salad

—Pam McCune, Eau Claire, Wisconsin

*The lemon and garlic give this salad so much flavor.
It is very filling and satisfying.*

Prep time: 10 minutes
Cook time: 10 to 12 minutes

- 1 teaspoon + 3 tablespoons extra-virgin olive oil
- 2 boneless, skinless chicken breasts (about 10–12 ounces)
- 2 tablespoons lemon juice
- 2 cloves garlic, minced
- ¼ teaspoon coarse salt
- 1 head romaine lettuce, coarsely shredded (about 8 ounces)
- 3 tablespoons shredded Parmesan cheese
  Freshly ground black pepper

In a nonstick skillet over medium-high heat, warm 1 teaspoon of the oil. Place the chicken in the pan. Cook for 5 to 6 minutes per side, or until golden and a thermometer inserted in the thickest portion registers 160°F and the juices run clear.

In a large bowl, combine the remaining 3 tablespoons oil, the lemon juice, garlic, and salt. Whisk to blend. Add the lettuce and cheese. Toss to mix. Transfer to 4 serving plates. Thinly slice the chicken breasts crosswise. Divide the slices evenly over the salad. Season to taste with pepper.

Makes 6 servings

Per serving: 135 calories, 11 g protein, 2 g carbohydrate, 9 g fat, 25 mg cholesterol, 148 mg sodium, 0 g fiber

Diet Exchanges: *0 milk, 0 vegetable, 0 fruit, 0 bread, 1½ meat, 1½ fat*

0 Carb Choices

It Worked for Me!

Sharon Hildebrandt, 41

VITAL STATS

Weight lost: 75 pounds

Time to initial goal: 4 years

Greatest challenge: changing her lifestyle to learn to like healthy foods

In old family photos, Sharon Hildebrandt was the skinny one. "I was 130 pounds when I married my husband, Michael," says the Sayre, Pennsylvania, schoolteacher. In 1992, however, when she became pregnant at 27, she stopped being active and started eating for two—and more. As a result, she added 50-plus pounds to her 5'7" frame. After giving birth to her son, Trey, only 20 came off. In 1995, she became pregnant with daughter Paige and gained 60 more pounds.

Sharon's turning point came on an August morning in 2001. "I saw myself literally roll out of bed in this huge mirror we have. I thought, 'What have I done?' I lost it—cried and cried and cried." She weighed 231 pounds.

That afternoon, Sharon enrolled in LA Weight Loss, which requires its participants to keep food diaries and weigh in each week. "They made me focus on what I was eating

and helped me realize that I'm an emotional eater."

Sharon consumed 1,200 to 1,400 calories a day in carefully portioned meals and snacks of lean protein (fish, chicken, eggs), fruits and vegetables, and low-fat dairy. She learned to eat breakfast—she'd always skipped it before—and to drink water to quell hunger pangs. She also started to move her body—any activity from Tae Bo class to using a push mower to cut her lawn. By March 2002, Sharon had lost 60 pounds. By 2005, she'd lost another 15.

She's now more relaxed about her eating. "When I crave something, like ice cream, I have it. I just watch the portions." She's also a more creative and health-conscious cook.

"My success was a result of a true change in lifestyle," says Sharon. "It was the most difficult obstacle I've ever had to overcome. But I did overcome it by starting each day new, believing in myself."

19 Calories

Ranch Dressing

—Terry Thompson, Casper, Wyoming

This luscious dressing is extra special when you make it with fresh minced garlic and parsley.

Prep time: 5 minutes

- 1 **cup reduced-fat buttermilk**
- 1 **cup fat-free mayonnaise**
- 1 **tablespoon minced or grated onion or 2 teaspoons dehydrated onion**
- 1 **tablespoon finely chopped parsley**
- ½ **teaspoon minced or dried garlic**
- ⅛ **teaspoon salt**

In a bowl, combine the buttermilk, mayonnaise, onion, parsley, garlic, and salt. Whisk to blend.

Makes 16 servings; 2 tablespoons per serving (2 cups)

Per serving: *19 calories, 1 g protein, 3 g carbohydrate, 1 g fat, 3 mg cholesterol, 155 mg sodium, 0 g fiber*

Diet Exchanges: *0 milk, 0 vegetable, 0 fruit, 0 bread, 0 meat, 0 fat*

0 Carb Choices

SECRETS OF WEIGHT-LOSS WINNERS

• Exercise. It's not only great for you, but you'll look years younger and feel more energetic. Do aerobic exercise at least 30 minutes a day with any activity that gets your heart rate up for 30 minutes. Follow with weight training for about 15 minutes, and if you have time, try yoga or Pilates. It will work wonders on shaping your body.

—Chitra Pamadi, Downingtown, Pennsylvania

• My tip is to exercise and use portion control. It's the only safe and effective way to lose weight. So far I have lost 50 pounds doing it this way.

—Tammy Gauf, Mauston, Wisconsin

• When I am upstairs, I go downstairs to use the bathroom. If I am downstairs, I go upstairs to use the bathroom.

—Terri Gray, Ligonier, Iowa

158 Calories

Cream of Broccoli Soup

—Susan Showalter, Delavan, Wisconsin

"Success in my diet depends upon making easy, healthy meals that my children and husband enjoy. This is a simple, hearty soup that works with broccoli or cauliflower. Adding a hearty, whole grain bread is even more satisfying. It's also a great leftover for my lunch the next day."

Prep time: 5 minutes
Cook time: 20 minutes

- 1 bag (14 ounces) (4½ cups) frozen loose-pack broccoli
- 1 tablespoon butter or trans-free margarine
- ¼ cup finely chopped onion
- 1 tablespoon flour
- 2 cups fat-free reduced-sodium chicken broth
- 1 cup fat-free evaporated milk
- ½ teaspoon salt
- ¼ teaspoon ground black pepper
- ½ cup shredded reduced-fat sharp Cheddar cheese

Cook the broccoli according to package directions. Drain and set aside.

In a large heavy saucepan over medium heat, warm the butter or margarine. Add the onion. Cook, stirring occasionally, for 2 minutes, or until tender. Place the flour in a bowl. Gradually add the broth, whisking constantly, until the flour is dissolved. Add the broth mixture and milk to the pot. Cook, stirring constantly, for 5 to 7 minutes, or until bubbly and slightly thickened. Add the reserved broccoli, salt, and pepper. Simmer for 5 minutes.

In a blender or food processor, puree the soup, in batches if necessary, and return to the pot. Stir in the cheese. Cook, stirring, over low heat for about 1 minute, or until the cheese melts.

Makes 4 servings

Per serving: *158 calories, 11 g protein, 15 g carbohydrate, 6 g fat, 20 mg cholesterol, 853 mg sodium, 3 g fiber*

Diet Exchanges: *0 milk, 1 vegetable, 0 fruit, 0 bread, ½ meat, 1 fat*

1 Carb Choice

157 Calories

Gianna's Lentil Soup

—Giovanna Kranenberg, Cambridge, Minnesota

"It's so filling, healthy, and ohhh so good!"

Prep time: 20 minutes
Cook time: 45 minutes

  2 **tablespoons olive oil**
  1 **small yellow onion, chopped**
  1 **medium carrot, finely chopped**
  1 **rib celery, finely chopped**
  2 **cloves garlic, minced**
  8 **ounces brown lentils, rinsed and drained**
  1 **medium potato, peeled and chopped**
  ½ **cup canned crushed petite diced tomatoes**
  2 **bay leaves**
  6 **cups vegetable broth or water**
  ½ **teaspoon dried thyme**
  2 **tablespoons chopped fresh parsley**
  ½ **teaspoon salt**
  ½ **teaspoon ground black pepper**

In a large saucepan over medium heat, warm the oil. Add the onion, carrot, celery, and garlic. Cook, stirring, for about 5 minutes, or until the carrot starts to soften. Add the lentils, potato, tomatoes, and bay leaves. Stir to mix. Cook for 2 minutes for the flavors to blend. Add the broth or water and thyme. Bring to a boil, then lower the heat to simmer.

Cook for about 35 minutes, or until the lentils are very tender.

Add the parsley, salt, and pepper. Remove the bay leaves and discard.

Makes 8 servings

Per serving: *157 calories, 8 g protein, 24 g carbohydrate, 3.5 g fat, 0 mg cholesterol, 492 mg sodium, 9 g fiber*

Diet Exchanges: *0 milk, 1 vegetable, 0 fruit, 0 bread, 0 meat, ½ fat*

1½ Carb Choices

Easy Chinese Vegetable Soup

—Stephanie Patrick, Mill Creek, Washington

*This oh-so-simple soup tastes better than any takeout
and contains a fraction of the fat.*

**Prep time: 20 minutes
Cook time: 25 minutes**

- 1 tablespoon vegetable oil
- ½ medium onion, chopped
- 2 teaspoons minced garlic
- 4 cups fat-free reduced-sodium chicken broth
- 3 cups chopped vegetables (such as carrots and mushrooms)
- 1 cup bean sprouts
- 2 tablespoons reduced-sodium soy sauce
- ½ teaspoon ground black pepper
- ½ teaspoon toasted sesame oil

In a soup pot over medium heat, warm the vegetable oil. Add the onion and garlic. Cook, stirring, for 1 minute. Add the broth, vegetables, sprouts, soy sauce, and pepper. Bring to a boil. Turn down the heat and simmer for about 20 minutes, or until the vegetables are tender. Stir in the sesame oil.

Makes 4 servings

Per serving: *92 calories, 4 g protein, 10 g carbohydrate, 4.5 g fat, 0 mg cholesterol, 789 mg sodium, 2 g fiber*

Diet Exchanges: *0 milk, 1½ vegetable, 0 fruit, 0 bread, 0 meat, 1 fat*

1 Carb Choice

SECRETS OF WEIGHT-LOSS WINNERS

- Prepare snacks ahead of time so when you're hungry you'll have something handy and convenient.

—Brenda Robinson, Charleston, West Virginia

- Find a hobby that you enjoy, and spend at least 30 minutes a day doing it to get rid of your stress.

—Sher Sosine, Concord, California

78 Calories

Cabbage & Beef Soup

—Rosemary Fahlen, Rockford, Michigan

*Prepare a batch of this hearty soup on the weekend
to reheat for a fast weeknight supper.*

Prep time: 15 minutes
Cook time: 40 minutes

- 1 tablespoon olive oil
- 1 cup chopped onion
- ½ teaspoon thyme
- 8 ounces 99% lean ground beef
- 6 cups thinly sliced green cabbage
- 1 cup thinly sliced carrots
- 6 cups fat-free reduced-sodium chicken broth
- ½ teaspoon salt
- ½ teaspoon ground black pepper

In a large saucepan over medium heat, warm the oil. Add the onion and thyme. Cook, stirring occasionally, for about 5 minutes, or until softened. Add the beef. Cook, stirring occasionally, for about 4 minutes longer, or until no longer pink. Add the cabbage, carrots, broth, salt, and pepper. Bring to a boil. Reduce the heat. Simmer for 30 minutes, or until the cabbage is very tender.

Makes 8 servings

Per serving: *78 calories, 7 g protein, 6 g carbohydrate, 3 g fat, 15 mg cholesterol, 518 mg sodium, 2 g fiber*

Diet Exchanges: *0 milk, 1 vegetable, 0 fruit, 0 bread, 1 meat, ½ fat*

½ **Carb Choice**

84 Calories

Cold Soup à la Tomato

—Winston Banford, Mount Holly, New Jersey

This dish is heaven when prepared with seasonal ripe tomatoes, either from your own garden or the farmers' market.

Prep time: 25 minutes
Chill time: several hours

6 large very ripe tomatoes, cut into quarters

1 cucumber, peeled, cut into chunks

1 green bell pepper, cut into chunks

1 Portuguese bread roll (about 4 ounces), cut into pieces and soaked in enough water to cover (about ½ cup)

5 garlic cloves, peeled

¼ cup white wine vinegar

2 tablespoons extra-virgin olive oil

½ teaspoon salt

In a blender or a food processor fitted with a metal blade, pulse the tomatoes, cucumber, pepper, bread, and garlic. Pulse for 1 to 2 minutes, or until the mixture is a chunky puree. Pour into a large bowl. Add the vinegar, oil, and salt. Cover and refrigerate for several hours.

Makes 10 servings

Per serving: *84 calories, 2 g protein, 12 g carbohydrate, 3.5 g fat, 0 mg cholesterol, 192 mg sodium, 2 g fiber*

Diet Exchanges: *0 milk, 1 vegetable, 0 fruit, ½ bread, 0 meat, ½ fat*

1 Carb Choice

154
Calories

Michelle's Hearty Bean & Pasta Soup

—Michelle Barr, Pine Mountain Club, California

"This dish is rich with different textures and tastes, low in fat, high in protein, and hearty enough to satisfy the hungriest member of my family."

Prep time: 20 minutes
Cook time: 30 minutes

　1　**cup cooked whole wheat pasta shells or spirals (about 2 ounces dry)**
　¾　**cup canned chickpeas, rinsed and drained**
　2　**teaspoons olive oil**
　¾　**cup finely chopped onion**
　½　**cup finely chopped red bell pepper**
　2　**cloves garlic, minced**
　1　**can (14½ ounces) stewed or diced tomatoes**
　1　**can (15½ ounces) black-eyed peas, drained and rinsed**
1½　**cups vegetable broth or water**
　½　**teaspoon dried oregano**
　½　**teaspoon dried basil**
　¼　**teaspoon black pepper**

Preheat the oven to 350°F. Cook the pasta according to package directions. Drain and set aside.

Meanwhile, spread the chickpeas on a baking sheet. Coat lightly with cooking spray. Sprinkle lightly with salt. Bake, stirring occasionally, for 10 to 12 minutes, or until golden.

In a large saucepan over medium heat, warm the oil. Add the onion, bell pepper, and garlic. Cook, stirring occasionally, for 5 minutes, or until soft.

Add the tomatoes, black-eyed peas, reserved pasta, broth or water, oregano, basil, salt, and pepper. Bring to a boil, cover, and simmer gently for about 10 minutes, or until the vegetables are tender.

Add the reserved chickpeas and serve.

Makes 6 servings

Per serving: *154 calories, 6 g protein, 27 g carbohydrate, 3 g fat, 0 mg cholesterol, 463 mg sodium, 5 g fiber*

Diet Exchanges: *0 milk, 1½ vegetable, 0 fruit, 1 bread, 0 meat, ½ fat*

2 Carb Choices

Southwest Soup I "Can" Do

—Johnna Troglin, Collinsville, Oklahoma

Incredibly easy and surprisingly satisfying.

Prep time: 5 minutes
Cook time: 5 minutes

1 can (14½ ounces) **diced tomatoes with green chilies**

1 can (15 ounces) **fat-free refried beans**

1 can (15 ounces) **no-salt-added black beans**

1 can (14½ ounces) **fat-free reduced-sodium chicken broth**

4 tablespoons **fat-free sour cream or fat-free plain yogurt** (optional)

Chopped fresh cilantro (optional)

In a large saucepan, combine the tomatoes, refried beans, black beans, and broth. Stir to mix well. Simmer over medium heat for 5 minutes, or until hot.

Serve with a dollop of sour cream or yogurt and a sprinkling of cilantro, if using.

Makes 6 servings

Per serving: *137 calories, 9 g protein, 24 g carbohydrate, 0 g fat, 1 mg cholesterol, 658 mg sodium, 7 g fiber*

Diet Exchanges: *0 milk, ½ vegetable, 0 fruit, 1 bread, ½ meat, 0 fat*

1½ Carb Choices

SHOPPING SAVVY

Out of the (Fat) Kettle

The mission of privately owned Oregon-based Kettle Foods is to produce great tasting, all-natural snacks with a caring commitment to its employees, craft, and community. Now, this company is also looking after your waistline with the introduction of Pita Chips to their Bakes line of savory snacks.

Made from organic wheat flour, Kettle brand Bakes Pita Chips start with authentic pita bread sprinkled with seasonings and toasted, not fried, until crisp and golden brown. Made with just a hint of healthy canola oil, the crispy chips contain no trans fats, with 120 calories and 3.5 grams of fat per 1-ounce serving.

Two flavorings are available in super-markets and natural foods stores: Salt & Pepper Bakes Pita Chips, which can be enjoyed alone or with dips and spreads, and Salt Kissed Bakes Pita Chips, which are the perfect complement to hummus or light cheese spreads.

For more information, visit www.kettlebakes.com.

83 Calories

Manhattan Clam Chowder

—Nancy O'Brien, Mount Airy, Maryland

Load up on healthy lycopene with this tomato-based seafood stew.

Prep time: 15 minutes
Cook time: 15 minutes

 1 tablespoon canola oil
½ cup chopped onion
½ cup chopped bell pepper (any color)
 1 medium potato, peeled and chopped
½ cup chopped celery
½ teaspoon dried thyme
⅛ teaspoon paprika
⅛ teaspoon salt
 1 can (14½ ounces) petite diced tomatoes
 1 tablespoon tomato paste
 1 can (14½ ounces) vegetable broth or fat-free reduced-sodium chicken broth
 1 container (6 ounces) baby clams or littleneck clams, drained

In a pot over medium heat, warm the oil. Add the onion, pepper, potato, celery, thyme, paprika, and salt. Cook, stirring, for about 5 minutes, or until the vegetables start to soften. Add the tomatoes, tomato paste, and broth. Simmer for 10 minutes. Add the clams. Heat gently just until hot.

Makes 6 servings

Per serving: *83 calories, 5 g protein, 8 g carbohydrate, 3 g fat, 10 mg cholesterol, 388 mg sodium, 2 g fiber*

Diet Exchanges: *0 milk, 1 vegetable, 0 fruit, 0 bread, ½ meat, ½ fat*

½ **Carb Choice**

Turkey Noodle Soup with Spinach

—Maggie McDowell, Oak Park, Illinois

Any short shape of whole wheat pasta, such as macaroni or shells, works nicely if noodles aren't available.

Prep time: 15 minutes
Cook time: 25 minutes

  4 ounces whole wheat noodles, cooked
  1 tablespoon canola oil
  ½ cup chopped onion
  ½ cup chopped carrot
  ½ cup chopped celery
  1 teaspoon dried sage
12 ounces ground turkey breast
  2 cans (14½ ounces each) fat-free reduced-sodium chicken broth
  4 cups water
  1 tablespoon balsamic vinegar
  ½ teaspoon salt
  1 bag (6 ounces) baby spinach leaves
  Ground black pepper

Cook the noodles according to the package directions. Drain and set aside.

Meanwhile, in a pot over medium heat, warm the oil. Add the onion, carrot, celery, and sage. Cook, stirring occasionally, for 5 minutes, or until the vegetables start to soften. Add the turkey. Cook, breaking up the turkey with the back of a spoon, for about 4 minutes longer, or until the turkey is no longer pink.

Add the broth, water, vinegar, and salt. Simmer for about 5 minutes, or until hot. Do not boil. Stir in the spinach and reserved noodles. Remove from the heat and let rest for 5 minutes. Season with pepper to taste.

Makes 8 servings

Per serving: *135 calories, 14 g protein, 15 g carbohydrate, 3 g fat, 17 mg cholesterol, 447 mg sodium, 2 g fiber*

Diet Exchanges: *1 vegetable, 1½ meat, ½ fat*

1 Carb Choice

Snacks and Appetizers, Sandwiches and Pizzas, and Sides

SIDES

Garlic Chili Popcorn

—Amy Joy Goertz, London, Ontario, Canada

"After watching my father prepare popcorn every night with ¼ cup of butter each time, I decided to give him an alternative. This recipe not only satisfied his 'salty tooth,' but he now prefers the flavor and is greatly reducing his sodium intake. The decrease in fat alone, and the benefits of olive oil, should convince anyone to switch over to this tasty and weight-reducing snack."

Prep time: 2 minutes
Cook time: 2 minutes
Cool time: 5 minutes

   2 tablespoons extra-virgin olive oil
   1 clove garlic, minced
   1 teaspoon red-pepper flakes
  10 cups freshly air-popped popcorn
      (about ½ cup dry)
      Pinch of salt

In a small skillet, combine the oil, garlic, and pepper flakes. Cook over medium-low heat for about 2 minutes, or until the garlic is soft and the mixture is aromatic. Cool for 5 minutes. Place the popcorn in a large bowl. Pour the oil mixture over the popcorn. Add the salt. Toss to coat. Serve immediately.

Makes 10 servings, 1 cup each

Per serving: *57 calories, 1 g protein, 6 g carbohydrate, 3 g fat, 0 mg cholesterol, 15 mg sodium, 1 g fiber*

Diet Exchanges: *0 milk, 0 vegetable, 0 fruit, ½ bread, 0 meat, ½ fat*

½ Carb Choice

Swedish Nuts

—Avis Birk, Waterbury, Connecticut

"I love to snack! Instead of cookies and potato chips, these are healthier and delicious!"

Prep time: 5 minutes
Bake time: 25 to 30 minutes

1 egg white

1 tablespoon water

2 cups mixed plain nuts (pecans, walnuts, and almonds)

2 tablespoons Splenda

2 teaspoons ground cinnamon

½ teaspoon pure vanilla extract

Preheat the oven to 350°F. Coat a large shallow baking sheet with cooking spray.

In a bowl, beat the egg white and water with a fork. Add the nuts. Toss to coat thoroughly with the egg mixture. Place on the baking sheet.

In a small bowl, combine the Splenda and cinnamon. Stir to mix. Sprinkle the mixture over the nuts. Drizzle with the vanilla extract. Toss the nuts to coat evenly with the Splenda mixture. Spread the nuts out in a single layer.

Bake, stirring occasionally, for about 25 to 30 minutes, or until toasted.

Makes 10 servings; 2 tablespoons per serving

Per serving: *168 calories, 5 g protein, 8 g carbohydrate, 14 g fat, 0 mg cholesterol, 9 mg sodium, 3 g fiber*

Diet Exchanges: *0 milk, 0 vegetable, 0 fruit, ½ bread, 1 meat, 2½ fat*

½ Carb Choice

9 Calories

Cucumber Zingers

—Brandie Sieffert, Sedro Woolley, Washington

"This is a good snack when you are craving something sweet. It helps me not eat candy and cookies. Just about a quarter of a cup seems to curb the craving."

Prep time: 5 minutes
Chill time: 1 hour

  1 **English cucumber, halved lengthwise**
  ½ **sweet onion, coarsely chopped (about ⅔ cup)**
  ½ **cup water**
  ½ **cup apple cider vinegar**
  1 **teaspoon Splenda or sugar**
  1 **teaspoon ground black pepper**
  ½ **teaspoon salt**

Cut the cucumber halves into thin slices. Place in a large bowl. Add the onion, water, vinegar, Splenda or sugar, pepper, and salt. Stir to mix well. Cover and refrigerate for at least 1 hour, or up to overnight.

Makes 16 servings, ¼ cup each

Per serving: *9 calories, 0 g protein, 2 g carbohydrate, 0 g fat, 0 mg cholesterol, 74 mg sodium, 0 g fiber*

Diet Exchanges: *0 milk, ½ vegetable, 0 fruit, 0 bread, 0 meat, 0 fat*

0 Carb Choices

SECRETS OF WEIGHT-LOSS WINNERS

• Take a walk instead of opening the refrigerator.

—Louise Hintz, Yuma, Colorado

• Exercise with a friend, so you would feel as if you were letting her down if you skipped.

—Pat Krasnowski, Tolono, Illinois

• Have cheat night once a week so you feel like you're not left out of the good stuff.

—Kimberly Bennett, Kunkletown, Pennsylvania

168 Calories

Turkey Taco Nachos

—Wendy Stanton, Clarks Summit, Pennsylvania

This Tex-Mex treat keeps the zesty flavors and satisfying textures but kicks the fat and calories way low.

Prep time: 10 minutes
Cook time: 10 minutes
Bake time: 10 minutes

  2 teaspoons canola oil
½ cup chopped onion
  1 green bell pepper, chopped
  1 red bell pepper, chopped
  2 teaspoons minced garlic
  2 teaspoons chili powder
  1 teaspoon ground cumin
¼ teaspoon salt
  1 pound lean ground turkey breast
  4 cups baked tortilla chips, coarsely broken
¾ cup shredded reduced-fat sharp Cheddar cheese
  2 cups shredded lettuce
  1 tomato, chopped
½ cup fat-free sour cream
    Hot-pepper sauce

Preheat the oven to 350°F. Lightly coat a 2-quart baking dish with cooking spray.

In a nonstick skillet over medium heat, warm the oil. Add the onion, bell peppers, garlic, chili powder, cumin, and salt. Cook, stirring frequently, for about 5 minutes, or until the vegetables are softened. Crumble the turkey into the skillet. Cook, breaking up the turkey with the back of a spoon, for 5 minutes longer, or until the turkey is no longer pink.

Spread the turkey mixture in the dish. Top with half of the tortilla chips and sprinkle with cheese.

Bake for about 10 minutes, or until the cheese is melted. Cover with the rest of the chips and the shredded lettuce. Top with the tomato and a few dollops of sour cream. Serve with hot-pepper sauce.

Makes 8 servings

Per serving: *168 calories, 18 g protein, 15 g carbohydrate, 5 g fat, 30 mg cholesterol, 293 mg sodium, 2 g fiber*

Diet Exchanges: *0 milk, ½ vegetable, 0 fruit, 1 bread, ½ meat, ½ fat*

1 Carb Choice

31 Calories

Mom's Treat

—Linda Parker, Lincoln, Illinois

"This recipe has helped me lose weight because it is low in calories. It's great for snacks. My sons just love this, and it is so easy to make."

Prep time: 10 minutes
Chill time: 1 to 2 hours

8 ounces reduced-fat cream cheese, at room temperature

3 tablespoons creamy horseradish

2 tablespoons grated Parmesan cheese

5 slices (3½ ounces) low-fat ham or turkey, chopped

Crackers, radicchio leaves, or endive leaves

In a bowl, combine the cream cheese, horseradish, and Parmesan cheese. With a fork, mash the mixture and then stir to mix. Add the ham or turkey. Stir to mix.

Place half of the mixture on a work surface. Mixture will be very sticky. Roll into a 1" thick log about 6" long. Wrap in plastic wrap or waxed paper. Repeat with the remaining mixture. Refrigerate for 1 to 2 hours until chilled through, or up to 2 days.

To serve, cut into ½" slices. Serve on crackers or small radicchio or endive leaves.

Makes 24 servings

Per serving: *31 calories, 2 g protein, 1 g carbohydrate, 2 g fat, 6 mg cholesterol, 112 mg sodium, 0 g fiber*

Diet Exchanges: *0 milk, 0 vegetable, 0 fruit, 0 bread, 0 meat, ½ fat*

0 Carb Choices

Tuna Yachts

—Bonnie Jessee, Saint Petersburg, Florida

"I changed my snacking from chips and ice cream at night to a better choice."

Prep time: 5 minutes

1 can (6 ounces) albacore tuna in water, drained

1 hard-cooked egg, chopped

1 tablespoon finely chopped red onion

1 tablespoon finely chopped celery

2 tablespoons low-fat mayonnaise

¼ teaspoon salt

  Ground black pepper

1 head Belgian endive

In a bowl, combine the tuna, egg, onion, celery, mayonnaise, salt, and pepper. Separate the endive leaves and arrange on a platter. Fill each leaf with some of the tuna salad.

Makes 12 servings

Per serving: *30 calories, 4 g protein, 1 g carbohydrate, 1 g fat, 24 mg cholesterol, 129 mg sodium, 0 g fiber*

Diet Exchanges: *0 milk, 0 vegetable, 0 fruit, 0 bread, ½ meat, 0 fat*

0 Carb Choices

SECRETS OF WEIGHT-LOSS WINNERS

• Take a portion you would normally take—and then put half back!

**—Jessica Lagana,
Pittsburgh, Pennsylvania**

• Prepare your meals ahead of time and freeze for the week. They will be a lot healthier than the premade frozen dinners.

**—Catherine Cole,
Long Reach, Nebraska**

• Cycling and not eating meat were my tickets to weight loss.

—Robert Root, Roseville, California

• I cut out junk food and lost 12 pounds! If it's junk, it's not for me! I also make homemade soup for my lunch every day. It is healthy, delicious, and nutritious!

**—Unita Esau, Meadow Lake,
Saskatchewan, Canada**

Pomegranate Salsa

—Judith Weems, La Crescenta, California

"Serve with jicama slices and celery sticks or baked tortilla chips—also great over roasted, sliced meats."

Prep time: 15 minutes
Chill time: several hours

- 1 pomegranate
- 1 medium red onion, finely chopped
- 1–2 jalapeño chile peppers, finely chopped (wear plastic gloves when handling)
- Juice of 2 limes
- ¼ teaspoon salt

Cut the pomegranate in half. Working over a fine sieve set over a bowl, use your fingers or a small spoon to extract the pulp-encased seeds from the light-colored membrane. Allow any juice to fall into the bowl. Add the onion, 1 or 2 chiles (depending upon desired heat), lime juice, and salt. Stir to mix. Cover and refrigerate for several hours.

Makes 8 servings, 2 tablespoons each

Per serving: *22 calories, 0 g protein, 6 g carbohydrate, 0 g fat, 0 mg cholesterol, 74 mg sodium, 0 g fiber*

Diet Exchanges: *0 milk, 0 vegetable, 0 fruit, 0 bread, 0 meat, 0 fat*

½ **Carb Choice**

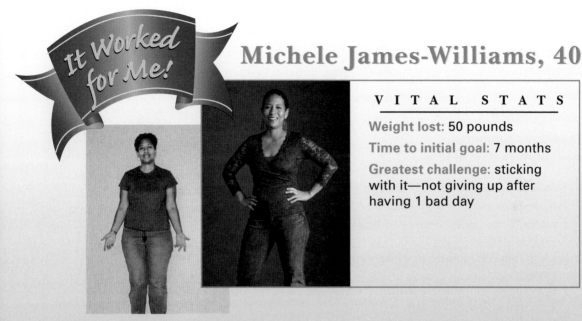

It Worked for Me!

Michele James-Williams, 40

VITAL STATS

Weight lost: 50 pounds

Time to initial goal: 7 months

Greatest challenge: sticking with it—not giving up after having 1 bad day

"I'm not the poster child for weight loss," says Michele James-Williams. "It's not like I sat around and ate bon-bons and all of a sudden I discovered healthy eating."

What she did discover: support. And it made all the difference.

In 2005, 5'6" Michele weighed in at 204 pounds. When she tried to lose weight, she kept it to herself, fearing that her friends and family would judge her if she failed. And inevitably, she did.

Then, on a 2005 flight, Michele saw a program about people in their eighties who looked 50—and took a hard look at herself. "Maybe the show brought out my fear of aging," she says. Or maybe her divorce-in-progress made her long for a fresh start with her son.

When Michele got home to California, she joined an online diet site called spark-people.com, received a customized food plan, and stuck to it, consuming between 1,200 and 1,550 calories a day.

But Michele, the Frank Sinatra of dieters, did it her way. "There wasn't a major change

in what I ate," says the 40-year-old director of finance for a software company. "I just ate less of it." To accomplish that, Michele broke out the measuring cups and food scale to measure out her portions. She cooked more and ate out less. She ate fewer chips and snack crackers and more apples. The needle on the scale started to move.

Michele also used her elliptical trainer for 10 to 30 minutes a day, four times a week, while her son slept. The more weight she lost, the more she wanted to exercise.

In 7 months, Michele shed 50 pounds and now weighs 154. While she rarely eats sweets, she won't give up her favorite cereals (including Honey Bunches of Oats and Honey-Comb).

Although a diet rebel, Michele doesn't stand alone. She credits her online support system for her success. "I couldn't have [lost the weight] without them." Now she hopes to similarly inspire her son. "I want to instill in him that being active and healthy is normal. I want us both to be around for a very long time."

Skinny Crab Dip

—Jean Wagner, Eugene, Oregon

Serve with wheat crackers or tiny radicchio leaves.

Prep time: 5 minutes
Chill time: several hours

2 ounces (¼ cup) low-fat cream cheese

2 tablespoons low-fat mayonnaise

2 tablespoons finely chopped chives or scallion greens

2 teaspoons lemon juice or white wine vinegar

1 tablespoon chopped fresh dill or 1 teaspoon dried dillweed

⅛ teaspoon ground black pepper
Pinch of salt

2 cans (8 ounces each) crabmeat, well drained

In a bowl, combine the cream cheese and mayonnaise. Stir until very smooth. Add the chives or scallions, lemon juice or vinegar, dill, pepper, and salt. Stir to mix thoroughly. Add the crab. Stir to mix. Cover and refrigerate for several hours.

Makes 12 servings, 2 tablespoons each

Per serving: *71 calories, 10 g protein, 1 g carbohydrate, 2½ g fat, 45 mg cholesterol, 142 mg sodium, 0 g fiber*

Diet Exchanges: *0 milk, 0 vegetable, 0 fruit, 0 bread, 0 meat, ½ fat*

0 Carb Choices

Front, Skinny Crab Dip (opposite page) and
Back, Strawberry Mock Daiquiri (page 248)

Cajun Chicken Fingers with Cool Cuke Dip

—Bill Linden, Chicago, Illinois

This appetizer jazzes up any get-together.

Prep time: 15 minutes
Chill time: 1 hour
Grill time: 4 to 6 minutes

DIP

½ cup fat-free sour cream

½ cup coarsely shredded hot-house cucumber

1 tablespoon minced scallions

1 teaspoon lemon juice

⅛ teaspoon salt

⅛ teaspoon ground black pepper

CHICKEN

1 pound chicken breast tenders

2 teaspoons olive oil

2 teaspoons Cajun seasoning rub

Hot-pepper sauce (optional)

To prepare the dip: In a bowl, combine the sour cream, cucumber, scallions, lemon juice, salt, and pepper. Stir to mix. Cover and refrigerate for at least 1 hour.

To prepare the chicken: Place the chicken, oil, and seasoning rub in a resealable plastic storage bag. Seal the bag and massage to coat the chicken evenly. Refrigerate for 1 hour.

Preheat a grill or stove-top griddle pan. Cook the chicken on the grill or pan for 2 to 3 minutes on each side, or until no longer pink and the juices run clear. Serve with the dip and hot-pepper sauce, if using.

Makes 4 servings

Per serving: *161 calories, 28 g protein, 6 g carbohydrate, 3 g fat, 70 mg cholesterol, 549 mg sodium, 0 g fiber*

Diet Exchanges: *3 meat, ½ fat*

½ Carb Choice

Cheddar-Bacon Potato Wedges

—Bill Linden, Chicago, Illinois

These gooey noshes are almost as decadent as the popular restaurant version.

Prep time: 10 minutes
Bake time: 45 minutes

3 medium russet potatoes, cut into thick wedges

Pinch of ground red pepper

2 teaspoons olive oil

¾ cup reduced-fat sharp Cheddar cheese

2 tablespoons crumbled cooked bacon

1 tablespoon chopped scallions

Pinch of salt

Preheat the oven to 400°F. Coat a large baking sheet with cooking spray.

Pat the potatoes dry and place on the baking sheet. In a small dish, mix the pepper with the oil. Drizzle on the potatoes. Toss to coat evenly. Bake for about 20 minutes, or until golden on the bottom. Turn over the potatoes and continue baking for 20 minutes, or until golden and crisp. Sprinkle the cheese and bacon on top. Bake for about 5 minutes, or until the cheese melts. Remove the potatoes to a serving platter and sprinkle with the scallions and salt.

Makes 4 servings

Per serving: *191 calories, 9 g protein, 21 g carbohydrate, 8.5 g fat, 19 mg cholesterol, 276 mg sodium, 2 g fiber*

Diet Exchanges: *0 milk, 0 vegetable, 0 fruit, 1 bread, 1 meat, 1 fat*

1½ Carb Choices

85 Calories

Spinach Party Dip

—Wendy Henrichs, Iowa City, Iowa

"The dip can be put in a small, hollowed rye bread round with whole grain crackers, dippable veggies, and small pieces of rye bread around the top."

Prep time: 10 minutes
Chill time: several hours

2 teaspoons canola oil

1 cup chopped red bell pepper

1 cup chopped scallions

2 packages (10 ounces each) frozen chopped spinach, thawed and squeezed dry

1 cup fat-free sour cream

½ cup water chestnuts, drained and chopped

½ cup mayonnaise

1 tablespoon finely chopped fresh dill or 1 teaspoon dried dillweed

½ teaspoon salt

1 teaspoon salt-free seasoning blend

¼ teaspoon ground red pepper

Heat the oil in a nonstick skillet over medium heat. Add the bell pepper. Cook, stirring, for about 3 minutes, or until tender. Add the scallions. Cook for about 2 minutes longer, or until the scallions are wilted. Transfer to a bowl. Add the spinach, sour cream, water chestnuts, mayonnaise, dill, salt, seasoning, and ground red pepper. Stir to mix thoroughly. Cover and refrigerate for several hours.

Makes 16 servings, generous ¼ cup each

Per serving: *85 calories, 2 g protein, 5 g carbohydrate, 6 g fat, 5 mg cholesterol, 152 mg sodium, 1 g fiber*

Diet Exchanges: *0 milk, ½ vegetable, 0 fruit, 0 bread, 0 meat, 1 fat*

0 Carb Choices

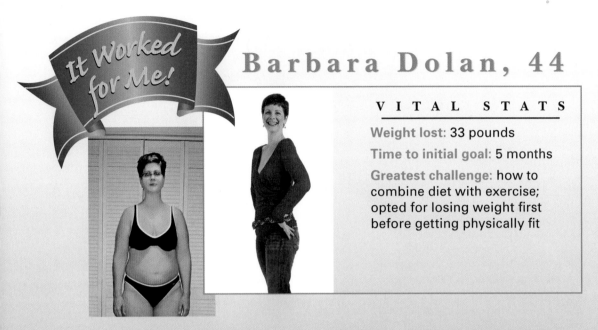

It Worked for Me!

Barbara Dolan, 44

VITAL STATS

Weight lost: 33 pounds

Time to initial goal: 5 months

Greatest challenge: how to combine diet with exercise; opted for losing weight first before getting physically fit

Until age 36, Barbara Dolan's on-the-go lifestyle and regular dance classes kept her fit. But things changed in 1999, when she gained 40 pounds carrying her first son, Levi, and hung on to 13 of them. In 2002, during her second pregnancy with son Drew, Barbara gained another 40 pounds—and kept 20.

As an exhausted mother of two, the Oak Park, Illinois, resident now 44, discovered convenience foods.

What finally sparked her resolve to get fit? "One little thing after another," she says. "I just wasn't comfortable in my larger body anymore."

Barbara tried Weight Watchers for 3 months but, disliking the weigh-ins, switched to its online program. "Logging in everything I ate made me think of calories in real-world terms."

Barbara, who used the Weight Watchers POINTS system, estimates she consumed 1,200 to 1,800 calories a day, fewer as her weight dropped. "Smaller portions were key," she says. "I just made sure the foods I chose were healthy and easy to prepare." She stuck to lean protein, steamed and raw veggies,

whole grain bread and high-fiber cereals, and fat-free plain yogurt with honey. As a nod to convenience, she also nuked frozen diet meals and whole grain waffles and snacked on fat-free popcorn. "And I made a conscious effort to avoid fast food."

Five months later, 5'9" Barbara had hit her goal weight of 142 pounds—a 33-pound loss in total—and had shrunk from a size 16 to a 6.

Signing up for a regular Pilates class enabled her to firm up her smaller body. And a stint with the Windy City Rollers, Chicago's first all-girl, flat-track Roller Derby league, helped her lose an additional 7 pounds.

Barbara notes that she didn't work out in earnest while she lost the weight. "Many women beat themselves up because they don't get to the gym every day. But when you're overweight, you lack energy, and exercise is the enemy.

"Losing weight is a function of calories in, calories out. If you're not ready for the calories-out part of the deal, put fewer calories in. Lose the weight first. Once you have more energy and feel better about yourself, you'll be more motivated to exercise."

Healthy Black-Bean Dip

—Christi Jensen, Des Moines, Iowa

"Serve with pita crisps or baked tortilla chips or as a spread on tacos or quesadillas. Delicious and good for you."

Prep time: 5 minutes
Microwave time: 2 to 3 minutes

- 2 **cans (15 ounces each) black beans, rinsed and drained**
- ¾ **cup green chile salsa**
- **Juice of 1 lime**
- 1 **teaspoon ground cumin**
- ½ **cup shredded reduced-fat sharp Cheddar cheese**

In the bowl of a food processor fitted with a metal blade, combine the beans, salsa, lime juice, and cumin. Process into a coarse puree. Transfer to a shallow microwaveable dish. Sprinkle with the cheese. Microwave on high power for 2 to 3 minutes, or until the cheese melts and is heated through.

Makes 12 servings, ¼ cup each

Per serving: *59 calories, 4 g protein, 9 g carbohydrate, 1 g fat, 3 mg cholesterol, 310 mg sodium, 3 g fiber*

Diet Exchanges: *0 milk, 0 vegetable, 0 fruit, ½ bread, 0 meat, 0 fat*

1 Carb Choice

SHOPPING SAVVY

Better Beans

Dry beans are excellent sources of plant protein and also provide other nutrients such as iron, zinc, and folate. Canned beans are a convenient alternative to dried beans. The only drawback to canned beans has been their high sodium content. But Goya's low-sodium canned beans have two-thirds less sodium than Goya's standard Blue Label line of beans. You can choose black beans, pinto beans, red kidney beans, pink beans, or chickpeas. A ½-cup serving of low-sodium red kidney beans, for instance, contains 110 milligrams of sodium, compared with 350 milligrams in the regular canned red kidney beans. (And remember, rinsing and draining any canned beans before using washes away about 25 percent of the sodium content.) Look for Goya products in supermarkets or at www.goyafoods.com.

Asian Pork Meatballs
on Shredded Vegetables

—Bonnie Boyd, Oak Park, Illinois

This sophisticated appetizer is a delightful first course for a special dinner.

Prep time: 15 minutes
Bake time: 10 minutes

MEATBALLS

1 medium cucumber, shredded
1 medium carrot, shredded
1 pound ground lean pork
3 pieces water chestnut, finely chopped
1 tablespoon finely chopped scallion
2 tablespoons reduced-sodium soy sauce
2 large eggs
¼ teaspoon ground black pepper
¼ cup panko bread crumbs

DIPPING SAUCE

3 tablespoons reduced-sodium soy sauce
1 tablespoon canola oil
1 teaspoon toasted sesame oil
1 scallion, sliced
½ teaspoon grated fresh ginger

To prepare the meatballs: In a small bowl, combine the cucumber and carrot. Set aside. In a food processor fitted with a metal blade, combine the pork, water chestnut, scallion, soy sauce, eggs, pepper, and bread crumbs. Pulse several times just to combine.

Preheat the oven to 375°F.

With a melon baller or fingers, shape the meat mixture into balls and place on a baking sheet. Bake for 10 minutes, turning meatballs once, until the pork is no longer pink and the juices run clear.

To prepare the dipping sauce: While the meatballs are baking, in a small bowl, combine the soy sauce, canola oil, sesame oil, scallion, and ginger. Stir to mix. Set aside.

Arrange the reserved cucumber-carrot mixture in small mounds on a serving plate. Arrange the meatballs around the vegetables. Drizzle with a small amount of the sauce. Serve the remaining sauce on the side.

Makes 8 servings

Per serving: *204 calories, 12 g protein, 3 g carbohydrate, 16 g fat, 94 mg cholesterol, 433 mg sodium, 1 g fiber*

Diet Exchanges: *0 milk, ½ vegetable, 0 fruit, 0 bread, 2 meat, 2 fat*

0 Carb Choices

Herbed Rice Bread

—Virginia Moon, Harvest, Alabama

Low in fat and flavored with mixed herbs and a dusting of Parmesan cheese, this unique rice-and-cornmeal bread is a real delight—a perfect complement to the Chicken, Corn, & Tomatillo Chili, page 190.

Prep time: 10 minutes
Bake time: 30 minutes
Cool time: 10 minutes

1 cup white cornmeal

1 tablespoon grated Parmesan cheese

1 teaspoon baking powder

1 teaspoon onion powder

½ teaspoon garlic powder

½ teaspoon dried mixed herbs, such as fines herbes

¼ teaspoon salt (optional)

¼ cup fat-free egg substitute or 2 large egg whites

1 cup fat-free milk

¼ cup fat-free sour cream or plain yogurt

1 cup cold cooked Uncle Ben's Converted Rice

1 tablespoon light margarine, melted

Preheat the oven to 400°F. Coat an 8" × 8" baking dish with cooking spray.

In a small bowl, mix the cornmeal, cheese, baking powder, onion powder, garlic powder, herbs, and salt.

In a large bowl, whisk the egg substitute or egg whites until frothy. Whisk in the milk and sour cream or yogurt. Stir in the dry ingredients.

Place the rice in a small bowl. Drizzle with the margarine. Mix and mash the rice with a fork or potato masher. Add to the cornmeal mixture and stir to combine. Spoon the batter into the baking dish.

Bake for 30 minutes, or until a tester inserted in the center comes out clean. Cool on a rack for 10 minutes before serving.

Makes 9 servings

Per serving: *122 calories, 4 g protein, 22 g carbohydrate, 2 g fat, 2 mg cholesterol, 197 mg sodium, 1 g fiber*

Diet Exchanges: *0 milk, 0 vegetable, 0 fruit, 1 bread, 0 meat, ½ fat*

1½ Carb Choices

221 Calories

Pork & Beans in Buns

—Brandi McKoy, Norfolk, Virginia

"By using lean pork tenderloin instead of bacon or ham, my family can enjoy this dish without too much fat."

Prep time: 20 minutes
Cook time: 10 minutes
Bake time: 1 hour 30 minutes

- 2 teaspoons canola oil
- 1 cup chopped onion
- 1 cup chopped red bell pepper
- 1 tablespoon minced garlic
- 1 tablespoon chili powder
- ½ teaspoon salt
- 1 can (15½ ounces) pinto beans, drained and rinsed
- 1 can (15½ ounces) tomato puree
- 1 pound boneless pork tenderloin
- 12 whole wheat hamburger buns, toasted
  Hot-pepper sauce

In a large saucepan over medium-high heat, warm the oil. Add the onion, bell pepper, garlic, chili powder, and salt. Cook, stirring, for about 10 minutes, or until softened. Add the beans and tomato puree. Stir to mix. Place the pork in the pot, spooning the sauce over to cover.

Cover and cook at a simmer for about 1½ hours, or until the pork is fork-tender.

Remove the pork. With 2 forks, shred the meat into small pieces. Return to the pot. Mix.

To serve, spoon the mixture onto the buns. Pass the hot-pepper sauce at the table.

Makes 12 servings

Per serving: *221 calories, 16 g protein, 28 g carbohydrate, 4½ g fat, 25 mg cholesterol, 529 mg sodium, 4 g fiber*

Diet Exchanges: *0 milk, 1 vegetable, 0 fruit, 1 bread, 1 meat, 0 fat*

2 Carb Choices

50 LOW-FAT SNACKS AT 100 CALORIES OR LESS

Run amok with snacks, and you'll gain weight. But experts say that an occasional indulgence won't hurt. And an occasional treat may actually help by preventing feelings of deprivation. The secret to successful snacking, say nutritionists, is to be selective. Instead of snacking mindlessly, think about your choices. Here are 50 indulgences that, when eaten in the portions listed, can help keep eating fun without packing on the pounds.

These items are available at most supermarkets. Individual brands can vary, so be sure to read package labels. Items listed as having no fat have less than 1 gram per serving.

Food Item	Portion	Calories	Fat (g)
Apple	1 medium	81	0
Applesauce, unsweetened	½ c	53	0
Apricots, dried	5	83	0
Apricots, fresh	3 medium	51	0
Bagel	½	81	0
Banana	1 medium	100	0
Blueberries	1 c	82	0
Bread, sourdough	1 slice	70	1
Butterscotch candy	4 pieces	88	1
Cantaloupe	½ c	57	0
Carrot	1 medium	31	0
Celery	1 stalk	6	0
Cereal, frosted wheat	4 biscuits	100	0
Cottage cheese, low-fat	½ c	81	1
Cucumber	1 medium	16	0
Devil's food cookies, low-fat	1	50	0
Fruit roll candy	1 roll	81	1
Gummi Bears candy	3 pieces	20	0
Fig bars, fat-free	2	100	0
Fruit juice bar, frozen	1	25	0
Grapefruit, pink or white	½ medium	37	0

Food Item	Portion	Calories	Fat (g)
Grapes	1 c	58	0
Honeydew melon	1 c	60	0
Jelly beans	8 large	83	0
LifeSavers candy, all flavors	1	9	0
Orange, navel	1 medium	65	0
Peach, dried	1	62	0
Peach, fresh	1 medium	37	0
Pecan cookies, low-fat	1	70	3
Pepper, bell	1 large	20	0
Potato chips, fat-free	30	110	0
Saltines	5	60	1
Pickle, dill	1 medium	12	0
Pineapple	1 c	77	0
Popcorn, caramel, low-fat	1 c	100	0
Popcorn, light	1 c	45	3
Pretzels, thin	10	70	0
Pretzels, whole wheat	1 small	51	0
Pudding cup, chocolate	1 (4 oz)	100	0
Raisins, seedless	⅛ c	55	0
Rice cake, plain	1	21	0
Strawberries	1 c	45	0
String cheese, low-fat	1 piece	60	3
Tomato juice	½ c	20	0
Tortilla chips, baked, low-fat, with salsa	10	90	1
Tuna, light, packed in water	2 oz	65	0
Whole grain crackers, fat-free	5	60	0
Whole wheat crackers	6	96	3
Yogurt, nonfat	½ c	60	0
Yogurt bar, frozen, nonfat	1	45	0

Portobello Sandwich

—Jennifer Stewart, Stevensville, Maryland

This sandwich is so tasty and succulent that you won't miss the meat.

Prep time: 5 minutes
Cook time: 10 minutes
Bake time: 5 minutes

1 teaspoon olive oil
1 onion slice, ¼" thick
¼ red bell pepper, cut into thick strips
1 medium portobello mushroom cap
 Salt
1 slice reduced-fat provolone cheese
1 teaspoon prepared pesto
1 focaccia roll or 1–2" slice focaccia bread (about 2 ounces)
1 lettuce leaf
1 slice tomato

Preheat the oven to 400°F.

In a nonstick skillet over medium heat, warm the oil. Add the onion and bell pepper. Cook, tossing occasionally, for about 5 minutes or until softened. Scrape the vegetables to the side. Place the mushroom in the pan, top side up. Cook for about 2 minutes longer. Turn over and cook for 2 minutes more, or until softened. Season the mushroom cap and vegetables lightly with salt. Transfer the mushroom to a baking pan or piece of heavy aluminum foil. Top with the onion, pepper, and cheese.

Bake for 5 minutes, or until the cheese bubbles. Meanwhile, spread the pesto on both sides of the roll or bread. Transfer the mushroom, onion, and pepper to the bottom bun. Top with lettuce, tomato, and top bun. Slice in half and serve.

Makes 1 serving

Per serving: *302 calories, 12 g protein, 39 g carbohydrate, 12 g fat, 12 mg cholesterol, 650 mg sodium, 3 g fiber*

Diet Exchanges: *0 milk, 1½ vegetable, 0 fruit, 2 bread, 1½ meat, 1½ fat*

2½ Carb Choices

Ted's Open-Face Blue Cheese Chicken Salad Sandwiches

—Ted Kranenberg, Cambridge, Minnesota

Just a touch of tangy blue cheese really livens up a chicken salad.

Prep time: 15 minutes

1 can (12½ ounces) chunk white chicken, drained and rinsed, or 1½ cups chopped cooked chicken breast

3 tablespoons crumbled blue cheese

3 tablespoons fat-free mayonnaise

1 medium carrot, shredded

¼ cup finely chopped celery

2 tablespoons finely chopped white onion

1 clove garlic, finely chopped

Pinch of salt

Ground black pepper

6 slices sourdough or dark rye sandwich bread, toasted

In a mixing bowl, combine the chicken, cheese, mayonnaise, carrot, celery, onion, garlic, salt, and pepper to taste. Stir to mix. Spread on the toasted bread.

Makes 6 servings

Per serving: *265 calories, 19 g protein, 40 g carbohydrate, 3½ g fat, 24 mg cholesterol, 844 mg sodium, 2 g fiber*

Diet Exchanges: *0 milk, ½ vegetable, 0 fruit, 2½ bread, 1½ meat, 0 fat*

3 Carb Choices

142 Calories

Pita Stuffed with Hummus and Veggies

—C. Kent, Columbus, Ohio

"I like this with chilled melon for a light meal."

Prep time: 10 minutes

2 whole wheat pitas (6" diameter), toasted

4 tablespoons prepared roasted garlic hummus

4 tablespoons fat-free plain yogurt

¼ teaspoon dried oregano

Ground black pepper

½ small seedless cucumber, peeled and chopped

½ small red onion, thinly sliced

¼ cup crumbled reduced-fat feta cheese

4 lettuce or spinach leaves, shredded

Sliced bottled or fresh hot peppers (optional)

Cut the pitas in half. Open carefully. Spread 1 tablespoon each of the hummus and yogurt into each pocket. Season lightly with the oregano and black pepper. Stuff with the cucumber, onion, cheese, lettuce, and hot peppers, if using.

Makes 4 servings

Per serving: *142 calories, 7 g protein, 23 g carbohydrate, 3.5 g fat, 4 mg cholesterol, 360 mg sodium, 4 g fiber*

Diet Exchanges: *0 milk, ½ vegetable, 0 fruit, 1 bread, 0 meat, ½ fat*

1½ Carb Choices

California Special

—Billie Kroger, Surprise, Arizona

Serve with a chunky vegetable soup.

Prep time: 5 minutes

4 **slices multigrain bread, toasted**
1 **tablespoon stone-ground mustard**
2 **slices red onion, ¼" thick**
1 **ripe avocado, sliced**
2 **slices tomato, ¼" thick**
2 **thin slices (1½ ounces) Monterey Jack cheese**
1 **cup alfalfa sprouts**

Lay 2 slices of the bread on a work surface. Spread with the mustard. Separate the onion slices and distribute on the bread. Top with the avocado, tomato, cheese, sprouts, and remaining bread slices. Cut each sandwich diagonally.

Makes 4 servings

Per serving: *204 calories, 8 g protein, 20 g carbohydrate, 11 g fat, 10 mg cholesterol, 208 mg sodium, 8 g fiber*

Diet Exchanges: *0 milk, ½ vegetable, 0 fruit, 1 bread, ½ meat, 2 fat*

1 Carb Choice

SHOPPING SAVVY

Raising the Bar

Gnu Foods Flavor & Fiber Bars help you increase your fiber intake. Fiber, which passes through the body undigested, contains no nutrients but has been cited in study after study as a valuable dietary tool in staving off diabetes and heart disease. One 40-gram bar contains 12 grams of fiber, more than one-third of the daily recommended requirement. Each bar has only 3 grams of fat and is a mere 2 POINTS on the Weight Watchers program—all for 130 calories (140 for the Chocolate Brownie). Four fabulous flavors are available: Chocolate Brownie, Orange Cranberry, Banana Walnut, and Cinnamon Raisin. The bars are 100% sweetened with fruit juice—no high-fructose corn syrup or trans fats. Look for these fiber phenoms at some supermarkets, specialty food stores, and www.gnufoods.com.

Tuna Rice-Paper Wrap

—Harris, Calgary, Alberta, Canada

Rice-paper wrappers make this recipe different and fun.

Prep time: 10 minutes

1 can (12 ounces) water-packed light tuna, drained
2 tablespoons reduced-fat mayonnaise
1 tablespoon chopped scallion
1 tablespoon chopped celery
1 tablespoon finely shredded carrot
1 tablespoon finely chopped cilantro or Thai basil + some leaves for garnish
½ teaspoon toasted sesame oil
   Pinch of salt
   Pinch of ground black pepper
   Hot-pepper sauce (optional)
4 round rice-paper wrappers

In a bowl, combine the tuna, mayonnaise, scallion, celery, carrot, cilantro or basil, oil, salt, pepper, and a few drops of hot-pepper sauce (if using). Stir to mix well.

Prepare the rice-paper wrappers according to the package directions. Lay the papers on a moistened tray or work surface. Spoon one-fourth of the tuna mixture and spoon on one side of each wrapper. Roll into packets, folding sides in first and rolling from the bottom into a tube. Garnish with cilantro or basil leaves and serve immediately.

Makes 4 servings

Per serving: *120 calories, 20 g protein, 2 g carbohydrate, 3½ g fat, 23 mg cholesterol, 371 mg sodium, 0 g fiber*

Diet Exchanges: *0 milk, 0 vegetable, 0 fruit, 0 bread, 2½ meat, ½ fat*

0 Carb Choices

— *Kitchen Tip* —

Rice-paper wrappers, made from rice flour, water, and salt, are brittle, dried flatbreads that are sold in Asian groceries and some supermarkets. They must be reconstituted in hot water before using in wraps and other recipes.

248 Calories

Tuna Curry Sandwich

—Elizabeth Goldstein, Yardley, Pennsylvania

A most unlikely combination—curry, mustard, tuna, and, yes, banana—gives a tangy, pungent twist to everyday tuna.

Prep time: 5 minutes

1 can (6½ ounces) water-packed albacore tuna, drained and flaked

¼ cup chopped onion

2 tablespoons low-fat mayonnaise

1 teaspoon Dijon mustard

½ teaspoon curry powder

1 banana, sliced

4 slices pumpernickel or rye bread

4 cucumber slices (optional)

In a medium bowl, combine the tuna, onion, mayonnaise, mustard, and curry powder. Fold in the banana.

Spread the mixture on 2 slices of the bread. Top with the cucumbers and the remaining bread. Slice in half and serve.

Makes 2 servings

Per serving: *248 calories, 24 g protein, 24 g carbohydrate, 6 g fat, 36 mg cholesterol, 783 mg sodium, 3 g fiber*

Diet Exchanges: *0 milk, ½ vegetable, 0 fruit, 1 bread, 3½ meat, ½ fat*

1½ Carb Choices

148 Calories

Indian Potato Flatbread

—Lakshmi Nannur, Troy, Michigan

"After my child was born, I gained a lot of weight. I started eating potato bread for dinner everyday. Now I am back to my weight, and I am very healthy."

Prep time: 15 minutes
Cool time: 10 minutes
Stand time: 10 minutes
Cook time: 25 minutes

- 1 **pound russet potatoes, peeled and cut into chunks**
- 2 **serrano or other green chile peppers, cut into pieces (wear plastic gloves when handling)**
- 1 **teaspoon salt**
- 2 **tablespoons chopped cilantro**
- 1 **teaspoon garam masala**
- 1 **cup whole wheat flour**
  Water

In a saucepan, combine the potato, peppers, and ½ teaspoon of the salt. Add enough water to cover. Cover the pan and set over high heat. Bring to a boil. Reduce the heat to medium. Cook for about 20 minutes, or until the potatoes are very tender. Drain. Add the cilantro and garam masala and mash with a potato ricer or masher. Set aside for about 10 minutes to cool to room temperature.

In a mixing bowl, combine the potato mixture with the flour and the remaining ½ teaspoon salt. Stir, adding 1 tablespoon of water at a time, to make a moist but not sticky dough. Turn onto a lightly floured work surface. Knead lightly for about 30 seconds, or until the dough forms a smooth ball. Cover with a cloth and let stand for 10 minutes.

Lightly dust your hands with flour. Divide the ball into 12 pieces. With your palms, shape each piece into a ball. Cover the dough while working with one ball at a time. With a rolling pin on a work surface lightly dusted with flour, roll each ball into a 6" circle. Dust lightly with flour; set aside. Continue rolling until all the breads are ready.

Lightly coat a stove-top griddle or other heavy skillet with cooking spray and set over medium-high heat. Place several breads in a single layer on the griddle. Cook for about 1½ minutes, or until brown spots form on the bottom. Turn over and cook for about 1 minute longer, or until cooked through. Remove. Continue until all the breads are cooked. Serve immediately.

Makes 12 servings

Per serving: *148 calories, 2 g protein, 15 g carbohydrate, 0 g fat, 0 mg cholesterol, 148 mg sodium, 2 g fiber*

Diet Exchanges: *0 milk, 0 vegetable, 0 fruit, 1 bread, 0 meat, 0 fat*

1 Carb Choice

319 Calories

Caribbean Jerk Chicken Pan Pizza

—Larry Elder, Charlotte, North Carolina

The robust flavors really give your tastebuds something to rave about.

Prep time: 12 minutes
Bake time: 25 to 32 minutes

1 tablespoon canola oil
1 cup cornmeal
¾ cup fat-free plain yogurt
1 teaspoon ground cumin
2 cups diced cooked chicken breast
1 cup low-fat salsa
2 tablespoons Worcestershire sauce
1 tablespoon lime juice
½ teaspoon dried thyme
¼ teaspoon ground allspice
½ cup shredded reduced-fat Monterey Jack cheese with jalapeño chiles
¼ cup chopped scallions
¼ cup diced red bell pepper

Preheat the oven to 400°F.

Brush a large cast-iron skillet or other heavy ovenproof frying pan with the oil. Bake for 5 minutes, or until hot.

In a small bowl, combine the cornmeal, yogurt, and cumin. Stir to mix. Carefully remove the pan from the oven and spoon the cornmeal mixture into it, spreading it evenly over the bottom.

Bake for 10 to 15 minutes, or until just firm and set but not browned. Remove from the oven.

In a medium bowl, combine the chicken, salsa, Worcestershire sauce, lime juice, thyme, and allspice. Stir to mix. Spread evenly over the cornmeal mixture. Sprinkle with the cheese, scallions, and pepper. Bake for 10 to 12 minutes, or until bubbly.

Makes 4 servings

Per serving: 350 calories, 30 g protein, 35 g carbohydrate, 10 g fat, 71 mg cholesterol, 3 g fiber, 497 mg sodium

Diet Exchanges: *0 milk, 0 vegetable, 0 fruit, 1½ bread, 3½ meat, 1 fat*

2 Carb Choices

YES Pizzas

—Nancy Moore, San Antonio, Texas

Served with a yummy fresh salad, this pizza is so filling and pleasing that no one feels deprived.

Prep time: 4 minutes
Cook time: 6 minutes
Bake time: 8 minutes

 2 teaspoons olive oil
 8 ounces sliced mushrooms
 1 cup grape tomatoes, sliced
 ½ teaspoon dried oregano
    Pinch of salt
    Pinch of ground black pepper
 4 low-fat tortillas (7" diameter)
 ⅓ cup pizza sauce
 ½ cup (2 ounces) shredded part-skim
    mozzarella cheese
    Red-pepper flakes (optional)

Preheat the oven to 400°F.

In a nonstick skillet over medium-high heat, warm the oil. Add the mushrooms. Toss. Cover and cook, tossing occasionally, for about 4 minutes, or until liquid pools in the pan. Uncover and cook for about 2 minutes longer, or until the liquid is gone. Add the tomatoes, oregano, salt, and pepper. Remove from the heat.

Lay the tortillas on a large baking sheet. With the back of a spoon, spread the sauce evenly over the tortillas. Evenly sprinkle on half of the cheese. Top evenly with the mushroom mixture and the remaining cheese.

Bake for about 8 minutes, or until the cheese is bubbly. Sprinkle with the red-pepper flakes, if desired.

Makes 4 servings

Per serving: *200 calories, 8 g protein, 23 g carbohydrate, 8 g fat, 0 mg cholesterol, 408 mg sodium, 5 g fiber*

Diet Exchanges: *0 milk, 1 vegetable, 0 fruit, 0 bread, ½ meat, 1 fat*

1½ Carb Choices

285 Calories

Guilt-Free Alfredo Pizza

—Lynn Johnson, Paragould, Arkansas

This unusual pizza is bound to get your tastebuds' attention.

Prep time: 10 minutes
Bake time: 7 to 10 minutes

2 teaspoons olive oil

1 teaspoon minced garlic

1 bag (6 ounces) fresh baby spinach

4 low-fat flour tortillas (7" diameter)

3 tablespoons grated Parmesan cheese

1 can (5–6 ounces) white chicken meat, drained, or 1½ cups chopped cooked chicken breast

3 slices turkey bacon, cooked and crumbled

¾ cup (3 ounces) shredded mozzarella cheese

Preheat the oven to 400°F.

In a nonstick skillet over low heat, warm the oil and garlic for about 1 minute, or until the garlic sizzles. Add the spinach. Cook, tossing, for about 2 minutes, or until wilted.

Set the tortillas in a single layer on a baking sheet. Sprinkle each with the Parmesan cheese. Cover with an even layer of the spinach and chicken. Top each pizza with the bacon. Sprinkle the mozzarella on top.

Bake for 7 to 10 minutes, or until the cheese is bubbly. Cut each pizza into wedges.

Makes 4 servings

Per serving: *285 calories, 18 g protein, 24 g carbohydrate, 13 g fat, 39 mg cholesterol, 773 mg sodium, 5 g fiber*

Diet Exchanges: *0 milk, 1 vegetable, 0 fruit, 0 bread, 2 meat, 1 fat*

1½ Carb Choices

164 Calories

Hawaiian Muffin Pizza

—Betty Romano, San Gabriel, California

Delicious, fast, and easy!

Prep time: 10 minutes
Bake time: 12 minutes

3 **English muffins, split and lightly toasted**

4 **ounces reduced-fat ham, cut into small cubes**

1 **green bell pepper, chopped**

1 **cup pineapple tidbits in juice, drained, or finely chopped fresh pineapple**

4 **ounces shredded reduced-fat sharp Cheddar cheese**

Preheat the oven to 375°F. Set the muffins, cut side up, on a baking sheet. Top with the ham, pepper, pineapple, and cheese. Bake for 12 minutes, or until the cheese is bubbly.

Makes 6 servings

Per serving: *164 calories, 11 g protein, 18 g carbohydrate, 5 g fat, 19 mg cholesterol, 504 mg sodium, 1 g fiber*

Diet Exchanges: *0 milk, 0 vegetable, 0 fruit, 1 bread, 1 meat, ½ fat*

1 Carb Choice

110 Calories

Grilled Mixed Vegetables

—Lisa Mishaga, South Euclid, Ohio

"This is a great recipe because it makes you love to eat vegetables."

Prep time: 15 minutes
Grill time: 20 minutes

1 red bell pepper, quartered

1 yellow squash, sliced lengthwise into ½" thick pieces

1 zucchini, sliced lengthwise into ½" thick pieces

1 Japanese eggplant, sliced lengthwise into ½" thick pieces

4 cremini mushrooms

4 ounces asparagus

3 scallions

2 tablespoons olive oil

1 tablespoon balsamic vinegar

1 garlic clove, minced

1 tablespoon chopped fresh Italian parsley

1 tablespoon chopped fresh basil

1 teaspoon finely chopped fresh rosemary

¼ teaspoon salt

Freshly ground black pepper

Place a grill pan over medium-high heat or preheat the barbecue to medium-high heat. Brush the vegetables lightly with some of the oil to coat. Working in batches, grill the vegetables until tender and lightly charred all over, about 8 to 10 minutes for the bell pepper; 7 minutes for the yellow squash, zucchini, eggplant, and mushrooms; and 4 minutes for the asparagus and scallions. Arrange the vegetables on a platter. Meanwhile, in a small bowl, whisk the remaining oil, the vinegar, garlic, parsley, basil, rosemary, and salt to blend. Drizzle the herb mixture over the vegetables. Season to taste with black pepper. Serve warm or at room temperature.

Makes 4 servings

Per serving: *110 calories, 3 g protein, 11 g carbohydrate, 7 g fat, 0 mg cholesterol, 158 mg sodium, 4 g fiber*

Diet Exchanges: *0 milk, 2 vegetable, 0 fruit, 0 bread, 0 meat, 1½ fat*

1 Carb Choice

86 Calories

Summer Squash Parmigiana

—Pat Zashkoff, Yonkers, New York

"This is a great recipe for losing weight because it is quick and easy, and you get vegetables and dairy in your diet. It is filling and not many calories."

Prep time: 12 minutes
Microwave time: 18 minutes

1 can (14½ ounces) tomato sauce

2 teaspoons dried Italian seasoning

1 clove garlic, minced

¼ teaspoon salt

¼ teaspoon ground black pepper

3 small yellow squash or zucchini, unpeeled, cut into 1" chunks

3 tablespoons seasoned dry bread crumbs

¼ cup grated Parmesan cheese

½ cup shredded part-skim mozzarella cheese

Coat a 2-quart microwaveable gratin dish or other shallow baking dish with cooking spray.

In a bowl, combine the tomato sauce, seasoning, garlic, salt, and pepper. Spread a few tablespoons of the sauce on the bottom of the prepared dish. Cover with a layer of the squash. Repeat with 2 more layers of sauce and squash, ending with the remaining sauce. Sprinkle with the bread crumbs, Parmesan, and mozzarella.

Microwave on high power for about 18 minutes, or until the squash is cooked and the cheese is bubbly.

Makes 6 servings

Per serving: *86 calories, 6 g protein, 10 g carbohydrate, 3 g fat, 9 mg cholesterol, 606 mg sodium, 2 g fiber*

Diet Exchanges: *0 milk, 1 vegetable, 0 fruit, 0 bread, ½ meat, 0 fat*

1 Carb Choice

Gianna's Grilled Stuffed Eggplant

—Giovanna Kranenberg, Cambridge, Minnesota

"This recipe is especially great when all the ingredients come fresh from your garden!"

Prep time: 15 minutes
Grill time: 20 to 25 minutes

3 small eggplants, halved lengthwise
¼ cup grated Parmesan cheese
¼ cup seasoned dry bread crumbs
3 plum tomatoes, finely chopped
1 tablespoon chopped parsley
4 cloves garlic, minced
¼ teaspoon salt
¼ teaspoon ground black pepper
2 tablespoons olive oil

Preheat the grill to medium-high.

With a small, sharp knife, cut a grid of ½" squares in each eggplant half as close to the skin as possible without cutting through. Scoop out the flesh of each eggplant and place in a medium bowl. Add the cheese, bread crumbs, tomatoes, parsley, garlic, salt, and pepper. Stir to mix. Stuff the mixture tightly into each eggplant half. Drizzle with the oil.

Place the eggplant halves on a disposable aluminum foil pan. Set on the grill.

Cover and grill for 20 to 25 minutes, or until the eggplant is soft and the top is golden and crisp.

Makes 6 servings

Per serving: *150 calories, 5 g protein, 21 g carbohydrate, 6.5 g fat, 3 mg cholesterol, 244 mg sodium, 10 g fiber*

Diet Exchanges: *0 milk, 3 vegetable, 0 fruit, 0 bread, 0 meat, 1 fat*

1½ Carb Choices

115 Calories

Squash & Corn Delight

—Phyllis Ostrowski, Berkeley, Illinois

"Everything in this dish is vegetables. It's easy to make and tastes great."

Prep time: 15 minutes
Cook time: 10 minutes

1 tablespoon canola oil

1 small onion, finely chopped

4 medium yellow squash or zucchini or a combination, unpeeled, cubed

   Kernels cut from 2 ears of corn (about 1¾ cups)

1 jalapeño chile pepper, chopped (wear plastic gloves when handling)

½ teaspoon salt

In a large skillet over medium heat, warm the oil. Add the onion. Cook, stirring occasionally, for about 2 minutes, or until onion begins to soften. Add the squash. Turn the heat to high. Cook, stirring frequently, for about 6 minutes, or until softened and golden. Add the corn, chile pepper, and salt. Cook for about 2 minutes, or until the corn is heated through.

Makes 4 servings

Per serving: *115 calories, 5 g protein, 16 g carbohydrate, 5 g fat, 0 mg cholesterol, 303 mg sodium, 4 g fiber*

Diet Exchanges: *0 milk, 3½ vegetable, 0 fruit, 0 bread, 0 meat, 1 fat*

1 Carb Choice

SHOPPING SAVVY

Get Steamed

Eating your antioxidant-rich vegetables has just gotten a whole lot easier and faster with Green Giant Simply Steam no-sauce-added vegetables. With fewer than 70 calories per serving, the vegetables cook right in the bag in the microwave. A built-in steam seam helps retain natural flavor and texture while the vegetables cook. Sold in 8-ounce packages in the grocer's freezer section, the selections include individual varieties such as Asparagus Cuts, Baby Sweet Peas, Sugar Snap Peas, Shoepeg White Corn, Baby Lima Beans, Sweet Peas & Pearl Onions, and Niblets Corn, as well as Broccoli & Carrots, Green Beans & Almonds, and Garden Vegetable Medley, a combination of sugar snap peas, roasted potatoes, red peppers, garlic, and herbs. For more information, visit www.greengiant.com.

53 Calories

Green Beans with Dill

—Harry Rust, Columbus, Ohio

*"The aromatic fresh dill really makes this dish for me.
Fresh basil is also good if you don't have dill."*

Prep time: 10 minutes
Cook time: 5 minutes

1 pound green beans, cut into 2" lengths

2 teaspoons butter or trans-free margarine

½ cup chopped red onion

1 tablespoon finely chopped fresh dill or 1 teaspoon dried dillweed

¼ teaspoon salt

¼ teaspoon ground black pepper

Boil or steam the beans until tender but still crisp. Drain and set aside.

In a nonstick skillet over medium heat, melt the butter or margarine. Add the onion. Cook, stirring occasionally, for about 3 minutes, or until slightly softened. Add the reserved beans, the dill, salt, and pepper. Toss for about 2 minutes, or until the flavors combine.

Makes 4 servings

Per serving: *53 calories, 2 g protein, 9 g carbohydrate, 2 g fat, 5 mg cholesterol, 160 mg sodium, 4 g fiber*

Diet Exchanges: *0 milk, 1½ vegetable, 0 fruit, 0 bread, 0 meat, ½ fat*

1 Carb Choice

155 Calories

Tomatoes Stuffed with White Bean Salad

—Tracy Anderson, Austin, Texas

"This makes a great lunch-box treat or light supper. It can also be a great side dish with grilled fish. I love it!"

Prep time: 15 minutes

- 2 tablespoons Italian parsley, chopped + several sprigs for garnish
- 1 tablespoon lemon juice
- 1 tablespoon extra-virgin olive oil
- 2 teaspoons capers, rinsed and drained
- 2 cloves garlic, minced
- ¼ teaspoon salt
- ¼ teaspoon freshly ground black pepper
- 1 can (15½ ounces) navy beans, drained and rinsed
- 4 medium tomatoes

In medium bowl, combine the parsley, lemon juice, oil, capers, garlic, salt, and pepper. Whisk to mix. Add the beans. Toss thoroughly to mix. For a slightly creamier texture, mash one-quarter of the beans roughly with the back of a fork.

Slice ¼" from the tops of the tomatoes. Scoop out the seeds and discard. Spoon the bean salad into the tomatoes. Garnish with parsley sprigs.

Makes 4 servings

Per serving: 155 calories, 8 g protein, 24 g carbohydrate, 4 g fat, 0 mg cholesterol, 572 mg sodium, 0 g fiber

Diet Exchanges: *0 milk, 1 vegetable, 0 fruit, 1 bread, 0 meat, 1 fat*

1½ Carb Choices

All-Purpose Skillet Veggies

—Veronica Noone, Joppa, Maryland

"You can eat this as a meal, a side dish, or a filling for anything! I put it on a large tortilla with some mozzarella cheese and a little green chile sauce."

Prep time: 20 minutes
Cook time: 15 minutes

1 tablespoon olive oil
1 bell pepper, any color, chopped
½ sweet onion, chopped
4 garlic cloves, thinly sliced
1 medium zucchini, chopped
1 medium yellow squash, chopped
1 large tomato, chopped
2 tablespoons chopped parsley
½ teaspoon dried oregano
½ teaspoon dried basil
¼ teaspoon salt
¼ teaspoon ground black pepper

In a large nonstick skillet over medium heat, warm the oil. Add the bell pepper, onion, and garlic. Cook, stirring occasionally, for about 4 minutes, or until starting to soften. Add the zucchini and squash. Turn the heat to high. Cook, stirring frequently, for about 6 minutes, or until the squash starts to turn golden. Add the tomato. Cook, stirring, for about 3 minutes, or until the tomato softens. Add the parsley, oregano, basil, salt, and pepper. Cook for 1 minute for the seasonings to blend.

Makes 4 servings

Per serving: *80 calories, 2 g protein, 11 g carbohydrate, 4 g fat, 0 mg cholesterol, 160 mg sodium, 0 g fiber*

Diet Exchanges: *0 milk, 2 vegetable, 0 fruit, 0 bread, 0 meat, 1 fat*

1 Carb Choice

154 Calories

Vegan Sesame Grill

—Wendy Battin, Mystic, Connecticut

"The brilliant flavor of grilled vegetables is so satisfying!"

Prep time: 10 minutes
Cook time: 20 to 25 minutes

2 sweet potatoes, peeled, cut into walnut-sized chunks

8 ounces Brussels sprouts, halved

4 garlic cloves, thinly sliced

2 teaspoons canola oil

¼ teaspoon salt

½ teaspoon regular or hot toasted sesame oil

Freshly ground black pepper

Preheat a covered grill.

In a large bowl, combine the sweet potatoes, Brussels sprouts, garlic, canola oil, and salt. Toss to coat. Place the vegetables in a grill basket or portable grill rack. Set on the grill and cover. Grill, turning occasionally, for 20 to 25 minutes, or until tender.

Transfer the vegetables to a platter. Drizzle the sesame oil on top. Season to taste with black pepper. Toss.

Makes 4 servings

Per serving: *154 calories, 4 g protein, 23 g carbohydrate, 5 g fat, 0 mg cholesterol, 183 mg sodium, 0 g fiber*

Diet Exchanges: *0 milk, 1 vegetable, 0 fruit, 1 bread, 0 meat, 1 fat*

1½ Carb Choices

90 Calories

Kale with Pumpkin Seeds

—Wendy Battin, Mystic, Connecticut

"Filling, nutritious, low-calorie."

Prep time: 10 minutes
Stand time: 30 minutes
Cook time: 5 minutes

½ teaspoon + ⅛ teaspoon salt
1 pound kale leaves, coarsely chopped
1 tablespoon canola oil
2 teaspoons rice vinegar
1 tablespoon toasted pumpkin seeds

In a pot, combine ½ teaspoon salt and kale in enough water to cover. Let stand for 30 minutes. Drain the kale, leaving any water clinging to leaves.

In the same pot over medium-high heat, warm the oil. Add the kale and cook, tossing occasionally, for about 5 minutes, or until wilted. Add the vinegar and the remaining ⅛ teaspoon salt. Toss. Serve sprinkled with the seeds. Pass additional vinegar at the table.

Makes 4 servings

Per serving: *90 calories, 4 g protein, 12 g carbohydrate, 4.5 g fat, 0 mg cholesterol, 340 mg sodium, 2 g fiber*

Diet Exchanges: *0 milk, 2½ vegetable, 0 fruit, 0 bread, 0 meat, 1 fat*

1 Carb Choice

Carrot and Pineapple-Orange Gelatin Mold

—Nancy Kevorkian, Port Charlotte, Florida

"Junk snacking is my downfall. I have been able to lose weight and control it because this gelatin recipe satisfies so many different cravings. Most important, I substitute low-calorie/light ingredients without sacrificing flavor. Also, this recipe is really forgiving if you have to substitute a few veggie ingredients."

Prep time: 25 minutes
Chill time: 2 hours

- 1 large package (6 ounces) orange gelatin
- 2 cups boiling water
- ¼ cup pineapple juice
- 2 cups grated carrots
- 1½ cups reduced-fat small-curd cottage cheese
- 1 cup crushed unsweetened pineapple, drained
- ½ cup light mayonnaise
- ¼ cup slivered almonds

Coat a 9" × 13" glass or ceramic dish with cooking spray.

In a large bowl, combine the gelatin, water, and juice. Stir until the gelatin is dissolved. Refrigerate for 1 hour, or until slightly congealed.

With a hand-held electric beater or whisk, beat the gelatin mixture until frothy.

Add the carrots, cottage cheese, pineapple, mayonnaise, and almonds. Fold to combine. Transfer to the prepared dish.

Cover and refrigerate for 1 hour, or until set.

Makes 12 servings

Per serving: *122 calories, 6 g protein, 20 g carbohydrate, 3 g fat, 1 mg cholesterol, 267 mg sodium, 1 g fiber*

Diet Exchanges: *0 milk, ½ vegetable, 0 fruit, 1 bread, ½ meat, ½ fat*

1 Carb Choice

Gianna's Garlic-Lemon Potatoes

—Giovanna Kranenberg, Cambridge, Minnesota

"They're healthy and very flavorful!"

Prep time: 10 minutes
Cook time: 15 minutes

1½ **pounds red-skin or yellow potatoes,**
    cubed
½ **teaspoon salt**
1 **tablespoon olive oil**
2 **tablespoons lemon juice**
2 **cloves garlic, minced**
    Freshly ground black pepper

In a saucepan, combine the potatoes and salt with enough water to cover by 1". Cook over medium heat for about 15 minutes or until tender. Drain and return to the pan.

Add the oil, lemon juice, garlic, and pepper to taste. Toss to mix thoroughly.

Makes 6 servings

Per serving: *102 calories, 2 g protein, 19 g carbohydrate, 2½ g fat, 0 mg cholesterol, 201 mg sodium, 2 g fiber*

Diet Exchanges: *0 milk, 0 vegetable, 0 fruit, 1 bread, 0 meat, ½ fat*

1 Carb Choice

SECRETS OF WEIGHT-LOSS WINNERS

• Start each meal with some fruit. I find the natural sweetness of any fruit will help curb overeating at meal time.

**—Silvana Cox, Edmonton,
Alberta, Canada**

• I try to visualize in my mind everything I consume in one day. It keeps it real, as far as calories.

**—Rose Ardanaz, Langley,
British Columbia, Canada**

• If you like to walk but get tired of all the routes around your house, find some new routes near a friend's house or any nice neighborhood.

**—Patrice Pruitte, Greenville,
South Carolina**

Instant Rice Pilaf

—Harry Rust, Columbus, Ohio

*"I love getting the fiber and nutrients in brown rice with a fraction
of the cooking time that regular brown rice takes."*

Prep time: 5 minutes
Cook time: 15 minutes
Stand time: 5 minutes

  2 **teaspoons butter or trans-free
    margarine**
  2 **tablespoons chopped onion or scallion**
  1 **teaspoon salt-free seasoning blend**
  ½ **teaspoon salt**
  1 **cup instant brown rice**
  1 **can (14½ ounces) reduced-sodium
    chicken broth or water**
  1 **tablespoon chopped parsley or fresh
    chives**

In a saucepan over medium heat, melt the butter or margarine. Add the onion or scallion, seasoning, and salt. Cook, stirring, for about 2 minutes, or until the onion is sizzling. Add the rice. Stir to coat. Add the broth or water. Bring to a boil. Reduce the heat to a simmer and cover.

Cook for 10 minutes. Remove from the heat and set aside for 5 minutes.

Fluff with a fork, sprinkle with the parsley or chives, and serve.

Makes 4 servings

Per serving: *111 calories, 4 g protein, 18 g carbohydrate, 2½ g fat, 5 mg cholesterol, 407 mg sodium, 1 g fiber*

Diet Exchanges: *0 milk, 0 vegetable, 0 fruit, 1 bread, 0 meat, ½ fat*

1 Carb Choice

Tasty & Colorful Quinoa

—Theresa Malone, Higganum, Connecticut

"I replaced buttered potatoes or buttered white rice with this side.
As an added benefit, it helps lower cholesterol."

Prep time: 15 minutes
Cook time: 25 minutes

1½ tablespoons extra-virgin olive oil
½ cup chopped red bell pepper
½ cup chopped yellow onion
½ cup chopped celery
½ teaspoon adobo seasoning
¼ teaspoon salt
1 cup quinoa
2 cups reduced-sodium fat-free chicken broth
½ cup fresh or frozen corn kernels
2 scallions, sliced thinly

In a saucepan over medium heat, warm 1 tablespoon of the oil. Add the bell pepper, onion, celery, seasoning, and salt. Cook, stirring frequently, for 4 minutes, or until the pepper starts to soften. Add the quinoa. Stir to coat. Add the broth and corn. Bring to a boil and cover, then reduce the heat to low. Simmer for 20 minutes, or until all the liquid is absorbed. Stir in the remaining ½ tablespoon oil. Sprinkle with the scallions.

Makes 4 servings

Per serving: *243 calories, 7 g protein, 37 g carbohydrate, 8 g fat, 0 mg cholesterol, 567 mg sodium, 4 g fiber*

Diet Exchanges: *0 milk, 1 vegetable, 0 fruit, 2 bread, 0 meat, 1 fat*

2½ Carb Choices

209 Calories

Celebration Rice

—Marjorie "GeGe" Kingston, Stockbridge, Massachusetts

*This side dish flavors crunchy roasted sesame seeds and wild rice
with lively spices and a hint of citrus.*

Prep time: 5 minutes
Cook time: 50 to 55 minutes

¾ cup Uncle Ben's Brown Rice
¼ cup wild rice
2 cups water
½ teaspoon salt
⅓ cup orange juice
1 tablespoon low-sodium soy sauce
1½ teaspoons olive oil
1 teaspoon grated orange rind
1 teaspoon curry powder
2 tablespoons chopped chives or
    scallions
2 tablespoons chopped red bell pepper
1 tablespoon toasted sesame seeds

In a 2-quart saucepan over medium heat, stir the brown rice and wild rice for 5 minutes, or until lightly toasted.

Add the water, salt, orange juice, soy sauce, oil, orange rind, and curry powder. Cover the pan tightly and cook over low heat for 45 to 50 minutes, or until all the liquid has been absorbed and the rice is tender.

Fluff the rice with a fork. Stir in the chopped chives or scallions, pepper, and sesame seeds.

Makes 4 servings

Per serving: *209 calories, 5 g protein, 38 g carbohydrate, 4 g fat, 0 mg cholesterol, 2 g fiber, 449 mg sodium*

Diet Exchanges: *0 milk, 0 vegetable, 0 fruit, 2 bread, 0 meat, 2½ fat*

2½ Carb Choices

Main Dishes

VEGETARIAN

SEAFOOD AND FISH

CHICKEN AND TURKEY

BEEF AND PORK

Rigatoni with Summer Squash and Mushrooms

—Alison Siller, West Springfield, Massachusetts

"Very simple, healthy, and quick. And delicious!"

Prep time: 10 minutes
Cook time: 12 minutes

  8 ounces rigatoni pasta

  2 tablespoons olive oil

  1 medium yellow or green summer squash, halved lengthwise and sliced (about 2 cups)

  1 cup sliced mushrooms (about 8–10 mushrooms)

  ½ cup sliced carrots (1 small)

  ½ cup sliced scallions, all parts (about 6 scallions)

  2 tablespoons chopped fresh dill or 2 teaspoons dried dillweed

  ½ teaspoon crushed red-pepper flakes

  ¼ teaspoon salt

  ½ cup (2 ounces) shredded reduced-fat Swiss cheese

Cook the pasta according to the package directions. Scoop out ½ cup pasta-cooling water and reserve. Drain the pasta and return to the cooking pot to keep warm.

Meanwhile, in a large nonstick skillet over medium-high heat, warm the oil. Add the squash, mushrooms, and carrot. Toss to mix. Cover and cook, stirring occasionally, for 3 to 4 minutes, or until tender-crisp. Add the scallions. Cook for about 2 minutes, or until the carrots are tender and the scallions are wilted. Add the dill, pepper flakes, and salt. Remove from the heat and set aside.

Add the pasta to the vegetable mixture. Moisten with a few tablespoons of the reserved cooking water. Add the cheese. Toss over low heat for about 1 minute, or until the cheese melts. Serve warm or at room temperature.

Makes 4 servings

Per serving: *325 calories, 13 g protein, 48 g carbohydrate, 9 g fat, 5 mg cholesterol, 200 mg sodium, 3 g fiber*

Diet Exchanges: *0 milk, 1 vegetable, 0 fruit, 2½ bread, ½ meat, 1½ fat*

3 Carb Choices

347 Calories

Smothered Bean Burritos

—Pam Harris, Martin, Tennessee

Beans, an excellent source of low-fat protein and fiber, are a power diet food.

Prep time: 10 minutes
Cook time: 5 minutes
Bake time: 18 minutes

  2 teaspoons canola or olive oil
½ cup chopped onion (1 small)
½ cup chopped red or yellow bell pepper
    (½ large)
  1 tablespoon chili powder
  1 can (16 ounces) fat-free refried beans
  4 whole wheat or regular flour tortillas
    (8" diameter)
  1 can (14½ ounces) diced tomatoes
  2 jalapeño chile peppers, finely chopped
    (wear plastic gloves when handling)
  1 cup (4 ounces) shredded reduced-fat
    Cheddar cheese

Preheat the oven to 350°F. Coat a 13" × 9" baking dish with cooking spray.

In a small nonstick skillet over medium heat, warm the oil. Add the onion, bell pepper, and chili powder. Cook, stirring occasionally, for about 4 minutes, or until the onion is softened. Set aside half (about ¼ cup) of the mixture in a bowl. Add the beans to the skillet and break them up with a spoon. Add a few tablespoonfuls of water, if needed, to loosen the mixture slightly.

Lay the tortillas in a single layer on a work surface. Spoon one-quarter (about ½ cup) of the bean mixture on each tortilla, then fold opposite sides of each tortilla to meet in the middle. Fold under the top and bottom of the roll to form a compact bundle. Place the burritos seam side down in the dish.

Add the tomatoes (with juice) and the chile peppers to the reserved onion-and-pepper mixture. Stir to mix. Spread over the burritos. Sprinkle the cheese on top.

Bake for about 18 minutes, or until the cheese melts and the mixture bubbles.

Makes 4 servings

Per serving: *347 calories, 16 g protein, 43 g carbohydrate, 11 g fat, 20 mg cholesterol, 902 mg sodium, 8 g fiber*

Diet Exchanges: *0 milk, 1 vegetable, 0 fruit, 0 bread, 1 meat, 1 fat*

3 Carb Choices

106 Calories

Black-Bean Vegetable Noodle Stir-Fry

—Janet Utz, Kenmore, New York

"I created this recipe after reading about the health benefits of black beans and the carb-cutting benefits of shirataki noodles. I've lost over 30 pounds and learned the importance of creative cooking as a tool of success in reaching and maintaining my goal. This recipe is easy, delicious, and filling."

Prep time: 15 minutes
Cook time: 8 minutes

2 teaspoons olive oil

1 medium red bell pepper, chopped (about ¾ cup)

1 medium green bell pepper, chopped (about ¾ cup)

1 small onion, chopped (about ½ cup)

1 small zucchini, halved and cut into chunks (about 1 cup)

2 cloves garlic, minced

1 bag (16 ounces) shirataki noodles, drained and rinsed in hot water

1 cup canned black beans, drained and rinsed (about half of a 15–16 ounce can)

2 tablespoons reduced-sodium soy sauce

1½ teaspoons sodium-free seasoning mix

2 tablespoons chopped fresh cilantro or parsley

Hot-pepper sauce

In a wok or large nonstick skillet over high heat, warm the oil. Add the bell peppers, onion, zucchini, and garlic. Reduce the heat to medium-high and cook, stirring frequently, for 4 minutes, or until the vegetables start to soften. Add the noodles, beans, soy sauce, and seasoning mix. Reduce the heat to medium. Cook, stirring frequently, for 3 to 4 minutes longer, or until the mixture is hot. Add the cilantro or parsley. Toss to mix.

Pass the hot-pepper sauce at the table.

Makes 4 servings

Per serving: *106 calories, 5 g protein, 18 g carbohydrate, 3 g fat, 0 mg cholesterol, 537 mg sodium, 5 g fiber*

Diet Exchanges: *0 milk, 1 vegetable, 0 fruit, 1 bread, 0 meat, ½ fat*

1 Carb Choice

Kitchen Tip

Shirataki noodles, prepared from Japanese yam flour, are wheat- and gluten-free. They can be purchased in Asian food stores, on the Web, or in some supermarkets.

420 Calories

Bow Tie Pasta with Spinach, Tomato, and Olives

—Marcie Fisher, Cleburne, Texas

With appealing Mediterranean flavorings, you'll feel like you're vacationing, not watching your waistline. For a nonveg variation, toss in some grilled shrimp or chicken breast.

Prep time: 10 minutes
Cook time: 10 minutes

12 ounces bow tie pasta
2 tablespoons olive oil
2 cloves garlic, finely chopped
2 cups chopped fresh or canned tomato
2 cups, packed (2 ounces) baby spinach leaves, roughly chopped
2 tablespoons lemon juice, preferably freshly squeezed
2 tablespoons sliced kalamata or other ripe olives (about 5 to 6 olives)
2 tablespoons capers, drained and rinsed
¼ teaspoon ground black pepper
⅛ teaspoon salt
2 tablespoons grated Parmesan cheese

Cook the pasta according to the package directions. Before draining, scoop out ½ cup of the pasta-cooking water and reserve. Drain the pasta and return it to the cooking pot to keep warm.

Meanwhile, in a large, nonstick skillet over medium-low heat, combine the oil and garlic. Cook for about 2 minutes, or until the garlic is soft and fragrant. Do not brown. Add the tomato and cook for about 4 minutes longer, or until the tomato starts to soften. Add the spinach and cook, tossing, for about 1 minute more, or until wilted. Stir in the lemon juice, olives, capers, pepper, and salt. Reduce the heat to low.

Add the tomato mixture to the reserved pasta and toss to coat. Add a few tablespoons of the reserved cooking water, if needed, to moisten the pasta.

Serve sprinkled with cheese.

Makes 4 servings

Per serving: *420 calories, 14 g protein, 70 g carbohydrate, 10 g fat, 2 mg cholesterol, 343 mg sodium, 0 g fiber*

Diet Exchanges: *0 milk, 1 vegetable, 0 fruit, 4 bread, 0 meat, 1½ fat*

4½ Carb Choices

263 Calories

Vegetarian Cabbage "Lasagna"

—Sue Ellis, Watertown, Wisconsin

This tasty, protein-packed lasagna layers savory sautéed vegetables and tofu between leaves of tender cabbage. No one will know there's tofu in it!

Prep time: 20 minutes
Microwave time: 8–12 minutes
Cook time: 11 minutes
Bake time: 30 minutes

1 head (1½ pounds) green cabbage (about 12 large leaves), cored

1 tablespoon olive oil

½ cup finely chopped onion (about 1 small)

1 pound sliced mushrooms

6 ounces baby spinach leaves, cut into slices (about 8 cups loosely packed)

1 tablespoon Italian seasoning blend

1 package (12 to 14 ounces) silken tofu, drained

2 large eggs, beaten

¼ cup (1 ounce) grated Parmesan/ Romano cheese blend

½ teaspoon ground black pepper

¼ teaspoon salt

¼ teaspoon ground nutmeg

1 jar (26 ounces) marinara sauce

1 cup (4 ounces) shredded part-skim mozzarella cheese

Separate the cabbage leaves and wash in cold water. Reserve the remaining cabbage in the refrigerator for another use. Place 4 to 6 leaves in a resealable plastic storage bag. Microwave on high power for 3 to 4 minutes, rotating, until wilted. Using oven mitts, remove and set aside. Fill another bag with leaves. Microwave until wilted. Empty the first bag; fill it with leaves and microwave.

Continue until all the leaves are steamed.

Preheat the oven to 350°F. Coat a 13" × 9" pan with cooking spray.

In a large nonstick skillet over medium-high heat, warm the oil. Add the onion and mushrooms. Toss to coat. Cover and cook for about 5 minutes, or until the liquid pools in the pan. Uncover and cook for about 4 minutes longer, or until the liquid has evaporated. Add the spinach and seasoning. Cook, stirring, for about 2 minutes, or until the spinach is wilted.

In a bowl, combine the tofu, eggs, Parmesan/Romano, pepper, salt, and nutmeg. Stir to blend completely. Coat the bottom of the pan with ¼ cup of the sauce. Line the pan with 4 of the cabbage leaves. Top with half of the tofu mixture, half of the mushroom mixture, and about ⅔ cup sauce. Cover with 4 of the cabbage leaves. Top with the remaining tofu mixture, mushroom mixture, and ⅔ cup sauce. Cover with the remaining leaves and sauce. Sprinkle the mozzarella on top. Bake for about 30 minutes, or until bubbly and the cheese is golden.

Makes 6 servings

Per serving: *263 calories, 18 g protein, 23 g carbohydrate, 12 g fat, 88 mg cholesterol, 978 mg sodium, 7 g fiber*

Diet Exchanges: *0 milk, 2 vegetable, 0 fruit, 0 bread, 1 meat, 1½ fat*

1½ Carb Choices

195 Calories

Brown Rice Dolmades

—Azita Saffold, Dallas, Texas

You can prepare these tasty stuffed bundles in advance.
Reheat individual portions in the microwave.

Prep time: 30 minutes
Soak time: 10 minutes
Cook time: 45 minutes

   1 cup brown rice (about 3 cups cooked rice)
 36 drained, preserved grape leaves (5–6 ounces), well rinsed
   2 tablespoons olive oil
   1 cup chopped sweet onion
 ¼ cup tomato sauce
 ¼ cup raisins
 ¼ cup chopped fresh parsley
 ½ teaspoon dried oregano
    Pinch of ground allspice
   1 teaspoon salt
 ½ teaspoon ground black pepper
   1 lemon, thinly sliced
   1 cup water

Prepare the rice according to the package directions.

Rinse the grape leaves well under cold running water. Place in a large bowl and cover with boiling water. Set aside for 10 minutes. Drain and rinse the leaves again in cold water. Set aside.

In a large nonstick skillet over medium-high heat, warm the oil. Add the onion. Cook, stirring often, for about 8 minutes, or until golden. Add the rice, tomato sauce, raisins, parsley, oregano, allspice, salt, and pepper. Reduce the heat to low. Cook,

stirring, for about 5 minutes longer. Remove from the heat. Let stand to cool slightly.

Coat a large pot with cooking spray. Scatter a few lemon slices over the bottom of the pan. Set aside.

Open several grape leaves at a time and lay them, vein side up, on a work surface. Spoon about 1 tablespoon of the reserved filling in the center. Fold the stem end over the filling, then the two sides toward the middle. Roll into a tight tube. Place the stuffed leaves seam side down into the pan. Continue filling, rolling, and packing the leaves into the pan until all the leaves are used. Place the remaining lemon slices on top. Place a heavy heat-proof plate over the leaves to prevent them from floating. Add the water.

Cover and simmer over medium-low heat for about 30 minutes, or until tender.

Makes 6 servings

Per serving: *195 calories, 4 g protein, 33 g carbohydrate, 6 g fat, 0 mg cholesterol, 1,124 mg sodium, 3 g fiber*

Diet Exchanges: *0 milk, 1 vegetable, ½ fruit, 1½ bread, 0 meat, 1 fat*

2 Carb Choices

Kitchen Tip

For those on a restricted-sodium diet, fresh grape leaves may be used if available. Blanch them in boiling water before filling.

189 Calories

Zesty Eggplant Stew

—Arnita Somerville, Oregon, Illinois

"This dish is really satisfying. I get all the healthy veggies, plus so much flavor for very few calories."

Prep time: 12 minutes
Cook time: 45 minutes

- 1 tablespoon olive oil
- 1 medium eggplant, peeled and chopped (about 4 cups)
- 1 medium green bell pepper, chopped (about ¾ cup)
- 1 medium onion, chopped (about 1 cup)
- 2 cloves garlic, finely chopped
- 1 tablespoon chili powder
- 1 teaspoon paprika
- ½ teaspoon ground black pepper
- ¼ teaspoon salt
- 1 tablespoon flour
- 2 cans (14½ ounces each) diced tomatoes
- 1 can (15 ounces) tomato sauce
- 1 can (15½ ounces) kidney or pinto beans, rinsed and drained
- ⅓ cup chopped fresh cilantro or parsley leaves
- ¼ cup grated Parmesan/Romano cheese blend

In a large, deep nonstick skillet over medium-high heat, warm the oil. Add the eggplant, bell pepper, onion, garlic, chili powder, paprika, black pepper, and salt. Cook, stirring, for about 5 minutes, or until the vegetables start to soften.

Sprinkle the flour over the mixture. Stir to mix. Add the tomatoes, tomato sauce, and beans. Stir to mix. Reduce the heat to low. Simmer for about 40 minutes, or until the vegetables are tender and the flavors are blended. Stir in the cilantro or parsley.

Serve garnished with the cheese.

Makes 6 servings

Per serving: *189 calories, 9 g protein, 28 g carbohydrate, 4 g fat, 5 mg cholesterol, 872 mg sodium, 9 g fiber*

Diet Exchanges: *0 milk, 3 vegetable, 0 fruit, 1 bread, 0 meat, 1 fat*

2 Carb Choices

315 Calories

Black Beans and Corn with Rice

—Stephanie Stewart, Grandview, Missouri

Simple but vibrant, this dish comes together in a snap.

Prep time: 10 minutes
Cook time: 15 minutes

 2 cups instant or regular brown rice
    (6 cups cooked)
 2 teaspoons olive or canola oil
 ½ cup finely chopped onion (1 small
    onion)
 1 cup finely chopped red bell pepper
    (1 large pepper)
 1 teaspoon dried oregano
 ½ teaspoon ground cumin
 ⅛ teaspoon ground red pepper
 ¼ teaspoon salt
 ¼ teaspoon ground black pepper
 1 can (15½ ounces) black beans, rinsed
    and drained
 1 cup sweet white corn kernels
 1 cup vegetable broth or water
 ¼ cup freshly squeezed lime juice
 1 teaspoon grated lime peel

Prepare the rice according to the package directions.

Meanwhile, in a large nonstick skillet over medium heat, warm the oil. Add the onion, bell pepper, oregano, cumin, ground red pepper, salt, and black pepper. Cook, stirring, for about 5 minutes, or until the vegetables are starting to soften. Add the beans and corn and stir until blended. Add the broth or water. Reduce the heat to low. Simmer for about 10 minutes.

With a fork, stir the rice into the bean mixture. Add the lime juice and peel. Toss to mix well.

Makes 6 servings

Per serving: *315 calories, 9 g protein, 63 g carbohydrate, 4 g fat, 0 mg cholesterol, 365 mg sodium, 8 g fiber*

Diet Exchanges: *0 milk, 1 vegetable, 0 fruit, 3½ bread, 0 meat, ½ fat*

4 Carb Choices

161 Calories

Vegetarian Curry Burgers

—Margeaux Gray, Bowling Green, Kentucky

Enjoy these spicy burgers on toasted wheat buns with Simple Slaw
(page 61) on the side.

Prep time: 15 minutes
Cook time: 17 minutes

2 tablespoons olive or canola oil

1 medium onion, chopped (about 1 cup)

1 teaspoon curry powder

½ teaspoon ground coriander

½ teaspoon crushed fennel seeds

1½ cups white button mushrooms, chopped

1½ cups cooked and drained chickpeas or 1 can (15½ ounces) chickpeas, rinsed and drained

1 medium carrot, grated (about 1 cup)

¼ cup chopped walnuts

3 tablespoons chopped cilantro

½ teaspoon salt

¼ teaspoon ground black pepper

Flour

In a medium nonstick skillet over medium-high heat, warm 1 tablespoon of the oil. Add the onion, curry powder, coriander, and fennel. Cook, stirring frequently, for about 2 minutes, or until the onion starts to soften. Add the mushrooms. Stir to mix. Cover and cook for about 4 minutes longer, or until the liquid pools in the pan. Uncover and cook for about 3 minutes more, or until the liquid is evaporated.

Transfer the mixture to the bowl of a food processor fitted with a metal blade. Add the chickpeas. Pulse until well chopped. Transfer to a bowl. Add the carrot, walnuts, cilantro, salt, and pepper and mix well.

Lightly dust hands with flour. Shape the mixture into six 4" wide patties.

In a large skillet over medium heat, warm the remaining 1 tablespoon oil. Place the patties in the pan. Cook for about 4 minutes, or until browned on the bottom. Flip and cook for about 4 minutes longer, or until heated through.

Makes 6 servings

Per serving: *161 calories, 5 g protein, 16 g carbohydrate, 9 g fat, 0 mg cholesterol, 212 mg sodium, 5 g fiber*

Diet Exchanges: *0 milk, 1 vegetable, 0 fruit, 1 bread, ½ meat, 1½ fat*

1 Carb Choice

298 Calories

Vegetable Fajitas

—Sara Hoyt, Lake Worth, Florida

It's the colorful vegetables and exciting seasonings that make fajitas so appealing!
By leaving out the meat, you lose a lot of calories and fat.

Prep time: 15 minutes
Cook time: 7 minutes

  2 tablespoons olive oil
  1 large onion, halved and sliced
  1 red bell pepper, cut into strips
  1 yellow bell pepper, cut into strips
  1 green bell pepper, cut into strips
  8 ounces mushrooms, stems removed, sliced
  1 tablespoon chili powder
  2 cloves garlic, minced
  ¼ teaspoon salt
  ⅛ teaspoon ground black pepper
  4 whole wheat tortillas (8" diameter)
  1 small ripe avocado, sliced
  ½ cup grape tomatoes, sliced (about 12 tomatoes)
  ¼ cup chopped fresh cilantro + sprigs for garnish (optional)

In a large nonstick skillet over high heat, warm the oil for 1 minute. Add the onion, bell peppers, mushrooms, chili powder, garlic, salt, and black pepper. Cook, tossing frequently, for about 6 minutes, or until the vegetables are just tender.

Meanwhile, heat the tortillas according to the package directions.

Spoon the vegetable mixture onto the tortillas. Top with avocado, tomatoes, and cilantro. Roll and serve garnished with cilantro sprigs, if desired.

Makes 4 servings

Per serving: *298 calories, 6 g protein, 35 g carbohydrate, 16 g fat, 0 mg cholesterol, 388 mg sodium, 9 g fiber*

Diet Exchanges: *0 milk, 2 vegetable, 0 fruit, 0 bread, 0 meat, 2½ fat*

2 Carb Choices

Grecian Scallop Salad

—Alex Fotopoulos, Cresskill, New Jersey

Try this light main dish for a summer meal with fresh fruit on the side.

Prep time: 10 minutes
Cook time: 6 to 7 minutes

SCALLOPS

16 medium sea scallops
2 tablespoons lemon juice
2 teaspoons minced garlic
1 teaspoon water
3 cups chopped romaine lettuce
2 medium tomatoes, chopped
1 medium cucumber, chopped
1 cup cooked rice
1 cup crushed tomatoes
¼ cup diced onion
2 tablespoons crumbled reduced-fat feta cheese

DRESSING

¼ cup red-wine vinegar
1½ tablespoons balsamic vinegar
1 tablespoon olive oil
1½ tablespoons minced fresh parsley
1 tablespoon dried basil
1 teaspoon garlic powder
1 teaspoon hot-pepper sauce (optional)
¼ teaspoon dried oregano
⅛ teaspoon ground black pepper

To prepare the scallops: Coat a large non-stick skillet with cooking spray. Over medium heat, cook the scallops for 4 minutes. Add the lemon juice, garlic, and water. Cook for 2 to 3 minutes longer, or until the scallops are opaque. Set aside to cool.

In a large bowl, toss together the lettuce, tomatoes, and cucumber. Cover with the rice, tomatoes, onion, and reserved scallops. Sprinkle with the cheese. Set aside.

To prepare the dressing: In a large bowl, combine the red wine vinegar, balsamic vinegar, oil, parsley, basil, garlic powder, hot-pepper sauce, oregano, and black pepper. Whisk. Pour over the salad and toss well.

Makes 4 servings

Per serving: *213 calories, 16 g protein, 27 g carbohydrate, 5 g fat, 21 mg cholesterol, 250 mg sodium, 4 g fiber*

Diet Exchanges: *0 milk, 2 vegetable, 0 fruit, 1 bread, 1½ meat, 1 fat*

2 Carb Choices

219 Calories

Catfish and Okra Stew

—Joy Austin, St. Petersburg, Florida

Fiber- and nutrient-rich instant brown rice is the perfect accompaniment for this Southern-style main dish.

Prep time: 10 minutes
Cook time: 25 minutes

 1 tablespoon vegetable oil
 ½ cup chopped onion
 1 cup chopped red bell pepper
 ½ cup sliced fresh or frozen okra
 1 teaspoon thyme
 ¼ teaspoon ground red pepper
 1 tablespoon flour
 1 teaspoon Worcestershire sauce
 2 bay leaves
 ¼ teaspoon salt
 ¼ teaspoon ground black pepper
 1 cup fat-free, reduced-sodium chicken broth
 1 pound catfish fillets (4 small fillets), cut into 1½" cubes

In a large, deep nonstick skillet over medium-high heat, warm the oil. Add the onion, bell pepper, and okra. Cook, stirring occasionally, for 5 minutes, or until softened. Add the thyme, ground red pepper, flour, Worcestershire sauce, bay leaves, salt, and black pepper. Cook, stirring, for about 1 minute, or until no flour is visible. Gradually add the broth, stirring constantly. Cook for about 3 minutes, or until thickened. Reduce the heat and simmer for 5 minutes, allowing the flavors to blend.

Add the fish. Stir gently. Simmer for about 10 minutes, or until the fish flakes easily with a fork. Remove and discard the bay leaves before serving.

Makes 4 servings

Per serving: *219 calories, 20 g protein, 8 g carbohydrate, 12 g fat, 53 mg cholesterol, 360 mg sodium, 2 g fiber*

Diet Exchanges: *0 milk, 1 vegetable, 0 fruit, 0 bread, 3 meat, 1 fat*

½ Carb Choice

329 Calories

Orange Coconut Shrimp

—Jacquelynn Franklin, Medford, Wisconsin

Even indulgence foods such as coconut are okay on a weight-loss diet. Just keep moderation in mind. This is great for an outdoor party!

Prep time: 10 minutes
Marinate time: 15 minutes
Cook time: 6 minutes

D I P

½ cup low-sugar or artificially sweetened orange marmalade

2 tablespoons spicy brown mustard

1 tablespoon lime juice, preferably freshly squeezed

S H R I M P

½ cup rice wine vinegar

2 tablespoons olive oil

2 teaspoons minced garlic

¼ teaspoon red pepper flakes

¼ teaspoon salt

⅛ teaspoon ground black pepper

1 pound jumbo shrimp, peeled, deveined, and rinsed

½ cup unsweetened flaked coconut

¼ cup low-sugar or artificially sweetened orange marmalade

Preheat the oven to 350°F.

To prepare the dip: In a saucepan, combine the marmalade, mustard, and lime juice. Cook, stirring constantly, over medium heat, for about 4 minutes, or until the mixture bubbles. Remove from the heat. Let stand to cool.

To prepare the shrimp: In a mixing bowl, combine the vinegar, oil, garlic, pepper flakes, salt, and black pepper. Whisk to mix. Add the shrimp. Toss to coat. Let stand for 15 minutes to marinate.

Meanwhile, scatter the coconut in a thin layer over a baking sheet. Bake, stirring occasionally, for about 7 minutes, or until lightly browned. Remove and let stand to cool.

Coat a stove-top griddle or baking sheet with cooking spray. Preheat the pan or broiler.

Drain the shrimp and discard the marinade. Thread 4 or 5 shrimp on each of 4 metal or soaked bamboo skewers. Cook for about 3 minutes per side, or until no longer opaque. Remove the shrimp to a tray. Brush both sides of the shrimp with the marmalade. Sprinkle on the coconut, pressing lightly to adhere. Serve with the dip.

Makes 4 servings

Per serving: *329 calories, 21 g protein, 23 g carbohydrate, 16 g fat, 151 mg cholesterol, 395 mg sodium, 1 g fiber*

Diet Exchanges: *0 milk, 0 vegetable, 0 fruit, 1 bread, 3 meat, 3 fat*

1½ Carb Choices

186 Calories

Roasted Orange Tilapia and Asparagus

—C. Kent, Columbus, Ohio

Roasting asparagus in the oven really concentrates the flavor and retains the nutrients. Any mild white-fleshed fish can take the place of the tilapia.

Prep time: 5 minutes
Bake time: 15 to 20 minutes

¼ cup orange juice

1½ tablespoons olive oil

2 teaspoons minced garlic (about 2–3 medium cloves)

1½ teaspoons herbes des Provence

¼ teaspoon salt

¼ teaspoon ground black pepper

1 pound tilapia fillets

12 ounces asparagus, trimmed
Orange slices

Preheat the oven to 375°F. Coat a 13" × 9" baking dish with cooking spray. Add the orange juice, oil, garlic, herbes de Provence, salt, and pepper. Stir to mix. Place the fish in the pan.

Cut the asparagus into 1½"-long pieces. Place in the pan around the fish. Flip the fish twice and stir the asparagus to thoroughly coat with the orange mixture.

Bake, stirring the asparagus once or twice, for 15 to 20 minutes, or until the fish flakes easily with a fork. Serve garnished with orange slices and drizzled with the pan juices.

Makes 4 servings

Per serving: *186 calories, 25 g protein, 6 g carbohydrate, 7 g fat, 57 mg cholesterol, 326 mg sodium, 2 g fiber*

Diet Exchanges: *0 milk, 1 vegetable, 0 fruit, 0 bread, 3 meat, 1 fat*

½ **Carb Choice**

275 Calories

Crabby Broccoli Casserole

—Sandra Makuaole, Kekaha, Hawaii

"I have to run a lot because people chase me, begging for my recipe."

Prep time: 10 minutes
Cook time: 22 minutes
Bake time: 15 minutes

  1 **pound broccoli crowns, broken into florets**
  2 **cans (6 ounces each) lump crabmeat, drained**
  1 **tablespoon trans-free margarine or butter**
  ⅓ **cup chopped onion**
  1 **pound sliced white mushrooms**
  2 **tablespoons flour**
  ½ **teaspoon dried thyme**
  ¼ **teaspoon ground black pepper**
     Pinch of ground nutmeg
  2 **cups fat-free milk**
  ¾ **cup shredded low-fat Swiss cheese**

Preheat the oven to 350°F. Coat a 13" × 9" baking dish with cooking spray. Set aside.

Steam or parboil the broccoli for 3 to 4 minutes, or until bright green and crisp-tender. Transfer to the baking dish. Scatter the crab over the broccoli. Set aside.

Heat a large nonstick skillet over medium heat. Add the margarine or butter. Add the onion. Cook, stirring occasionally, for about 3 minutes, or until sizzling. Add the mushrooms. Stir. Cover the skillet and cook, stirring occasionally, for about 4 minutes longer, or until the liquid pools in the skillet. Uncover and cook for about 3 minutes more, or until most of the liquid is gone. Add the flour and stir until the flour is completely incorporated. Add the thyme, pepper, and nutmeg. Stir to combine. Add the milk and cook, stirring, for 7 to 8 minutes, or until the mixture thickens. Pour evenly over the reserved broccoli and crab. Scatter the cheese evenly over the top.

Bake for about 15 minutes, or until golden and bubbly.

Makes 4 servings

Per serving: *275 calories, 37 g protein, 21 g carbohydrate, 5 g fat, 100 mg cholesterol, 500 mg sodium, 5 g fiber*

Diet Exchanges: *1½ milk, 2 vegetable, 0 fruit, 0 bread, 1 meat, 1 fat*

1½ Carb Choices

295 Calories

Tuna-Pineapple-Veggie Kebabs

—Alexis Todd, Plymouth, Minnesota

"This recipe encourages me to eat fish, veggies, and fruit in a fun finger-food manner."

Prep time: 15 minutes
Cook time: 10 minutes
Grill time: 8 to 10 minutes

½ cup low-sugar or artificially sweetened orange marmalade

2 tablespoons lemon juice

1 teaspoon canola oil

¼ teaspoon salt

¼ teaspoon ground black pepper

2 medium carrots, cut into 1" diagonal pieces

2 medium leeks, white and light green parts, cut into 1" diagonal pieces

1 pound tuna steaks, cut into 1" cubes

1 can (8 ounces) pineapple chunks packed in juice, drained

Coat a grill rack or stove-top grill pan with nonstick spray. Preheat a grill or stovetop grill pan.

In a bowl, combine the marmalade, lemon juice, oil, salt, and pepper. Stir to mix. Set aside.

Bring a medium saucepan of water to a boil over high heat. Add the carrots. Cook for about 8 minutes, or until tender but firm enough to skewer. Remove with a slotted spoon to a plate. Set aside. Add the leeks to the water. Cook for about 2 minutes, or just until blanched. Remove with a slotted spoon to a plate.

On 4 long (18") or 8 medium (12") metal or soaked bamboo skewers, alternately thread the fish, carrots, leeks, and pineapple, leaving ⅛" between pieces. Place on the grill rack or grill pan. Grill, uncovered, over medium-hot coals or medium heat, for 4 minutes. Turn the kebabs and grill for 4 to 6 minutes longer, or until the fish flakes easily with a fork. Brush with the reserved marmalade sauce during the last 2 minutes of cooking. If desired, transfer the remaining sauce to a small saucepan. Boil for 1 minute and serve with the kebabs.

Makes 4 servings

Per serving: *295 calories, 28 g protein, 30 g carbohydrate, 7 g fat, 43 mg cholesterol, 220 mg sodium, 2 g fiber*

Diet Exchanges: *0 milk, 2 vegetable, ½ fruit, 1 bread, 4 meat, 1 fat*

2 Carb Choices

168 Calories

Salmon Patties

—Theresa Cootway, Elcho, Wisconsin

Pair these patties alongside Kale with Pumpkin Seeds (page 146) for super flavor and nutrition. Canned salmon is a great source of calcium and omega-3 fatty acids, and dark leafy greens are bursting with antioxidants.

Prep time: 10 minutes
Cook time: 6 minutes

1 can (15 ounces) pink salmon, drained, skin removed

¼ cup finely chopped onion or scallions

1 large egg, beaten

⅓ cup dried whole wheat bread crumbs or crushed soda crackers

¼ teaspoon ground black pepper

Lemon wedges, coarse mustard, or prepared horseradish, for serving

In a mixing bowl, combine the salmon, onion or scallions, egg, bread crumbs or crackers, and pepper. With clean hands or 2 forks, mix until blended. Shape into 4 patties.

Coat a large nonstick skillet lightly with cooking spray and warm over medium heat. Place the patties in the pan and cook for about 3 minutes, or until golden on the bottom. Flip and cook for about 3 minutes longer, or until heated through.

Serve with lemon wedges, mustard, or horseradish.

Makes 4 servings

Per serving: *168 calories, 29 g protein, 4 g carbohydrate, 5 g fat, 129 mg cholesterol, 461 mg sodium, 1 g fiber*

Diet Exchanges: *0 milk, 0 vegetable, 0 fruit, 0 bread, 4 meat, 0 fat*

0 Carb Choices

Tuna Mushroom Melt Supreme

—Judith Michalski, Rochester Hills, Michigan

*This tuna mushroom mixture makes a quick and tasty light
family meal from pantry staples.*

Prep time: 10 minutes
Cook time: 9 minutes

2 tablespoons cold water

1½ tablespoons cornstarch

1 cup cold 1% milk

1 can (12 ounces) light tuna packed in water, drained

1 can (8 ounces) mushrooms, drained

1 tablespoon finely chopped fresh parsley (optional)

½ teaspoon paprika

⅛ teaspoon salt

⅛ teaspoon ground black pepper

4 slices whole grain high-fiber bread

1 cup shredded reduced-fat Swiss or Cheddar cheese

In a medium nonstick skillet, whisk together the water and cornstarch until smooth. Add the milk gradually, whisking until blended. Place the skillet over medium heat. Cook, whisking constantly, for about 3 minutes, or until thickened. Add the tuna, mushrooms, parsley (if using), paprika, salt, and pepper. Simmer for 2 to 3 minutes, or until heated through.

Set the bread slices on a broiler pan and top each with one-quarter of the tuna mixture and ¼ cup of the cheese. Broil for 2 to 3 minutes, or until the cheese is melted.

Makes 4 servings

Per serving: *257 calories, 35 g protein, 23 g carbohydrate, 3 g fat, 38 mg cholesterol, 719 mg sodium, 6 g fiber*

Diet Exchanges: *0 milk, ½ vegetable, 0 fruit, 1 bread, 4 meat, 0 fat*

1½ Carb Choices

126 Calories

Sesame Sea Bakers

—Mardee Kauffman, Ducktown, Tennessee

Japanese-style furikake seasoning is sold in health food stores and Japanese supermarkets. Toasted sesame seeds and a pinch of salt may replace it.

Prep time: 5 minutes
Microwave time: 7 minutes

1 **russet potato (about 6 ounces)**
½ **cup low-fat cottage cheese**
1 **teaspoon furikake seasoning**
4 **ounces imitation crab, cut into small chunks**

Pierce the potato several times. Microwave, rotating once, for about 5 minutes, or until tender when pierced with a sharp knife. Remove and set aside.

Meanwhile, in a microwaveable bowl, combine the cheese and seasoning. Microwave on medium power, stirring once, for about 2 minutes, or until warm. Fold in the crab. Cut the potato in half. Top with crab sauce.

Makes 2 servings

Per serving: *126 calories, 15 g protein, 14 g carbohydrate, 2 g fat, 17 mg cholesterol, 718 mg sodium, 2 g fiber*

Diet Exchanges: *0 milk, 0 vegetable, 0 fruit, 1 bread, 1½ meat, 0 fat*

1 Carb Choice

SHOPPING SAVVY

Out of the Frying Pan

Dietitians are always advising us to eat more fish, but many of us just don't know how to cook it properly. Now, the Maryland-based McCormick spice company has made cooking seafood just about foolproof. The flavoring experts have developed two varieties of Seafood Steamers, a single pouch that contains everything needed for perfectly seasoned steamed fish or shrimp. Lemon Garlic and Garlic Butter Seafood Steamers make it a snap to dress up weeknight meals. Simply place seafood, water, and seasoning in the steaming bag and microwave for 6 minutes. The specially designed steaming bag helps lock in moisture and flavor for perfect results every time. After supper, you just toss the empty bag—and the mess. The bags are available in supermarkets. For more information, visit www.mccormick.com.

260 Calories

Shrimp in Green Tea–Curry Sauce

—Richard Dait, Honolulu, Hawaii

This dish is so simple to prepare, yet it's sophisticated enough to share with guests. The delicate tea flavor is delightfully enhanced by the subtle curry.

Prep time: 10 minutes
Stand time: 5 minutes
Cook time: 10 minutes

    Salt
1 **cup boiling water**
1 **tablespoon green tea leaves**
8 **ounces dried linguine**
1 **tablespoon canola oil**
1 **pound large shrimp, peeled, deveined, and rinsed**
¼ **cup finely shopped scallions, white and light green parts**
2 **teaspoons minced garlic**
1½ **teaspoons hot or mild curry powder**
2 **tablespoons sake or dry white wine**
1 **teaspoon toasted sesame oil**
    Chopped cilantro and sliced scallions

Cook the linguine according to the package direction, subtracting 2 minutes of the cooking time. Drain and return to the cooking pot to keep warm.

In a heatproof container, combine the boiling water and tea. Cover and steep for 5 minutes.

Meanwhile, heat the canola oil in a large nonstick skillet or wok over high heat. Add the shrimp, scallions, garlic, and curry powder. Cook, tossing, for 1 minute. Add the sake or wine. Cook for 30 seconds. Add the tea and half of the tea leaves. Cook for 1 minute, or until the shrimp are opaque. With a slotted spoon, remove the shrimp and set aside.

Transfer the linguine to the skillet or wok. Reduce the heat to medium-low. Cook, tossing, for about 3 minutes, or until the linguine is al dente and the sauce has thickened. Return the shrimp to the pan. Drizzle with the sesame oil. Toss to combine. Garnish with the cilantro and scallions.

Makes 6 servings

Per serving: *260 calories, 21 g protein, 30 g carbohydrate, 5 g fat, 115 mg cholesterol, 115 mg sodium, 1 g fiber*

Diet Exchanges: *0 milk, 0 vegetable, 0 fruit, 2 bread, 2 meat, 1 fat*

2 Carb Choices

EZ Trim Fajitas

—Meredith Peters, Round Pond, Maine

"I use this recipe a few times a week and find it very satisfying because of its color and burst of fresh flavors. It can be changed with different veggies or spices, such as garam masala. Yum! It makes the whole house smell good!"

Prep time: 15 minutes
Cook time: 10 minutes

- 1 tablespoon canola oil
- 1 pound boneless, skinless chicken breast, cut into strips
- ½ green bell pepper, cut into strips
- ½ cup red bell pepper, cut into strips
- ½ small red onion, sliced
- 2 teaspoons ground cumin
- ¼ teaspoon salt
- ¼ teaspoon ground black pepper
- ½ cup bottled or homemade salsa
- 1 chopped or sliced jalapeño chile pepper (wear plastic gloves when handling)
- 12 whole wheat tortillas (7" diameter), heated
- 6 lime wedges
  Shredded lettuce
- 1 tomato, sliced
  Sliced scallions (optional)
  Sliced cucumber (optional)
  Shredded low-fat Cheddar cheese (optional)
  Fat-free sour cream (optional)

In a large nonstick skillet over medium heat, warm the oil. Add the chicken. Cook, stirring occasionally, for about 5 minutes, or until lightly browned. Test that the juices run clear and no pink remains. Add the bell peppers, onion, cumin, salt, and black pepper. Cook, tossing frequently, for about 4 minutes longer, or until the bell peppers are crisp-tender. Add the salsa and chile pepper. Cook for 1 minute more, or until heated through.

Serve with the tortillas, lime, lettuce, and tomato. Garnish each serving with scallions, cucumber, cheese, and sour cream, if desired.

Makes 6 servings (2 fajitas per serving)

Per serving: 333 calories, 22 g protein, 39 g carbohydrate, 8.5 g fat, 44 mg cholesterol, 685 mg sodium, 7 g fiber

Diet Exchanges: *0 milk, ½ vegetable, 0 fruit, 0 bread, 2½ meat, ½ fat*

2½ Carb Choices

333 Calories

It Worked for Me!

Janet Utz, 44

VITAL STATS

Weight lost: 100 pounds

Time to goal: 1½ years

Greatest challenge: beating the odds against regaining by maintaining the weight loss

In June 1999, Janet Utz looked down and hated what she saw: the bathroom scale telling her that she weighed 251 pounds.

During the next year and a half, the Kenmore, New York, woman dropped more than 100 pounds. In the past, when she saw appealing foods, she just ate them "almost like I was oblivious to the consequences of what I was doing." That came to a stop. She ate more salads and carefully considered the foods she was about to eat. She started exercising more, too.

After losing her excess weight, Janet met her future husband, Don. "After we got married, the weight started creeping back up. Before I knew it, I had put 25 pounds back on, and the number on the scale continued to climb."

She realized that losing the weight was the simple part—keeping it off was going to require more effort. So she started experimenting until she had created a lifestyle that would keep her at a healthy weight.

For starters, she lets Don eat his way, which is now starting to slowly come around to her way. Jan prepares healthy recipes for herself with lots of beans, fruits, and vegetables. "I experiment constantly with different foods," she says. "I've learned through research that beans and lentils are a great source of protein and fiber."

Jan believes planning is key and keeps three sets of measuring spoons, three sets of measuring cups, and a food scale in her kitchen, as well as a weekly menu posted on the refrigerator so she'll always know how to shop, prepare in advance, and practice portion control.

When she goes to a new restaurant, she investigates its menu online and sticks to her preplanned choice.

Janet also walks on the treadmill twice a week, does aerobics, lifts weights, and does yoga and Pilates. And every week she attends Weight Watchers meetings, which provide a powerful support network. "I'm involved in this long-term experiment with food. Statistics show the odds working against those of us who are trying to lose excess weight and keep it off. I've beaten those odds thus far and plan on winning."

Turn to page 156 for Janet's recipe.

356 Calories

Chicken Tetrazzini

—Cindy Reinhold, New Westminster, British Columbia, Canada

Chicken, pasta noodles, and a creamy sauce?
Who wouldn't want to be on a diet?

Prep time: 20 minutes
Cook time: 10 minutes
Bake time: 15 minutes

  1 package (9 ounces) spinach linguine, cooked and drained
  1 tablespoon canola oil
  1 onion, finely chopped
  4 ounces mushrooms, finely chopped
  3 cloves garlic, minced
  ¼ cup flour
1½ cups reduced-sodium chicken broth
1½ cups low-fat milk (1%)
  ½ teaspoon dried thyme
  ½ cup grated Parmesan/Romano cheese blend
  3 cooked boneless, skinless chicken breasts, cubed (3 cups)
  ½ teaspoon salt
  ½ teaspoon ground black pepper
   Paprika (optional)

Preheat the oven to 375°F. Coat a 13" × 9" baking dish with cooking spray. Set aside.

Cook the pasta according to the package directions. Drain the pasta and return to the cooking pot to keep warm.

Meanwhile, in a large nonstick skillet over medium-high heat, warm the oil. Add the onion, mushrooms, and garlic. Stir and cover. Cook, stirring occasionally, for about 5 minutes, or until the mushrooms have shrunk.

Stir in the flour with a wooden spoon. Gradually add the broth. Cook, stirring constantly, for about 3 minutes, or until thickened. Add the milk and thyme. Stir constantly for 2 minutes longer, or until thickened. Remove from the heat. Stir in the cheese until melted. Add the chicken, salt, and pepper. Stir to mix.

Place the pasta in the baking dish. Add the sauce and toss to combine. Sprinkle with the paprika, if using.

Bake for about 15 minutes, or until golden and bubbly.

Makes 8 servings

Per serving: *356 calories, 39 g protein, 30 g carbohydrate, 8 g fat, 85 mg cholesterol, 475 mg sodium, 2 g fiber*

Diet Exchanges: *0 milk, ½ vegetable, 0 fruit, 1½ bread, 4½ meat, 1 fat*

2 Carb Choices

Ted's Chicken à la Prosciutto

—Ted Kranenberg, Cambridge, Minnesota

*This chicken main dish is special enough for an occasion
yet remarkably low in calories.*

Prep time: 15 minutes
Cook time: 25 minutes

　4 **boneless, skinless chicken breasts
　　(1¼ pounds)**
3–4 **tablespoons flour**
　1 **tablespoon butter**
　1 **tablespoon extra-virgin olive oil**
　8 **ounces mushrooms, sliced**
　¾ **cup dry white wine**
　¾ **cup chicken broth**
　¼ **teaspoon salt**
　½ **teaspoon ground black pepper**
　4 **slices prosciutto ham**
　4 **slices (2 ounces) thinly sliced
　　provolone cheese**
　2 **tablespoons chopped fresh parsley**

Place the chicken on a work surface. Cover with plastic wrap. Pound to ½" thickness. Dust both sides of the chicken lightly with the flour. Shake off the excess.

In a large nonstick skillet over high heat, warm the butter and oil. Cook the chicken, in two batches, for about 3 minutes on each side, or until no longer pink and the juices run clear. Remove to a plate. Set aside.

Set the same skillet over medium-high heat. Add the mushrooms and toss. Cover and cook, stirring occasionally, for about 4 minutes, or until the mushrooms give off liquid. Uncover and cook for 2 minutes longer, or until the liquid evaporates. Add the wine. Cook for about 3 minutes, or until the liquid evaporates. Add the broth, salt, and pepper. Bring to a simmer. Return the reserved chicken to the pan. Reduce the heat to medium-low. Top with the prosciutto and cheese. Cover and cook for about 2 minutes, or until the cheese is melted. Place the chicken on a platter. Top with the mushrooms and sauce. Sprinkle with the parsley.

Makes 4 servings

Per serving: *368 calories, 43 g protein, 9 g carbohydrate, 14 g fat, 111 mg cholesterol, 836 mg sodium, 1 g fiber*

Diet Exchanges: *0 milk, ½ vegetable, 0 fruit, ½ bread, 6 meat, 2 fat*

½ Carb Choice

178 Calories

Paco's Favorite

—Deborah Damiani, Peoria, Arizona

Deborah's family loves this hearty, low-fat meal accompanied by low-fat sour cream and low-fat tortillas.

Prep time: 15 minutes
Cook time: 10 minutes
Bake time: 35 to 40 minutes

- 1 tablespoon olive oil
- 1 cup chopped onion (1 medium onion)
- 1 tablespoon minced garlic (3 small cloves)
- 4 small boneless, skinless chicken breasts (1 pound), cut into ½" strips
- 1 can (15 ounces) black beans, drained and rinsed
- 1 can (15 ounces) pinto beans, drained and rinsed
- 1 can (14½ ounces) diced tomatoes
- ¼ cup chopped cilantro, divided
- 1 Anaheim green chile pepper, chopped (wear plastic gloves when handling)
- ¼ teaspoon ground black pepper
- ½ cup shredded sharp reduced-fat Cheddar cheese

Preheat the oven to 350°F. Coat a 13" × 9" baking dish with cooking spray.

In a large nonstick skillet over medium-high heat, warm ½ tablespoon of the oil. Add the onion and garlic. Cook, stirring, for about 5 minutes, or until golden. Transfer to the baking dish.

Set the same skillet over high heat and warm the remaining oil. Place the chicken in the skillet and cook for about 1 to 2 minutes on each side, or until browned. (The chicken will not be cooked.)

In the baking dish, combine the black beans, pinto beans, tomatoes with juice, half of the cilantro, the chile pepper, black pepper, and salt with the onion mixture. Stir to mix. Place the chicken in the pan and spoon the bean mixture on top. Cover with aluminum foil.

Bake for 35 to 40 minutes, or until the chicken is no longer pink and the juices run clear. Remove from the oven. Sprinkle with the cheese and the remaining 2 tablespoons of cilantro. Broil 6" from the heat source for about 2 minutes, or until the cheese is bubbly.

Makes 8 servings

Per serving: *178 calories, 19 g protein, 16 g carbohydrate, 4 g fat, 38 mg cholesterol, 457 mg sodium, 4 g fiber*

Diet Exchanges: *0 milk, ½ vegetable, 0 fruit, 1 bread, 2 meat, ½ fat*

1 Carb Choice

255 Calories

Curried Chicken Broccoli Casserole

—Lisa Costello, Morgantown, West Virginia

*It's a cinch to assemble this oven-baked dinner up to a day ahead of cooking.
Simply cool the broccoli before putting all the ingredients together.
Cover with plastic wrap and refrigerate until baking time.*

Prep time: 15 minutes
Microwave time: 3 to 5 minutes
Bake time: 40 to 45 minutes

    1 pound broccoli florets
    ¼ cup water
    1 can reduced-sodium cream of
       mushroom soup
    ¼ cup mayonnaise
    1 tablespoon lemon juice
  1½ teaspoons curry powder
    ½ teaspoon salt
    ½ teaspoon ground black pepper
  1½ pounds boneless, skinless chicken
       breasts, cut into bite-size chunks
    ¼ cup shredded reduced-fat Colby or
       Swiss cheese

Preheat the oven to 350°F. Coat a 13" × 9" baking dish with cooking spray. Set aside.

Place the broccoli and water in a large resealable plastic storage bag. Microwave on high power, rotating occasionally, for about 3 to 5 minutes, or until bright green. Drain and set aside.

In a small bowl, mix the soup, mayonnaise, lemon juice, curry powder, salt, and pepper. Stir to mix. Line the baking dish with the reserved broccoli. Top with the chicken. Cover evenly with the soup mixture. Sprinkle with the cheese. Cover and bake for about 25 minutes. Uncover and bake for 15 to 20 minutes longer, or until golden and bubbling.

Makes 6 servings

Per serving: *255 calories, 30 g protein, 9 g carbohydrate, 11 g fat, 73 mg cholesterol, 571 mg sodium, 3 g fiber*

Diet Exchanges: *0 milk, 1 vegetable, 0 fruit, ½ bread, 4 meat, 2 fat*

½ Carb Choice

Chicken, Corn, & Tomatillo Chili

—Terry Thompson, Casper, Wyoming

If you can afford a few extra calories, sprinkle 2 teaspoons reduced-fat Cheddar cheese and 2 teaspoons mashed avocado or light sour cream on each serving.

Prep time: 15 minutes
Cook time: 25 minutes

1 tablespoon olive or canola oil

1 large onion, chopped

3 cloves garlic, minced

1 teaspoon ground cumin

1 teaspoon chili powder

½ teaspoon dried oregano

½ teaspoon ground coriander

¼ teaspoon salt

¼ teaspoon ground black pepper

12 ounces boneless, skinless chicken breast, cut into cubes

2 cans (14½ ounces each) fat-free reduced-sodium chicken broth

1 can (14½ ounces) salt-free diced tomatoes

1 can (4 ounces) tomatillos, drained and chopped

1 can (4 ounces) chopped green chilies, drained

1 package (10 ounces) frozen corn kernels, thawed

1 can (15 ounces) white beans or pinto beans, drained and rinsed

1 lime, cut into wedges

Chopped fresh cilantro

In a large, deep nonstick skillet over medium heat, warm the oil. Add the onion, garlic, cumin, chili powder, oregano, coriander, salt, and black pepper. Cook, stirring occasionally, for 3 to 5 minutes, or until the onion has softened. Add the chicken and continue cooking for 5 minutes longer, or until the chicken is browned. Add the broth, tomatoes (with juice), tomatillos, and chilies. Bring to a boil. Reduce the heat. Simmer, stirring occasionally, for 10 minutes, allowing the flavors to blend. Add the corn and beans. Cook, stirring occasionally, for 5 minutes longer. Serve with lime and cilantro.

Makes 8 servings

Per serving: *161 calories, 15 g protein, 19 g carbohydrate, 3 g fat, 25 mg cholesterol, 516 mg sodium, 4 g fiber*

Diet Exchanges: *0 milk, 1 vegetable, 0 fruit, 1 bread, 1½ meat, ½ fat*

1 Carb Choice

Mexicali Chicken Bake

—Honor Derbyshire, Fort Wayne, Indiana

Serve this robust dish with Spanish rice or with tortillas, fajita-style.

Prep time: 15 minutes
Cook time: 10 minutes
Bake time: 1 hour

  1 **tablespoon olive or canola oil**
  1 **onion, cut into rings**
  1 **green bell pepper, cut into strips**
  1 **tablespoon chili powder**
  1 **clove garlic**
  ¼ **teaspoon salt**
  2 **cups tomato puree**
  1 **cup canned vegetarian refried beans**
  ½ **cup low-fat sour cream (optional)**
  1 **jalapeño chile pepper, finely chopped
    (wear plastic gloves when handling)
    (optional)**
  1 **pound boneless, skinless chicken
    breasts, sliced crosswise**
  ¾ **cup shredded reduced-fat Colby Jack
    cheese**
    **Finely chopped fresh cilantro
    (optional)**

Preheat the oven to 350°F. Coat a 13" × 9" baking dish with cooking spray.

In a medium nonstick skillet over medium heat, warm the oil. Add the onion, bell pepper, chili powder, garlic, and salt. Stir to mix. Cover the skillet and cook, stirring occasionally, for 5 minutes, or until softened.

Add the tomato puree, beans, sour cream, and chile pepper (if using). Stir to mix. Simmer for about 3 minutes, or until heated through.

Place the chicken in the prepared dish. Cover with the sauce. Sprinkle the cheese on top. Cover with foil and bake for 1 hour, or until a thermometer inserted in the thickest portion registers 160°F and the juices run clear. Remove the foil. If desired, broil 6" from the heat source for about 2 minutes or until the cheese is bubbly.

Makes 6 servings

Per serving: *220 calories, 25 g protein, 17 g carbohydrate, 6 g fat, 51 mg cholesterol, 788 mg sodium, 4 g fiber*

Diet Exchanges: *0 milk, 2 vegetable, 0 fruit, ½ bread, 3 meat, 1 fat*

1 Carb Choice

SHOPPING SAVVY

Big Flavor

Frieda's, a specialty produce company, has taken over the time-consuming and messy task of roasting garlic cloves and extracting the resulting sweet, nutty puree. The California company starts with Elephant Garlic (which really is immense compared to regular cloves!), a milder and slightly sweeter alternative to traditional garlic, and roasts it to perfection. The Traditional variety has no spices added. Cajun and Italian versions are also available. To use, simply heat in the microwave.

Spread the Italian version on hot whole wheat bread, toss it with roasted tomatoes and peppers, add it to roasted potatoes, or create Chicken scallopine in a wine sauce. The Cajun version is perfect for combining with sautéed greens or for spicing up a shrimp and pasta dish. Blend the Traditional Roasted Elephant Garlic into dips and spreads. Or use it to top grilled chicken, stir into mashed potatoes, or create a garlic-barbecue sauce for roasted pork tenderloin. A tablespoon contains only 60 calories and 1.5 grams of fat. Look for it in the produce section of your supermarket. To find out more about Frieda's produce specialties, visit www.friedas.com.

212 Calories

Lemon Chicken Oregano

—Kate Mattox, Orlando, Florida

*Bake this chicken just until it's no longer pink in the center
and you'll be rewarded with a juicy, succulent supper.*

Prep time: 5 minutes
Bake time: 15 minutes

2 boneless, skinless chicken breasts
2 tablespoons lemon juice
1 tablespoon butter or trans-free margarine, melted
¾ teaspoon dried oregano
½ teaspoon lemon pepper seasoning
⅛ teaspoon salt
2 teaspoons finely chopped parsley or chives (optional)

Preheat the oven to 375°F. Coat a small baking dish with cooking spray. Place the chicken in a single layer in the dish. Pour the lemon juice and butter or margarine over the chicken. Sprinkle with the oregano, lemon pepper, and salt.

Bake for about 15 minutes, or until a thermometer inserted in the thickest portion registers 160°F and the juices run clear.

Serve drizzled with the pan juices. Sprinkle with the parsley or chives, if using.

Makes 2 servings

Per serving: *212 calories, 33 g protein, 2 g carbohydrate, 7.5 g fat, 97 mg cholesterol, 308 mg sodium, 0 g fiber*

Diet Exchanges: *0 milk, 0 vegetable, 0 fruit, 0 bread, 5 meat, 1 fat*

0 Carb Choices

SECRETS OF WEIGHT-LOSS WINNERS

• Don't miss workouts—think of them as your secret weapon.

—Nancy Gruzleski, Uniontown, Ohio

• My tip is to walk 2 miles three times a week and also do exercises at home at least twice a week.

—Loretta Exline, Brookings, Oregon

• Instead of trying to lose weight, decide to eat healthy and exercise. Before you know it, the weight will melt off.

—Peggy Miller, Crowley, Louisiana

Zesty Skillet Turkey and Noodles

—Elena Dodge, Erie, Pennsylvania

A big tossed salad goes nicely with this casual meal.

Prep time: 10 minutes
Cook time: 20 minutes

- 8 ounces (4 cups) yolk-free medium-wide noodles
- 2 teaspoons olive oil
- 1 bunch scallions, all parts, sliced (about 8 scallions)
- 1 pound lean ground turkey breast
- 2 cans (14½ ounces each) no-salt-added diced tomatoes
- ½ teaspoon Italian seasoning
- ¼ teaspoon salt
- ¼ teaspoon crushed red-pepper flakes
- ¼ cup grated Parmesan/Romano cheese blend
- 2 tablespoons chopped parsley

Cook the pasta according to the package directions. Drain the pasta and return to the cooking pot to keep warm.

In a large nonstick skillet over high heat, warm the oil. Add the scallions. Cook, stirring, for 1 minute. Add the turkey. Cook, breaking up the turkey with the back of a spoon, for 4 to 5 minutes, or until no pink remains. Add the tomatoes, seasoning, pepper flakes, and salt. Reduce the heat to medium-low. Cover and simmer for 10 to 15 minutes.

Toss the noodles with the turkey mixture. Top with cheese and parsley.

Makes 6 servings

Per serving: *290 calories, 27 g protein, 34 g carbohydrate, 4½ g fat, 35 mg cholesterol, 302 mg sodium, 3 g fiber*

Diet Exchanges: *0 milk, 1 vegetable, 0 fruit, 2 bread, 2½ meat, ½ fat*

2 Carb Choices

264 Calories

Turkey Lumpia

—Linda Chaput, North Bay, Ontario, Canada

In the Philippines and Indonesia, lumpia (egg rolls) are typically fried. This more delicate version cuts calories and fat by steaming the scrumptious bundles.

Prep time: 25 minutes
Cook time: 10 minutes

1½ **pounds lean ground turkey breast**
¼ **cup finely chopped scallions (about 2–3 scallions)**
2 **tablespoons reduced-sodium soy sauce**
2 **tablespoons rice vinegar**
1 **tablespoon toasted sesame seeds**
1½ **teaspoons grated fresh ginger**
1 **teaspoon toasted sesame oil**
2 **teaspoons minced garlic**
16 **spring roll/lumpia wrappers**
¼ **cup hot Chinese mustard**

Fill a large pot, or 2 pots, with about 2" of water. Coat a bamboo steamer or other heatproof rack lightly with cooking spray. Set into the pot(s). Cover and set over medium-high heat.

Meanwhile, in a bowl, combine the turkey, scallions, soy sauce, vinegar, sesame seeds, ginger, oil, and garlic. Mix well with 2 forks or clean hands.

Lay several of the wrappers on a work surface. Place about 2 tablespoons of the turkey mixture in a line down the center of each wrapper. The filling should be no wider than a thumb. Fold 1 corner of the wrapper over to the other. Fold the outer edges in slightly, and then continue to roll into a cylinder. With a wet finger, moisten the edge to seal. Repeat with the remaining wrappers and filling. Cover the stuffed wrappers with a moist towel to prevent drying.

Lay the lumpia in a single layer in the pot(s). Cover and steam over boiling water for about 10 minutes, or until heated through.

Serve with the mustard for dipping.

Makes 4 servings (4 lumpia per serving)

Per serving: *264 calories, 43 g protein, 5 g carbohydrate, 9 g fat, 68 mg cholesterol, 449 mg sodium, 1 g fiber*

Diet Exchanges: *0 milk, ½ vegetable, 0 fruit, 0 bread, 5 meat, ½ fat*

½ **Carb Choice**

152 Calories

Slow-Cooker Turkey with Baked Beans and Pineapple

—Linda Wall, Cedar Grove, Tennessee

This down-home barbecue-style dish is a treat served on toasted wheat buns.

Prep time: 10 minutes
Cook time: 4 to 5 hours

1½ pounds turkey breast tenderloins
  2 cans (16 ounces each) baked beans
  1 can (20 ounces) crushed pineapple, packed in juice
  ½ cup barbecue sauce
  1 medium green bell pepper, chopped
  1 medium red bell pepper, chopped
  ½ cup chopped onion
  ½ teaspoon ground black pepper
  ¼ teaspoon salt

Coat the inside of a 5- to 6-quart slow cooker pot with cooking spray. Place the turkey, beans, pineapple with juice, barbecue sauce, bell peppers, onion, black pepper, and salt in the pot.

Cover and cook on the low-heat setting for 4 to 5 hours, or until fork-tender. Remove tenderloins to a cutting board. Shred the meat with 2 forks and return to the cooker. Heat through and serve.

Makes 16 servings

Per serving: *152 calories, 15 g protein, 21 g carbohydrate, 1 g fat, 17 mg cholesterol, 234 mg sodium, 4 g fiber*

Diet Exchanges: *0 milk, 0 vegetable, ½ fruit, 1 bread, 1 meat, 0 fat*

1½ Carb Choices

SECRETS OF WEIGHT-LOSS WINNERS

• There really is no need to diet per se—just learn how to eat healthy, and the weight will come off automatically.
  —Terri DeProspero, Clearwater, Florida

• Have one or two servings of fruit with each meal.
  —Michael Simms, Libertyville, Illinois

• Start more meals with a salad.
  —Joel Fahnestock, Melbourne, Florida

• Eat foods that you enjoy (in moderation) and you will be less likely to snack.
  —Susan Leitch, Stittsville, Ontario, Canada

224
Calories

Turkey, Black Bean,
& Beer Chili

—K. K. Peters, Edmonton, Alberta, Canada

"This recipe is high in protein and complex carbohydrates but low in fat. It is extremely satisfying (the flavor is sufficiently complex to energize all the tastebuds) and fills you up. I serve it over high-protein pasta if I'm craving pasta as well."

Prep time: 20 minutes
Cook time: 2 hours 15 minutes

  2 **tablespoons extra-virgin olive oil**
  1 **medium yellow onion, chopped**
  1 **small yellow bell pepper, chopped (1 cup)**
  1 **small orange bell pepper, chopped (1 cup)**
  1 **rib celery, chopped (¼ cup)**
  1 **carrot, chopped (⅓ cup)**
  3 **cloves garlic, minced**
  2 **teaspoons chili powder**
  2 **teaspoons dried oregano**
  1 **teaspoon ground cumin**
  ½ **teaspoon salt**
1½ **pounds lean ground turkey breast**
  4 **cups chopped fresh plum tomatoes or canned plum tomatoes with juice**
  3 **cups cooked black beans**
  1 **bottle (12 ounces) light beer**
  ½ **teaspoon ground black pepper**

In a large, deep nonstick skillet set over medium-high heat, warm the oil. Add the onion, bell peppers, celery, carrot, garlic, chili powder, oregano, cumin, and salt. Stir. Cover and cook, stirring occasionally, for about 10 minutes, or until the peppers are softened.

Crumble the turkey into the skillet. Cook, breaking up the turkey with the back of a spoon, for about 5 minutes, or until no longer pink. Add the tomatoes, beans, and beer. Bring to a boil, then reduce the heat to a simmer. Cover the skillet and simmer for 1 hour, stirring occasionally to prevent sticking. Remove the cover and continue simmering, stirring occasionally, for 1 hour.

Makes 6 servings

Per serving: *224 calories, 30 g protein, 11 g carbohydrate, 6.6 g fat, 45 mg cholesterol, 283 mg sodium, 2 g fiber*

Diet Exchanges: *0 milk, 1½ vegetable, 0 fruit, 0 bread, 3½ meat, 1 fat*

1 Carb Choice

357 Calories

Turkey Sausage and Peppers

—Christine Ribaudo, Morris Plains, New Jersey

"With its leaner protein and lots of veggies, this is good traditional comfort food that is good for you. It's a perfect recipe to have on hand for parties, so all your family stays healthy!"

Prep time: 15 minutes
Cook time: 1 hour 15 minutes

2 tablespoons olive oil

1 large red bell pepper, cut into thin strips

1 large green bell pepper, cut into thin strips

2 medium yellow onions, cut into thin strips

3 cloves garlic, finely chopped

1 pound mild or hot Italian turkey sausage, cut into 4 equal pieces

1 can (28 ounces) crushed tomatoes in thick puree

1 teaspoon dried Italian seasoning

1 teaspoon crushed red-pepper flakes (optional)

Pinch of salt

In a large, deep nonstick skillet over medium heat, warm the oil. Add the bell peppers, onions, and garlic. Cook, stirring frequently, for about 10 minutes, or until the peppers are softened. Remove the vegetables to a bowl. Set aside.

Add the sausage to the same skillet. Cook, turning as needed, for 5 to 6 minutes, or until browned on all sides. Add the tomatoes, the reserved pepper-and-onion mixture, seasoning, pepper flakes (if using), and salt. Bring to a boil, then reduce to a simmer. Simmer for about 1 hour, or until the sausage is fork-tender.

Makes 4 servings

Per serving: *357 calories, 24 g protein, 27 g carbohydrate, 20 g fat, 68 mg cholesterol, 1,031 mg sodium, 6 g fiber*

Diet Exchanges: *0 milk, 4 vegetable, 0 fruit, 0 bread, 3 meat, 2 fat*

2 Carb Choices

146 Calories

Minced Meat Stew

—Kathleen Loeken, Atlanta, Georgia

Your family will love this homestyle main dish. Serve with noodles and a green vegetable such as Brussels sprouts or green beans.

Prep time: 10 minutes
Cook time: 30 minutes

  1 **tablespoon canola oil**
  1 **medium onion, chopped**
  2 **cups sliced mushrooms**
  1 **pound lean ground beef**
1½ **cups baby carrots (half bag)**
1½ **tablespoons flour**
  1 **teaspoon dried thyme**
½ **teaspoon salt**
½ **teaspoon ground black pepper**
1½ **cups fat-free reduced-sodium beef broth**

In a large, deep nonstick skillet over medium-high heat, warm the oil. Add the onion and mushrooms. Stir to mix. Cover the skillet. Cook, stirring occasionally, for about 5 minutes, or until liquid pools in the pot. Uncover. Cook, stirring occasionally, for about 3 minutes, or until the liquid is gone. Scrape the mushroom mixture to one side of the skillet. Crumble in the beef. Cook, stirring, for 5 minutes, or until no longer pink, incorporating the mushrooms and onions. Add the carrots, flour, thyme, salt, and pepper. Stir until the flour is no longer visible. Gradually add the broth while stirring constantly. Bring to a rapid simmer. Reduce the heat. Cover and simmer for about 17 minutes, or until the carrots are tender.

Makes 6 servings

Per serving: *146 calories, 17 g protein, 7 g carbohydrate, 5.5 g fat, 40 mg cholesterol, 366 mg sodium, 1 g fiber*

Diet Exchanges: *0 milk, 1 vegetable, 0 fruit, 0 bread, 2 meat, 1 fat*

½ **Carb Choice**

332 Calories

Winter Chili

—Sonya Miller, Gulfport, Mississippi

"Ground sirloin is a great alternative to ground chuck. The other ingredients contain lots of protein and vitamins without the high fat in some chili recipes."

Prep time: 15 minutes
Cook time: 1 hour 10 minutes

  1 tablespoon canola oil
  1 medium onion, chopped
  1 green bell pepper, chopped
  3 cloves garlic, minced
  1 pound ground top sirloin beef
1½ tablespoons mild or hot chili powder
1½ teaspoons ground cumin
  ½ teaspoon salt
  1 can (28 ounces) tomato puree
  1 can (28 ounces) petite diced tomatoes
  2 cans (15½ ounces each) dark red kidney beans, rinsed and drained
  Fresh chopped cilantro
  Shredded reduced-fat sharp Cheddar cheese (optional)

In a large, deep nonstick skillet over medium-high heat, warm the oil. Add the onion, pepper, and garlic. Stir to mix. Cover the skillet. Cook for about 4 minutes, or until the onions and pepper start to soften. Scrape to one side of the skillet. Crumble in the beef. Cook, stirring, for about 5 minutes, or until no longer pink. Add the chili powder, cumin, and salt. Cook, stirring, for 1 minute longer, or until the spices are fragrant. Add the tomato puree, tomatoes with juice, and beans. Stir to mix. Reduce the heat to medium-low. Partially cover the skillet. Cook, stirring occasionally, for about 1 hour, or until the flavors are well blended.

Sprinkle each serving with the cilantro and cheese, if using.

Makes 6 servings

Per serving: *332 calories, 28 g protein, 41 g carbohydrate, 7 g fat, 36 mg cholesterol, 585 mg sodium, 13 g fiber*

Diet Exchanges: *0 milk, 3½ vegetable, 0 fruit, 1½ bread, 2 meat, ½ fat*

3 Carb Choices

433 Calories

Beef and Mushroom Noodles

Andrea Skipton, Nova Scotia, Canada

"This is a filling meal that is quick and easy and one that the whole family will eat."

Prep time: 15 minutes
Cook time: 25 minutes

- 4 ounces whole wheat noodles
- 2 tablespoons cornstarch
- 2 cups fat-free reduced-sodium beef broth
- 1 tablespoon soy sauce
- 1 pound beef top round steak
- 2 tablespoons canola oil
- 12 ounces baby bella mushrooms, sliced
- 1 large sweet onion, halved and sliced
- 1 cup thinly sliced carrots
- 2 tablespoons chopped fresh parsley (optional)
- 2 teaspoons salt-free seasoning blend
- ½ teaspoon ground black pepper
- 4 teaspoons reduced-fat sour cream (optional)

Cook the noodles according to the package directions. Drain the noodles and return to the cooking pot to keep warm.

Meanwhile, place the cornstarch in a small bowl. Gradually add the broth while whisking constantly until the cornstarch is dissolved. Add the soy sauce and set aside. Cut the beef into thin slices across the grain. Set aside.

In a large nonstick skillet over high heat, warm 1 tablespoon of the oil. Add the mushrooms, onion, and carrots. Stir to mix. Cook, stirring frequently, for about 4 minutes, or until the vegetables start to soften. Remove to a plate and set aside.

Return the skillet to high heat. Add the remaining 1 tablespoon oil. Scatter the beef in the skillet. Cook, tossing frequently, for about 4 minutes, or until browned. Add the parsley (if using), seasoning blend, pepper, the reserved vegetables, and the broth mixture. Cook, stirring, for 4 minutes, or until bubbling and thickened.

Reduce the heat to medium-low. Simmer for about 10 minutes for the flavors to blend. Serve over noodles. Garnish each serving with 1 teaspoon of sour cream, if desired.

Makes 4 servings

Per serving: *433 calories, 34 g protein, 35 g carbohydrate, 17 g fat, 45 mg cholesterol, 478 mg sodium, 4 g fiber*

Diet Exchanges: *0 milk, 2 vegetable, 0 fruit, ½ bread, 4 meat, 3 fat*

2 Carb Choices

Kitchen Tip

Partially freezing the steaks makes it easier to slice them very thinly.

Slow-Cooker Barbecue Beef

—Tami Mertz, Algoma, Wisconsin

Either heap the tender meat onto toasted whole wheat buns or serve over rice.
Either way, coleslaw in oil and vinegar is a tasty companion.

Prep time: 10 minutes
Cook time: 8 to 9 hours

½ cup tomato puree

½ cup apple juice

2 tablespoons maple syrup

1 tablespoon flour

2 teaspoons chipotle chile powder or
   ground red pepper

½ teaspoon salt

½ teaspoon ground black pepper

3 pounds lean-only top round beef roast,
   cut into 3 or 4 large pieces

2 cups sliced sweet onion

Coat the inside of a 5- to 6-quart slow cooker pot with cooking spray. Add the tomato puree, apple juice, maple syrup, flour, chipotle powder or ground red pepper, salt, and black pepper. Whisk until smooth. Place the meat in the pot. Turn to coat well with the sauce. Add the onion. Cover and cook on the low-heat setting for 8 to 9 hours, or until fork tender. Remove the meat from the slow cooker to a cutting board. Shred the beef with a fork. Return to the slow cooker and combine with the sauce.

Makes 12 servings

Per serving: *130 calories, 24 g protein, 5 g carbohydrate, 3½ g fat, 50 mg cholesterol, 195 mg sodium, 0 g fiber*

Diet Exchanges: *0 milk, ½ vegetable, 0 fruit, 0 bread, 3 meat, ½ fat*

½ **Carb Choice**

····· SECRETS OF WEIGHT-LOSS WINNERS ·····

• Watching television helped me to lose weight! Yes, even though we have an image of the slothful couch potato, using my TiVo, I programmed my TV to find lots of healthy options for my viewing pleasure. I tape yoga on PBS, *Celebrity Fit Club* on VH1, and health

specials about weight loss on Discovery. It may seem strange, but your TV can become your personal weight-loss consultant!

**—Susan Mazur-Stommen,
Riverside, California**

321 Calories

Goodness Goulash

—Alexandria Rich, Willow Springs, Illinois

The genuine Hungarian meat stew doesn't contain tomatoes, which mask the sweet and spicy flavor of the paprika. More paprika can be added to taste.

Prep time: 10 minutes
Cook time: 1 hour 45 minutes

  2 **tablespoons canola oil**
  2 **pounds boneless top round beef, cut into 1" cubes**
  2 **large onions, cut into thin wedges**
  2 **tablespoons sweet paprika**
  ½ **teaspoon salt**
  ½ **teaspoon ground black pepper**
  ½ **teaspoon dried thyme**
  2 **bay leaves**
  1 **tablespoon flour**
  1 **cup reduced-sodium beef broth**
  1 **cup water**

In a large nonstick skillet over high heat, warm 1 tablespoon of the oil. Scatter the meat cubes into the skillet. Cook, turning as needed, for about 5 minutes, or until the meat is browned on all sides. (Cook meat in 2 batches if necessary to avoid crowding the pan.) Remove to a plate.

Add the remaining 1 tablespoon oil to the skillet. Add the onions, paprika, salt, pepper, thyme, and bay leaves. Stir. Cover and reduce the heat to medium. Cook, stirring occasionally, for about 5 minutes, or until the onions are softened. Stir in the flour until dissolved. Add the broth and water. Cook, stirring, until the mixture boils and thickens. Return the meat to the skillet. Reduce the heat and cover. Cook at a simmer for about 1½ hours, or until the meat is very tender. Remove the bay leaves and discard.

Makes 6 servings

Per serving: *321 calories, 34 g protein, 6 g carbohydrate, 17 g fat, 0 mg cholesterol, 362 mg sodium, 1 g fiber*

Diet Exchanges: *0 milk, 1 vegetable, 0 fruit, 0 bread, 5 meat, 3 fat*

½ **Carb Choice**

181 Calories

Homestyle Roast Beef

—Carmelita Falduto, Golf, Illinois

When you roast a heap of vegetables along with the lean beef, the whole meal takes on a healthier but no less satisfying profile.

Prep time: 10 minutes
Cook time: 50 minutes
Stand time: 10 minutes

1 boneless beef tri-tip roast (bottom sirloin) (1½–2 pounds)

2 cups frozen pearl onions, thawed

2 cups baby carrots

1 tablespoon canola oil

2 teaspoons garlic herb seasoning blend

½ teaspoon salt

1 cup fat-free reduced-sodium beef broth

Preheat the oven to 375°F. Coat the inside of a heavy roasting pan with cooking spray. Place the roast, onions, and carrots in the pan. Drizzle the oil over the meat and vegetables. Toss with clean hands to coat. Sprinkle with the seasoning blend and salt. Rub the seasonings all over the roast.

Roast for about 50 minutes, or until an instant read thermometer inserted into the center registers 155°F. Remove the roast and vegetables to a platter. Let stand for 10 minutes.

Meanwhile, place the roasting pan over medium heat. Add the broth and cook, scraping the pan bottom with a spatula to release the browned particles. Boil for a few minutes to reduce the sauce. Slice the roast. Serve the beef and vegetables drizzled with the pan juices.

Makes 8 servings

Per serving: *181 calories, 19 g protein, 10 g carbohydrate, 6.5 g fat, 37 mg cholesterol, 272 mg sodium, 1 g fiber*

Diet Exchanges: *0 milk, 2 vegetable, 0 fruit, 0 bread, 2½ meat, 1 fat*

1 Carb Choice

288 Calories

Apple-Cider Roast Pork

—Linda Tavani, Brooksville, Florida

"The pork is almost all white meat, with very little fat, and very delicious with the carrots and potatoes. There is no butter or milk on the potatoes, and the flavor is fabulous."

Prep time: 20 minutes
Cook time: 2 hours
Stand time: 10 minutes

1 sirloin pork roast (4½ pounds)

5 small red potatoes, quartered

5 medium carrots, quartered

2 tablespoons olive oil

1 teaspoon salt + more to season vegetables

1 teaspoon pepper + more to season vegetables

2 teaspoons crumbled dried sage

½ cup apple cider

Preheat the oven to 375°F. Coat a roasting pan with cooking spray. Set the roast in the pan. In a large bowl, toss the potatoes and carrots with the oil to coat. Sprinkle with salt and pepper. Scatter the potatoes and carrots around the roast. Combine the sage, 1 teaspoon salt, and 1 teaspoon pepper. With clean hands, rub the seasoning mixture evenly over the roast. Pour the cider into the bottom of the pan, taking care not to wash off the seasonings. Roast for 2 hours, tossing vegetables once every 30 minutes, or until the vegetables are very tender. Test that the juices run clear and an instant-read thermometer inserted into the center of the roast registers at least 155°F. Remove the roast and vegetables to a platter. Let stand for 10 minutes.

Place the pan juices and any loose browned bits of pork into a saucepan. Bring the juices to a boil and simmer for about 2 to 3 minutes, or until thickened slightly. Keep warm.

Slice the pork. Serve the pork and vegetables drizzled with the pan juices.

Makes 12 servings

Per serving: *288 calories, 37 g protein, 11 g carbohydrate, 10 g fat, 107 mg cholesterol, 302 mg sodium, 2 g fiber*

Diet Exchanges: *0 milk, ½ vegetable, 0 fruit, ½ bread, 5 meat, 1 fat*

1 Carb Choice

Fire Up the Flavor

Grilling icon Weber-Stephen Products Company has teamed with ACH Food Companies to expand its grilling expertise to seasonings with its Weber Grill Creations line. Seasoning mixes are amazing allies when it comes to healthy cooking.

There are eight different seasonings to choose from: Chicago Steak, Kick-N Chicken, Sweet & Tangy BBQ, N'Orleans Cajun, Smokey Mesquite, Gourmet Burger, Zesty Lemon Seasoning, and Veggie Grill. Also in the selection are six marinade mixes: White Wine & Herb, Black Peppercorn, Italian Herb, Chipotle, Tomato Garlic Pesto, and Mesquite. Look for Weber Grill Creations in supermarkets, mass merchandisers, wholesale clubs, and drugstores. Find out more about Weber products at www. weberbbq.com.

154 Calories

Glazed Ham with Mandarin Oranges

—Betty Enlund, Rosemount, Minnesota

You might not guess it, but a serving of glazed baked ham is low in calories and fat! This main dish is great for a gathering.

Prep time: 10 minutes
Cook time: 1 hour
Stand time: 10 minutes

- 1 **boneless fully cooked smoked ham (4 pounds)**
- 2 **cans (15 ounces each) mandarin oranges packed in juice**
- ¼ **cup honey**
- ¼ **cup Dijon mustard**
- ¼ **teaspoon ground cloves**

Preheat the oven to 325°F. Coat a roasting pan with cooking spray. Set the ham flat side down in the pan. With a small sharp knife, score the top in a grid pattern.

Place a small fine sieve over a bowl. Drain the oranges, reserving 1 cup of juice. Set the oranges aside. To the reserved juice, add the honey, mustard, and cloves. Whisk until well blended. Pour over the ham. Bake, basting every 15 minutes with pan juices, for 45 minutes. Add the oranges to the pan. Continue baking for about 15 minutes, or until an instant-read thermometer inserted in the center of the ham registers 140°F. Let stand for 10 minutes before slicing. Serve the ham drizzled with the pan juices and garnished with the oranges.

Makes 16 servings

Per serving: *154 calories, 19 g protein, 9 g carbohydrate, 4 g fat, 33 mg cholesterol, 1,523 mg sodium, 0 g fiber*

Diet Exchanges: *½ fruit, ½ bread, 3½ meat, 1 fat*

1 Carb Choice

292 Calories

Bacon Spaghetti

—Alana Villegas, Fort Worth, Texas

"This recipe fills you up with one serving, and you are not tempted to eat more than a regular serving size."

Prep time: 10 minutes
Cook time: 20 minutes

12 ounces spaghetti
4 strips bacon, cut into ½" pieces
1 teaspoon olive oil
½ cup finely chopped onion
2 teaspoons minced garlic
2 cans (14½ ounces each) salt-free diced tomatoes
1 teaspoon Italian seasoning
¼ teaspoon red-pepper flakes (optional)
2 tablespoons grated Parmesan cheese

Cook the spaghetti according to the package directions. Scoop out ½ cup of the cooking water and reserve. Drain the spaghetti and return to the cooking pot to keep warm.

Meanwhile, separate the bacon pieces and place in a large nonstick skillet. Cook over medium-high heat, stirring occasionally, for about 5 minutes, or until very crisp. Remove to a paper towel–lined plate. Set aside.

Pour off and discard all the bacon fat in the skillet. Return the skillet to medium heat. Add the oil, onion, and garlic. Cook, stirring occasionally, for about 5 minutes, or until the onion is golden. Add the tomatoes, seasoning, and pepper flakes (if using). Stir. Simmer over low heat for about 5 minutes longer, or until the flavors blend.

Add the spaghetti to the skillet. Toss to coat with tomatoes. Add a few tablespoonfuls of the reserved cooking water, if needed, to moisten the sauce.

Serve garnished with cheese, the reserved bacon, and additional pepper flakes (if desired).

Makes 6 servings

Per serving: *292 calories, 11 g protein, 49 g carbohydrate, 5 g fat, 6 mg cholesterol, 174 mg sodium, 3 g fiber*

Diet Exchanges: *0 milk, 1 vegetable, 0 fruit, 3 bread, ½ meat, ½ fat*

3 Carb Choices

249 Calories

Pork Kebabs Italiano

—Carmelita Falduto, Golf, Illinois

Robust Romano cheese and dried Italian herbs are all it takes to liven up lean pork tenderloin and healthy veggies. These kebabs are good enough for a party.

Prep time: 20 minutes
Grill time: 10 minutes

¼ cup dry bread crumbs

2 tablespoons grated Pecorino Romano cheese

2 teaspoons Italian seasoning

2 teaspoons minced garlic (2 medium cloves)

½ teaspoon salt

¼ teaspoon ground black pepper

12 ounces boneless pork loin, cut into 1" cubes

½ carton (5 ounces) grape or cherry tomatoes (about 1 cup)

1½ cups frozen pearl onions, thawed

1 tablespoon olive oil

Preheat the grill.

In a small bowl, combine the bread crumbs, cheese, seasoning, garlic, salt, and pepper. Toss to mix. Set aside.

In a medium bowl, combine the meat, tomatoes, and onions. Toss with the oil to coat.

Thread the meat, tomatoes, and onions alternately on 8 metal or soaked bamboo skewers. Put an even number of ingredients on each skewer. Place on a tray. Sprinkle with the seasoning mixture, making sure that all surfaces are coated evenly.

Grill the skewers, turning often, for about 10 minutes, or until the pork is no longer pink and the juices run clear.

Makes 4 servings (2 kebabs per serving)

Per serving: *249 calories, 20 g protein, 18 g carbohydrate, 11 g fat, 45 mg cholesterol, 884 mg sodium, 1 g fiber*

Diet Exchanges: *0 milk, 2 vegetable, 0 fruit, ½ bread, 2½ meat, 2 fat*

1 Carb Choice

— *Kitchen Tip* —

The kebabs may also be cooked in a 375°F oven or on a stove-top grill pan.

313 Calories

Cheryl's Favorite Pork and Sauerkraut

—Marjorie Lonigan, Falls City, Oregon

With this old-fashioned stick-to-your-ribs dinner, you just may forget you're watching your weight.

Prep time: 10 minutes
Cook time: 55 minutes

- 4 center-cut boneless pork chops, trimmed of visible fat (1 pound)
- ½ teaspoon thyme
- ½ teaspoon rubbed sage
- 1 tablespoon olive oil
- 3 medium white potatoes, cut into wedges
- 2 medium green or red apples, cored and quartered
- 1 medium onion, cut into wedges
- 1 bag (16 ounces) sauerkraut, drained and well rinsed
- ½ teaspoon ground black pepper

Rub the chops with the thyme and sage. In a Dutch oven over medium-high heat, warm the oil. Place the chops in the pan. Cook for about 2 minutes on each side, or until browned. Remove to a plate and set aside. Add the potatoes, apples, and onion to the pan. Cook, stirring occasionally, for about 6 minutes, or until the mixture starts to brown. Return the chops to the pan. Cover with the sauerkraut. Season with pepper. Cover and reduce the heat to medium-low. Cook for about 45 minutes, or until the pork is fork-tender.

Makes 4 servings

Per serving: *313 calories, 24 g protein, 22 g carbohydrate, 14 g fat, 59 mg cholesterol, 802 mg sodium, 7 g fiber*

Diet Exchanges: *0 milk, 1½ vegetable, ½ fruit, ½ bread, 3 meat, 1 fat*

1½ Carb Choices

234 Calories

Sweet-and-Sour Chinese Pork

—Karen Randolph, Chicago, Illinois

Serve with steamed broccoli and brown rice.

Prep time: 15 minutes
Cook time: 14 minutes

 2 **tablespoons reduced-sodium soy sauce**
 1 **tablespoon white or rice vinegar**
 1 **tablespoon cornstarch**
 1 **cup reduced-sodium chicken broth**
 1 **tablespoon canola oil**
12 **ounces pork loin, cut into 1" cubes**
 1 **cup chopped red onion**
 1 **red or yellow bell pepper, thinly sliced**
 1 **tablespoon minced garlic**
 1 **cup canned-in-juice pineapple chunks, drained**

In a small bowl, whisk the soy sauce, vinegar, cornstarch, and about ¼ cup of the broth until smooth. Gradually add the remaining ¾ cup broth, whisking constantly, until smooth. Set aside.

Heat a nonstick wok or large skillet over medium-high heat for 2 minutes. Add ½ tablespoon of the oil. Add the pork. Cook, tossing constantly, for 3 to 4 minutes longer, or until no longer pink. Remove and set aside.

Add the remaining ½ tablespoon oil to the pan. Add the onion, pepper, and garlic. Cook, tossing constantly, for 3 to 4 minutes, or until crisp-tender. Add the pineapple and the reserved pork to the pan. Add the reserved cornstarch mixture. Cook, stirring constantly, for 3 to 4 minutes longer, or until the mixture thickens and is heated through.

Makes 4 servings

Per serving: *234 calories, 18 g protein, 17 g carbohydrate, 10 g fat, 42 mg cholesterol, 748 mg sodium, 2 g fiber*

Diet Exchanges: *0 milk, 1 vegetable, ½ fruit, 0 bread, 2½ meat, 1½ fat*

1 Carb Choice

Pork Chops and Sweet Potatoes

—Brandi McKoy, Norfolk, Virginia

As this homey dish proves, comfort food does not have to pile on the calories and fat.

Prep time: 10 minutes
Cook time: 35 to 45 minutes

 2 large sweet potatoes, peeled
 1 large onion
 2 tablespoons canola oil
 2 teaspoons grated fresh ginger
 ¼ teaspoon salt
 4 thin-cut boneless pork chops (12 ounces)
 ¼ teaspoon ground cinnamon
   Ground black pepper
 ¼ cup hot chicken broth or water

Preheat the oven to 400°F. Coat a large shallow baking pan with cooking spray. Cut the sweet potatoes and onion into halves. Cut each half into 8 wedges. Transfer the vegetables to the pan.

In a small bowl, whisk the oil, ginger, and salt. Drizzle over the vegetables. With clean hands, rub the seasoning mixture evenly on the vegetables.

Bake for 25 to 30 minutes, tossing occasionally, or until the vegetables start to brown. Reduce the heat to 375°F. Add the pork to the pan. Sprinkle the cinnamon evenly on the pork. Roast for 10 to 15 minutes, or until the pork is no longer pink and the juices run clear. Remove the pork and vegetables to a platter. Add the broth or water to the pan juices. Stir to combine, scraping any browned bits in the pan. Drizzle the pan juices over the pork and vegetables.

Makes 4 servings

Per serving: *302 calories, 18 g protein, 23 g carbohydrate, 15 g fat, 44 mg cholesterol, 500 mg sodium, 4 g fiber*

Diet Exchanges: *0 milk, 1 vegetable, 0 fruit, 1 bread, 2 meat, 2 fat*

1½ Carb Choices

Breakfasts, Drinks, and Desserts

BREAKFASTS

DRINKS

152 Calories

Healthy Apples

—Carol Lauria, Smithtown, New York

*The dietary fiber from fresh fruit and whole grains has been proven
to assist in weight loss and promote heart health, too.*

Prep time: 10 minutes
Bake time: 40 to 45 minutes

  6 **apples, peeled and thinly sliced**
  ½ **cup unsweetened applesauce**
  1 **cup quick oats**
  2 **tablespoons brown sugar**
  2 **tablespoons wheat germ**
  ¼ **teaspoon ground cinnamon**
  ¼ **teaspoon salt**
  2 **tablespoons cold trans-free margarine
      or butter, cut into small pieces**

Preheat the oven to 350°F. Coat an 8" × 8" baking dish with cooking spray.

Scatter the apples into the dish. Add the applesauce and stir to mix.

In a large bowl, combine the oats, sugar, wheat germ, cinnamon, and salt. Cut in the margarine or butter with a pastry blender or 2 knives until the mixture forms small clumps. Scatter the mixture evenly over the apples.

Bake for 40 to 45 minutes, or until golden and bubbly.

Makes 6 servings

Per serving: *152 calories, 3 g protein, 34 g carbohydrate, 1.5 g fat, 0 mg cholesterol, 99 mg sodium, 4 g fiber*

Diet Exchanges: *0 milk, 0 vegetable, 1 fruit, 1 bread, 0 meat, 0 fat*

2 Carb Choices

Aromatica Rice Pudding

—Ellen Burr, Truro, Massachusetts

Chinese five-spice powder and grated tangerine peel are the secret ingredients that make this rice pudding unforgettable.

Prep time: 10 minutes
Cook time: 45 minutes

1 cup aromatic rice

1 tablespoon canola oil

2 cups water

1 tablespoon grated tangerine or orange peel

1 teaspoon five-spice powder

1 can (15 ounces) evaporated fat-free milk

½ cup chopped dates

¼ cup chopped dried black figs

2 tablespoons minced crystallized ginger

2 tablespoons toasted pine nuts

Ground cinnamon

In a saucepan over medium heat, combine the rice and oil. Cook, stirring, for about 5 minutes, or until glossy. Stir in the water, tangerine or orange peel, and five-spice powder. Bring to a boil. Reduce the heat so the mixture simmers. Cover and cook for 20 minutes.

Stir in the milk, dates, and figs. Cook over low heat for about 5 minutes, stirring often, until the mixture is thick and creamy. Serve warm, sprinkled with the ginger, pine nuts, and cinnamon to taste.

Makes 6 servings

Per serving: *217 calories, 7 g protein, 38 g carbohydrate, 4.5 g fat, 3 mg cholesterol, 87 mg sodium, 2 g dietary fiber*

Diet Exchanges: *½ milk, 0 vegetable, 1 fruit, 0 bread, 0 meat, 1 fat*

2½ Carb Choices

Apple Pancakes

—Maria Diehl, Schenectady, New York

*Top these hotcakes with 1 tablespoon of pure maple syrup
for only 50 additional calories!*

**Prep time: 5 minutes
Cook time: 3 to 5 minutes**

1½ cups reduced-fat baking and pancake
   mix
½ teaspoon apple pie spice
1 cup water
1 cup finely chopped apples (about
   1 medium apple)

In a large bowl, combine the pancake mix and apple pie spice. Stir to mix. Add the water. Mix well to combine. Stir in the apples.

Coat a large nonstick skillet or griddle pan lightly with butter-flavored cooking spray. Warm over medium heat. Scoop ¼-cup measures of batter onto the skillet or griddle. Cook for about 2 to 3 minutes, or until bubbles appear on the tops of the pancakes. Flip with a spatula and cook for about 1 to 2 minutes, or until cooked through.

**Makes 4 servings
(3 pancakes per serving)**

Per serving: *187 calories, 4 g protein, 36 g carbohydrate, 3 g fat, 0 mg cholesterol, 524 mg sodium, 1 g fiber*

Diet Exchanges: *0 milk, 0 vegetable, 0 fruit, 2 bread, 0 meat, 0 fat*

2 Carb Choices

— *Kitchen Tip* —

Apple pie spice is a bottled seasoning comprised of ground cinnamon and nutmeg, with additions that can include allspice, cloves, or ginger. If unavailable, replace it with ground cinnamon.

214 Calories

Peachy Oat Breakfast

—Linda Wood, Winfield, Illinois

When peaches are not in season, use thawed frozen peaches or canned or jarred peaches in juice, drained.

Prep time: 4 minutes
Microwave time: 2 minutes

1 cup water
¼ cup oat bran
2 tablespoons protein powder
1 teaspoon sugar
½ cup chopped fresh peaches
Ground cinnamon

In a microwaveable bowl, combine the water, oat bran, protein powder, and sugar. Stir to mix well. Microwave on high power for about 2 minutes, checking every 30 seconds, or until thickened and liquid is absorbed. Stir in the peaches and sprinkle with cinnamon to taste.

Makes 1 serving

Per serving: *214 calories, 25 g protein, 32 g carbohydrate, 3 g fat, 13 mg cholesterol, 41 mg sodium, 5 g fiber*

Diet Exchanges: *0 milk, 0 vegetable, ½ fruit, 1 bread, 0 meat, 0 fat*

2 Carb Choices

Healthy Pick-Me-Up

—Phyllis Briggs, Crawfordville, Florida

"Eating this healthy treat every evening has kept me away from junk food and helped me to easily lose weight."

Prep time: 3 minutes

  1 **medium banana, sliced**
  ¼ **cup fat-free plain yogurt**
  2 **tablespoons orange juice**
  ½ **tablespoon sliced almonds**

In a serving bowl, combine the banana, yogurt, and juice. Sprinkle the almonds on top.

Makes 1 serving

Per serving: *161 calories, 5 g protein, 36 g carbohydrate, 2 g fat, 1 mg cholesterol, 35 mg sodium, 3 g fiber*

Diet Exchanges: *½ milk, 0 vegetable, 2 fruit, 0 bread, 0 meat, 0 fat*

2½ Carb Choices

SHOPPING SAVVY

The Skinny on Cheese

Kraft Snackables Mozzarella String Cheese, made with 2 percent milk, is a handy portable snack that will help boost your protein and calcium intake for the day. Paired with a couple of whole wheat crackers, the string cheese can satisfy your late-afternoon hunger pangs and keep you satisfied until dinner. A 1-ounce serving contains 70 calories, 8 grams of protein, and 4 grams of fat, plus 15 percent of the Daily Value (DV) for calcium.

The company also produces an organic version called Kraft String-Ums String Cheese Organic Mozzarella with 80 calories, 6 grams of fat, 7 grams of protein, and 20 percent of the DV for calcium in a 1-ounce serving. Look for them in the dairy case of your local supermarket. For more information, visit www.kraftfoods.com.

125 Calories

Omelet Italian-Style

—Nanci Parker, Munford, Alabama

If you have some fresh basil leaves on hand, cut them into slivers and toss into the omelet with the tomatoes.

Prep time: 5 minutes
Cook time: 9 to 10 minutes

1 tablespoon chopped onion

1 tablespoon chopped green bell pepper

1 tablespoon chopped tomatoes + more for garnish

1 egg, beaten

2 egg whites, beaten

½ teaspoon Italian seasoning

1 teaspoon grated Parmesan cheese

In a medium nonstick skillet coated with cooking spray over medium heat, add the onion and peppers. Cook, stirring occasionally, for about 2 minutes, or until sizzling. Add the tomatoes. Cook for about 1 minute longer, or until just starting to soften. Add the egg and egg whites. Sprinkle with the seasoning. Reduce the heat to low and cook for about 5 minutes, lifting the cooked edges of the egg mixture with a fork so the uncooked egg can run underneath, or until the bottom is set. Cook for 1 to 2 minutes, or until the eggs are cooked through. Sprinkle with the cheese and fold the omelet in half.

Makes 1 serving

Per serving: 125 calories, 15 g protein, 3 g carbohydrate, 5½ g fat, 213 mg cholesterol, 208 mg sodium, 1 g fiber

Diet Exchanges: 0 milk, ½ vegetable, 0 fruit, 0 bread, 2 meat, ½ fat

0 Carb Choices

Yogurt-and-Bran Breakfast Feast

—Rachel Gregory, Lemont, Pennsylvania

"This recipe contains a lot of fiber, so it is low in calories and is filling, and it cleanses your system."

Prep time: 4 minutes

½ cup low-fat vanilla yogurt
⅓ cup Fiber One cereal
½ banana, sliced

In a serving bowl, combine the yogurt, cereal, and banana. Stir gently to mix.

Makes 1 serving

Per serving: *196 calories, 8 g protein, 47 g carbohydrate, 2 g fat, 6 mg cholesterol, 167 mg sodium, 11 g fiber*

Diet Exchanges: *0 milk, 0 vegetable, 1 fruit, 1½ bread, 0 meat, 0 fat*

3 Carb Choices

Pear-Raspberry Oven Pancake

—Gloria Bradley, Naperville, Illinois

Experts advise that variety can keep a diet from becoming ho-hum. Try this rustic fruit oven pancake to keep things interesting.

Prep time: 10 minutes
Bake time: 50 minutes

1 can (29 ounces) pear halves packed in juice, drained and chopped
¾ cup quick-cooking oats
1 cup fat-free milk
½ cup fat-free egg substitute
2 tablespoons vanilla
¼ cup sugar
1 teaspoon grated lemon peel
½ cup raspberries
¼ teaspoon ground cinnamon
Fat-free frozen raspberry yogurt (optional)

Preheat the oven to 350°F. Coat a deep 9" pie plate with cooking spray. Spread the pears in an even layer in the dish.

Place the oats in a blender. Cover and process on high for 1 minute, or until finely chopped. Add the milk, egg substitute, vanilla, sugar, and lemon peel. Process until well blended, stopping occasionally to scrape down the sides of the blender.

Gently ladle the batter over the pears. Sprinkle with the raspberries and cinnamon. Bake for 45 to 50 minutes, or until puffed and cooked through. Cool slightly.

Serve plain or with the frozen yogurt, if desired.

Makes 6 servings

Per serving: *167 calories, 5 g protein, 32 g carbohydrate, 1 g fat, 1 mg cholesterol, 68 mg sodium, 3 g fiber*

Diet Exchanges: *0 milk, 0 vegetable, 0 fruit, 1 bread, ½ meat, 0 fat*

2 Carb Choices

Mixed Fruit Parfait

—Ann Bilodeau, Ottawa, Ontario, Canada

A variety of fruits may be used in this parfait. Choose from pineapple,
kiwifruit, grapes, peaches, apples, pears, or mango.
The more types you add, the more interesting the taste.

Prep time: 5 minutes
Microwave time: 30 to 45 seconds

⅓ cup unsweetened applesauce
½ cup fresh fruit, chopped
¼ cup low-fat plain yogurt
2 tablespoons chopped walnuts

Combine the applesauce and fruit in a microwaveable serving bowl. Microwave on high for 30 to 45 seconds, or until hot.

Serve topped with the yogurt and walnuts.

Makes 1 serving

Per serving: *205 calories, 6 g protein, 24 g carbohydrate, 11 g fat, 4 mg cholesterol, 45 mg sodium, 3 g fiber*

Diet Exchanges: *½ milk, 0 vegetable, 1 fruit, 0 bread, ½ meat, 2 fat*

½ Carb Choices

Fruit and Veggie Smoothie

—Alan Josey, Irvine, California

"This is a great way to fill up on vegetables (get your five per day) and indulge your sweet tooth at the same time. You don't even taste the veggies! It's like berry-flavored frozen yogurt. Unbelievable!"

Prep time: 5 minutes

½ cup orange juice
½ cup low-fat vanilla yogurt
1 cup frozen loose-pack mixed berries
1 cup fresh spinach leaves
½ frozen banana, sliced
6 baby carrots

In a blender, combine the orange juice and yogurt. Add the berries, spinach, banana, and carrots. Pulse until smooth and frosty.

Makes 2 servings (1¼ cups per serving)

Per serving: *157 calories, 5 g protein, 33 g carbohydrate, 1 g fat, 3 mg cholesterol, 84 mg sodium, 4 g fiber*

Diet Exchanges: *0 milk, ½ vegetable, 1½ fruit, ½ bread, 0 meat, 0 fat*

2 Carb Choices

248 Calories

Tropical Fruit Smoothie

—Ruth Proch, Leesburg, Florida

"This is so tasty and filling. It makes a great balanced lunch along with a handful of almonds."

Prep time: 5 minutes

¾ cup fat-free plain yogurt

¾ cup frozen loose-pack tropical fruit blend

½ cup 2% milk

2 teaspoons sugar or 2 packets Splenda

In a blender, combine the yogurt, fruit, milk, and sugar or Splenda. Blend for about 20 seconds, or until smooth.

Makes 1 serving

Per serving: *248 calories, 13 g protein, 48 g carbohydrate, 2.5 g fat, 14 mg cholesterol, 151 mg sodium, 3 g fiber*

Diet Exchanges: *0 milk, 0 vegetable, 0 fruit, 1½ bread, 0 meat, 0 fat*

3 Carb Choices

SHOPPING SAVVY

Singular Satisfaction

An entire cake or batch of brownies sitting in the kitchen can turn into an exhausting battle of willpower that leaves a bitter taste in your mouth. Now Guiltless Gourmet has come up with a sweet solution to the dessert-portion dilemma. By factoring an occasional treat into your caloric total, you can savor single-serving Dessert Bowls in one of three seductive flavors: Hot Chocolate Brownie with Fudge Sauce, Black Velvet Cake with Caramel Sauce, and Bananas Foster Cake with Caramel Sauce. Each serving contains 200 calories and less than 3 grams of fat. Microwave in 40 seconds and you have that fresh-baked sensation. The confections each contain at least 3 grams of protein and no trans fat. Look for Dessert Bowls in the baking aisle at the supermarket or online at www.guiltlessgourmet.com.

Banana-Blueberry-Soy Smoothie

—Margaret Yannucci, Youngstown, Ohio

"I drink this for one meal a day. It is healthy and does not have a lot of calories."

Prep time: 5 minutes

1–1¼ cups light soy milk
  ½ cup frozen loose-pack blueberries
  ½ frozen banana, sliced
  2 teaspoons sugar or 2 packets artificial sweetener
  1 teaspoon pure vanilla extract

In a blender, combine 1 cup of the milk, the blueberries, banana, sugar or sweetener, and vanilla extract. Blend for 20 to 30 seconds, or until smooth. Add up to ¼ cup more milk if a thinner smoothie is desired.

Makes 2 servings (1 cup per serving)

Per serving: *125 calories, 3 g protein, 25 g carbohydrate, 2 g fat, 0 mg cholesterol, 60 mg sodium, 2 g fiber*

Diet Exchanges: *1 milk, 0 vegetable, 1 fruit, 0 bread, 0 meat, 0 fat*

2 Carb Choices

Front, Strawberry-Orange-Banana Smoothie (page 238); *Center Left,* Sunrise Shake-Up (page 243); *Center Right and Back Left, Banana-Blueberry-Soy Smoothie* (above); and *Back Right,* Papaya Smoothie (page 244)

Strawberry-Orange-Banana Smoothie

—Timothy Killoran, Shelton, Washington

"This smoothie helped me lose weight. Since I am always on the go, it was easier just to grab and go."

Prep time: 5 minutes

- 1 cup orange juice
- 1 cup fresh or frozen loose-pack strawberries
- 1 cup fat-free plain yogurt
- 1 cup crushed ice or 5 to 6 ice cubes
- 1 medium banana, cut into chunks

In a blender, combine the orange juice, strawberries, yogurt, ice, and banana. Process for about 30 seconds, or until smooth and frosty.

Makes 3 servings (1 cup per serving)

Per serving: *123 calories, 5 g protein, 28 g carbohydrate, 0.5 g fat, 2 mg cholesterol, 47 mg sodium, 2 g fiber*

Diet Exchanges: *½ milk, 0 vegetable, 1½ fruit, 0 bread, 0 meat, 0 fat*

2 Carb Choices

--- Kitchen Tip ---

To prepare a single serving, just reduce all the ingredients by two-thirds.

Pineapple-and-Strawberry Soy Shake

—Jean Londergan, La Crosse, Wisconsin

"After a lunchtime workout, this tides me over until the afternoon, when I have a high-protein, nutritious snack to rev up the metabolism until dinnertime."

Prep time: 5 minutes

½ cup low-fat vanilla yogurt
½ cup fat-free milk or fruit juice
½ cup frozen or fresh strawberries
½ cup pineapple chunks, fresh or packed in juice
2 tablespoons soy powder
½ teaspoon pure vanilla extract

In a blender, combine the yogurt, milk or juice, strawberries, pineapple, soy powder, and vanilla extract. Process for about 30 seconds, or until smooth.

Makes 2 servings (1 cup per serving)

Per serving: *181 calories, 7 g protein, 26 g carbohydrate, 5.5 g fat, 4 mg cholesterol, 69 mg sodium, 1 g fiber*

Diet Exchanges: *0 milk, 0 vegetable, 1 fruit, ½ bread, 0 meat, 0 fat*

1½ Carb Choices

Berry Good Workout Smoothie

—Victoria Coulter, Warner Robins, Georgia

"The best time to claim a lane in the swimming pool at my fitness center is 5:30 a.m. This drink is easy to throw together and gentle on the stomach; it's a tasty, well-rounded fuel to power me through my early morning swim."

Prep time: 5 minutes

 6 ounces cherry-flavored cranberry 100% juice blend
 ¾ cup mixed frozen loose-pack blackberries, raspberries, and blueberries
 ⅓ cup (3 ounces) light extra-firm silken tofu
 ½ large very ripe banana, fresh or frozen
 1 tablespoon ground flaxseed

In a blender, combine the juice, berries, tofu, banana, and flaxseed. Pulse for about 1 minute until chopped, then process until smooth.

Makes 2 servings (scant 1 cup per serving)

Per serving: *130 calories, 4 g protein, 24 g carbohydrate, 2 g fat, 0 mg cholesterol, 45 mg sodium, 3 g fiber*

Diet Exchanges: *0 milk, 0 vegetable, 1½ fruit, 0 bread, 1 meat, 0 fat*

1½ Carb Choices

— *Kitchen Tip* —

Whether you buy ground flaxseed or grind seeds yourself, store the ground seeds in an airtight container in the freezer for up to 3 months.
For those who don't like berry seeds, the fruit can be blended and strained before making the smoothie.

255 Calories

Morning Energy Drink

—Connie Toce, Middleburg, Florida

"This healthy shake curbs my appetite and keeps me from eating junk food throughout the day."

Prep time: 5 minutes

- 1 cup fat-free vanilla soy milk
- ½ cup fat-free plain yogurt
- 1 banana, sliced
- ¼ cup frozen loose-pack blueberries
- 2 tablespoons peanut butter
- 1 tablespoon wheat germ
- 1 tablespoon ground flaxseed

In a blender, combine the milk, yogurt, banana, blueberries, peanut butter, wheat germ, and flaxseed. Blend for about 30 seconds, or until smooth.

Makes 2 servings (1¼ cups per serving)

Per serving: *255 calories, 12 g protein, 33 g carbohydrate, 10 g fat, 1 mg cholesterol, 160 mg sodium, 5 g fiber*

Diet Exchanges: *1 milk, 0 vegetable, 1 fruit, 1 bread, 1 meat, 1½ fat*

2 Carb Choices

It Worked for Me!

Marni Halasa, 41

VITAL STATS

Weight lost: 29 pounds

Time to goal: 6 years

Greatest challenge: breaking the habit of eating too much

Growing up in a large Jordanian household, Marni Halasa routinely sat down to seven-course dinners—pita and hummus, tabbouleh, stuffed peppers, lamb and rice with yogurt sauce, spinach pies. "And you could never say no," recalls the 41-year-old New York City resident.

Although Marni started figure skating competitively at age 10, the weight started to creep on her 5'6" frame in her teens. By the time she graduated from journalism and law schools, she weighed 157.

In 1994, Marni took a job as a legal journalist and began teaching ice-skating on the side. She heard the other coaches raving about a gym and decided to try a class, which ignited her determination to get fit.

Soon Marni was a regular, taking intense boot camp and sculpting classes. Although she looked fit, after a year of intense physical activity, Marni had lost a measly 8 pounds. Her trainers advised her to change her diet to more protein and veggies, lose the refined carbohydrates, and monitor her caloric intake.

Marni began to eat small 250- to 300-calorie meals every few hours and follows this "minimeal" strategy to this day. Breakfast might be an egg-white omelet with a piece of American cheese. At midmorning, she snacks on a container of light yogurt or fruit. Lunch is a salad with low-fat dressing. Midafternoon, more fruit or yogurt. Dinner is usually chicken and a salad. "And I try not to eat after 7:00 p.m.," says Marni.

In 2001, Marni left her job in journalism to focus on figure skating. "The moment I decided to pursue skating professionally, everything seemed to fall into place. I was teaching others to do something I was passionate about." During the next year, she slimmed down to 135 pounds.

In 2003, Marni cut out refined carbohydrates like white flour and sugar and dropped another 10 pounds, to 125. Now at 129 pounds, Marni estimates that she consumes between 1,800 and 2,100 calories a day, mostly fruits, veggies, and lean protein.

"Learning to eat well took discipline, but the benefits were worth it," says Marni. "Eating well helps me do what I love— skating—better. It helps me live my life to the fullest."

244 Calories

Sunrise Shake-Up

—Phyllis Briggs, Crawfordville, Florida

"This healthy, easy morning shake, combined with exercise, helped me to lose weight."

Prep time: 5 minutes

1½ cups fat-free plain soy milk
1 carton (6 ounces) low-fat vanilla yogurt
1 ripe banana, sliced
2 tablespoons honey

In a blender, combine the milk, yogurt, banana, and honey. Process for about 20 seconds, or until smooth.

Makes 2 servings (1½ cups per serving)

Per serving: *244 calories, 9 g protein, 51 g carbohydrate, 1 g fat, 0 mg cholesterol, 136 mg sodium, 3 g fiber*

Diet Exchanges: *½ milk, 0 vegetable, 1 fruit, 2 bread, 0 meat, 0 fat*

3½ Carb Choices

299 Calories

Papaya Smoothie

—Suz Hall, Pinehurst, Idaho

"It's milk-shakey but good for you."

Prep time: 5 minutes

1 papaya, cut into chunks
1 cup fat-free plain yogurt
½ cup fresh pineapple chunks
½ cup crushed ice
1 teaspoon coconut extract
1 teaspoon ground flaxseed

In a blender, combine the papaya, yogurt, pineapple, ice, coconut extract, and flax-seed. Process for about 30 seconds, or until smooth and frosty.

Makes 1 serving

Per serving: *299 calories, 13 g protein, 64 g carbohydrate, 1.5 g fat, 5 mg cholesterol, 148 mg sodium, 7 g fiber*

Diet Exchanges: *1 milk, 0 vegetable, 3 fruit, 0 bread, 0 meat, 0 fat*

4 Carb Choices

It Worked for Me!

Terri Stewart, 45

VITAL STATS

Weight lost: 52 pounds

Time to goal: 6½ months

Greatest challenge: sticking to the Pritikin Program after returning home

On New Year's Eve 1999, Terri Stewart faced a painful realization: Her world was upside down. At 37, she was alone after divorcing her husband of more than 10 years, and missing her professional identity after selling her real-estate development business. Seeking comfort, she began to eat—a lot.

By the end of 2000, her weight had climbed from 120 pounds to over 170. "I was easily winded—I had absolutely no stamina," recalls the South Florida real-estate instructor/ broker who owns a real-estate school.

Terri's mother has high blood pressure; her father, coronary artery disease and diabetes. Approaching 40 and terrified she was heading down their unhealthy path, she booked a 2-week stay at the Pritikin Longevity Center & Spa in Aventura, Florida.

Terri lost 6 pounds during her stay. Her challenge: to stick with the program when she returned home. She swapped bacon-and-egg breakfasts with oatmeal and fruit, lunchtime pizza with salads or a baked potato, and fettuccine Alfredo dinners for another large salad with a bit of fish and

steamed broccoli or kale. She snacked on fruit or veggies and nonfat dressing.

Terri had begun a challenging daily exercise program at Pritikin—45 minutes on a treadmill set to a steep incline and an additional 30 to 45 minutes of strength training. When she got home, she created a program to emulate these activities, including daily walks and light weights.

After 7 months, Terri had lost 52 pounds, settling at 120, a weight she's held for 7 years. "I have more appreciation for food now," she says. "I know what I'm preparing is better than any medicine."

While Terri loves her new, tiny wardrobe, she loves her cholesterol and blood pressure levels—now normal—even more. She's also thrilled that she met the man of her dreams: Jeff Novick, Pritikin's director of nutrition. Their friendship, which began during Terri's stay, blossomed into more after she left.

"Changing one aspect of your life for the better begins a domino effect of positive change in other areas of your life—emotional, financial, spiritual, professional," she says.

28
Calories

Hot Spiced Tea Mix

—Nancy Booker, Dallas, Texas

"Just a cup of this very tasty drink satisfies my in-between meal cravings.
Also, it is nice to have a cup at night."

Prep time: 5 minutes

1 container (12 ounces) instant orange
  breakfast drink
¼ cup Splenda
1 tablespoon light lemonade mix
1 tablespoon ground cinnamon
1 tablespoon ground cloves
½ teaspoon nutmeg

In a large bowl, stir together the breakfast drink, Splenda, lemonade mix, cinnamon, cloves, and nutmeg. Pour into a jar. Seal tightly with a lid. Store in a cool cupboard for up to 3 months.

To make 1 cup of tea, spoon 1 tablespoon of the mix into a mug and add 1 cup of hot water. Stir until the powder is dissolved.

**Makes 48 servings, 1 tablespoon each
(Yield: 3 cups mix)**

Per serving: *28 calories, 0 g protein, 7 g carbohydrate, 0 g fat, 0 mg cholesterol, 1 mg sodium, 0 g fiber*

Diet Exchanges: *0 milk, 0 vegetable, 0 fruit, ½ bread, 0 meat, 0 fat*

½ **Carb Choice**

Strawberry Mock Daiquiri

—Jan Kerr, Hot Springs Village, Arkansas

"I can still have a fancy drink without the calories and not feel deprived."

Prep time: 5 minutes

- 2 cups diet ginger ale or lemon-lime soda
- 1 cup frozen strawberries
- 1 small package (0.3 ounce; 4 servings) sugar-free lemon gelatin

In a blender, combine the soda, strawberries, and gelatin. Process for 30 seconds, or until smooth. Serve in daiquiri glasses, if desired.

Makes 4 servings (scant 1 cup per serving)

Per serving: *24 calories, 1g protein, 3 g carbohydrate, 0 g fat, 0 mg cholesterol, 89 mg sodium, 1 g fiber*

Diet Exchanges: *0 milk, 0 vegetable, 0 fruit, 0 bread, 0 meat, 0 fat*

0 Carb Choices

Pumpkin Ricotta Pudding

—Julie Jones, Iowa City, Iowa

"Pumpkin contains beta-carotene and fiber. The ricotta is a good source of calcium without many carbohydrates. This is a very filling, nutritious, and tasty way to cure the sweets craving and not feel guilty!"

Prep time: 5 minutes
Chill time: 30 minutes

- 1 cup reduced-fat ricotta cheese
- 1 cup canned pumpkin
- ¼ cup pure maple syrup or 1–2 tablespoons Splenda
- 1 teaspoon pure vanilla extract
- ½ teaspoon pumpkin pie spice
- 1 tablespoon finely chopped crystallized ginger or toasted walnuts (optional)

In a medium bowl, beat the ricotta, pumpkin, maple syrup or Splenda, vanilla extract, and spice until well combined.

Cover and refrigerate for 30 minutes, or until chilled. Serve, sprinkled with crystallized ginger or walnuts, if desired.

Makes 4 servings

Per serving: *137 calories, 6 g protein, 22 g carbohydrate, 3 g fat, 15 mg cholesterol, 60 mg sodium, 2 g fiber*

Diet Exchanges: *0 milk, 0 vegetable, 0 fruit, 1 bread, 1 meat, ½ fat*

1½ Carb Choices

126 Calories

Banana Tapioca Pudding

—Marjorie Lonigan, Falls City, Oregon

Nutrients and fiber are up and fat is down in this revamped childhood favorite. It's light and delicious.

Prep time: 5 minutes
Cook time: 6 minutes
Cool time: 15 minutes
Chill time: several hours

1 package (3 ounces) tapioca pudding mix

2 cups fat-free milk

¼ cup finely chopped dates or raisins (optional)

2 large pasteurized egg whites

1 banana, sliced

In a saucepan, combine the pudding mix and milk. Stir until smooth. Cook according to the package directions. Stir in the dates or raisins, if using. Set aside for 15 minutes to cool.

Meanwhile, place the egg whites in the bowl of an electric mixer. Beat on medium speed until foamy. Increase the speed to high and beat for about 1 minute, or until soft peaks form.

Add the bananas and beaten egg whites to the reserved tapioca. Fold to incorporate. Cover and refrigerate for several hours, or until chilled.

Makes 6 servings

Per serving: *126 calories, 5 g protein, 28 g carbohydrate, 0 g fat, 1 mg cholesterol, 130 mg sodium, 1 g fiber*

Diet Exchanges: *½ milk, 0 vegetable, ½ fruit, 1 bread, 0 meat, 0 fat*

2 Carb Choices

Kitchen Tip

To avoid any risk of salmonella contamination from eating raw egg whites, use only pasteurized egg whites for this recipe. Packaged refrigerated egg whites are available in supermarkets and natural food stores.

Tropical Fruit Cream

—Lurline Neal, Carthage, Mississippi

"This is so refreshing. It provides a real pick-me-up while adding calcium and fruit to my diet."

Prep time: 5 minutes
Chill time: Several hours

1 **can (20 ounces) crushed pineapple in juice, drained**

1 **package (0.3 ounce; 4 servings) sugar-free lime gelatin**

1 **container (16 ounces) fat-free cottage cheese**

In a mixing bowl, stir together the pineapple and gelatin powder. Set aside.

Put the cottage cheese in the bowl of a food processor fitted with a metal blade. Process for about 2 minutes, scraping the sides of the bowl as needed, or until very creamy. Stir the cottage cheese into the reserved pineapple mixture. Cover and refrigerate for several hours, or until set.

Makes 6 servings

Per serving: *112 calories, 8 g protein, 18 g carbohydrate, 0 g fat, 6 mg cholesterol, 313 mg sodium, 1 g fiber*

Diet Exchanges: *½ milk, 0 vegetable, 1 fruit, 0 bread, 0 meat, 0 fat*

1 Carb Choice

123
Calories

Pineapple Fluff

—Janet Surber, Brownsburg, Indiana

"This is light, 'fluffy' comfort food that helps when my sweet tooth kicks in."

Prep time: 5 minutes
Chill time: 1 hour

1 can (20 ounces) crushed pineapple packed in juice

1 box (1.1 ounces; 4 servings) sugar-free instant vanilla pudding mix

1 cup frozen fat-free nondairy whipped topping, thawed

2 tablespoons toasted unsweetened flaked coconut (optional)

In a bowl, combine the pineapple with juice, pudding mix, and whipped topping. Stir to mix completely. Cover and refrigerate for at least 1 hour, or until set.

Serve garnished with the coconut, if using.

Makes 4 servings

Per serving: *123 calories, 1 g protein, 30 g carbohydrate, 0 g fat, 0 mg cholesterol, 109 mg sodium, 1 g fiber*

Diet Exchanges: *0 milk, 0 vegetable, 1½ fruit, 0 bread, 0 meat, 0 fat*

2 Carb Choices

Eggnog Pudding

—Maria Diehl, Schenectady, New York

"It's especially a favorite at the holiday time, when so many people who usually avoid sweets want to indulge."

Prep time: 10 minutes
Chill time: 1 hour

1 package (1.1 ounces; 4 servings) sugar-free instant vanilla pudding mix

2 cups fat-free milk

½ cup sugar-free frozen nondairy whipped topping, thawed

1 teaspoon rum or brandy extract

¼ teaspoon ground nutmeg

In a mixing bowl, combine the pudding mix and milk. Whisk for about 2 minutes, or until smooth. Add the whipped topping and rum or brandy extract. Whisk just until combined. Spoon the pudding mixture into 4 dessert dishes. Sprinkle with the nutmeg. Cover and refrigerate for 1 hour, or until set.

Makes 4 servings

Per serving: *111 calories, 4 g protein, 18 g carbohydrate, 0 g fat, 2 mg cholesterol, 376 mg sodium, 0 g fiber*

Diet Exchanges: *½ milk, 0 vegetable, 0 fruit, 0 bread, 0 meat, 0 fat*

1 Carb Choice

Fall Bread Pudding

—Tyler Hill, Chatham, Ontario, Canada

"This is something I can prepare all year round and enjoy without guilt. It satisfies my sweet craving, but all the ingredients are healthy, and I continue to lose weight without sabotaging my diet."

Prep time: 10 minutes
Cook time: 5 minutes
Bake time: 40 to 45 minutes

6 slices whole wheat bread, cut into ½" cubes

1 cup chopped apple or pear

1 tablespoon trans-free margarine

1 tablespoon flour

1 cup 1% milk

¼ cup three-fruit spread

¼ cup unsweetened orange juice

1 large egg, beaten

1 large egg white, lightly beaten

2 tablespoons brown sugar

1 teaspoon rum extract or 1 tablespoon dark rum

¼ teaspoon ground allspice

Preheat the oven to 350°F. Coat a 6-cup baking dish with cooking spray. Place the bread and apple or pear in the dish. Set aside.

In a large saucepan over low heat, melt the margarine. Stir in the flour. Add the milk, stirring constantly, and cook for about 5 minutes, or until the mixture thickens slightly. In a small bowl, stir together the three-fruit spread, orange juice, egg, egg white, sugar, rum extract or rum, and allspice. Add to the milk mixture and stir until well blended. Pour over the reserved bread cubes and apple or pear. Stir just until the bread is coated.

Bake for 40 to 45 minutes, or until the pudding is golden and set.

Serves 6

Per serving: *184 calories, 6 g protein, 32 g carbohydrate, 4 g fat, 37 mg cholesterol, 206 mg sodium, 3 g fiber*

Diet Exchanges: *0 milk, 0 vegetable, 0 fruit, 1½ bread, 0 meat, ½ fat*

2 Carb Choices

230 Calories

Double Dark Chocolate Biscotti

—Lynn Grossart, Chicago, Illinois

*These crisp cookies are so satisfying when dunked in a
cup of steaming tea or coffee.*

Prep time: 15 minutes
Bake time: 45 minutes
Stand time: 15 minutes

BISCOTTI

1½ cups flour

½ cup brown sugar

⅓ cup unsweetened cocoa powder

½ teaspoon baking powder

¼ teaspoon ground cinnamon

⅛ teaspoon salt

1 large egg

2 large egg whites, beaten

¼ cup trans-free margarine, melted

2 teaspoons pure vanilla extract

¼ cup very finely chopped bittersweet chocolate

GLAZE

½ cup confectioners' sugar

1 to 2 teaspoons fat-free milk

To prepare the biscotti: Preheat the oven to 350°F. Coat a large baking sheet with cooking spray.

In a mixing bowl, combine the flour, sugar, cocoa, baking powder, cinnamon, and salt. Stir to mix.

In another bowl, combine the egg, egg whites, margarine, and vanilla extract. Beat with a fork until well blended. Add to the reserved dry ingredients. Stir until well blended. Stir in the chocolate. Coat hands lightly with cooking spray. Shape the dough into a 12" log. Place on the baking sheet and pat to flatten slightly.

Bake for 25 minutes. Remove the cookie log from the oven and let stand for about 15 minutes, or until cool enough to move. With a serrated knife, cut into ½" thick slices. Place cut sides down on the baking sheet.

Bake for about 20 minutes more, or until crisp. Remove cookies to a rack and cool completely.

To prepare the glaze: In a small bowl, mix the confectioners' sugar and milk until smooth. Drizzle each biscotti with glaze.

Makes 9 servings (2 biscotti each)

Per serving: *230 calories, 2 g protein, 40 g carbohydrate, 6.5 g fat, 24 mg cholesterol, 122 mg sodium, 2 g fiber*

Diet Exchanges: *0 milk, 0 vegetable, 0 fruit, 2 bread, 0 meat, ½ fat*

2½ Carb Choices

163 Calories

Chocolate Cupcakes with Butterscotch Frosting

—Bonnie Boyd, Oak Park, Illinois

These little cakes are so low in fat and calories that they're cause for celebration.

Prep time: 20 minutes
Bake time: 18 to 22 minutes
Cool time: 15 minutes

CUPCAKES

1 box (18¼ ounces) devil's food reduced-sugar cake mix

FROSTING

1⅓ cups fat-free milk

1 package (3.4 ounces; 4 servings) sugar-free instant butterscotch pudding mix

2 packages (1.3 ounces each) whipped topping mix

TOPPING

2 tablespoons finely ground walnuts

2 tablespoons brown sugar

Pinch of ground cinnamon

Pinch of ground nutmeg

To prepare the cupcakes: Preheat the oven to 350°F. Coat two 12-cup muffin pans with cooking spray. Set aside.

Prepare the cake mix according to the package directions. Scoop the batter into the muffin pans.

Bake for 18 to 22 minutes, or until the cake springs back when gently pressed. Cool in the pan on a rack for 10 minutes. Remove to a rack to cool completely.

To prepare the frosting: Meanwhile, in the bowl of an electric mixer, stir together the milk, pudding mix, and topping mix. Beat on low speed until moistened. Increase the speed to high. Beat for 2 to 3 minutes, or until peaks form. Refrigerate for 5 minutes.

Spread the frosting on the cooled cupcakes.

To prepare the topping: In a small bowl, stir together the nuts, sugar, cinnamon, and nutmeg. Sprinkle on the cupcakes.

Makes 24 servings

Per serving: *163 calories, 2 g protein, 23 g carbohydrate, 7 g fat, 27 mg cholesterol, 238 mg sodium, 1 g fiber*

Diet Exchanges: *0 milk, 0 vegetable, 0 fruit, 0 bread, 0 meat, 1 fat*

1½ Carb Choices

Kitchen Tip

The batter can be baked in a 13" × 9" baking pan instead of muffin pans. Bake for 31 to 35 minutes.

199 Calories

Sheila's Raisin-Orange Spice Cake

—Lorraine Bromley, Portugal Cove, Newfoundland, Canada

Natural sweetness and fiber from dried fruits and whole wheat flour make this snack cake irresistible. Incredibly, no sugar is needed in the batter.

Prep time: 10 minutes
Cook time: 5 minutes
Cool time: 10 minutes
Bake time: 30 minutes

2 cups water
1 cup raisins
1 cup chopped dates
¾ cup canola oil
　Juice and grated peel of 1 navel orange
2 teaspoons orange or pure vanilla extract
2 cups whole wheat pastry flour
2 teaspoons ground cinnamon
1 teaspoon ground nutmeg
1 teaspoon baking powder
1 teaspoon baking soda
½ teaspoon salt
　Confectioners' sugar (optional)

In a saucepan, combine the water, raisins, and dates. Bring to a boil over high heat. Reduce the heat and simmer for 5 minutes. Remove from the heat and stir in the oil, orange juice and peel, and orange or vanilla extract. Let the mixture cool for about 10 minutes.

Preheat the oven to 350°F. Coat an 8" × 8" cake pan with cooking spray.

In a bowl, stir together the flour, cinnamon, nutmeg, baking powder, baking soda, and salt. Stir to mix.

Add the flour mixture to the reserved raisin mixture. Stir just until the batter is blended. Spoon into the prepared pan. Smooth the top evenly.

Bake for 30 minutes, or until a wooden toothpick inserted in the center comes out clean. Remove to a rack to cool completely. Dust with confectioners' sugar, if desired, before serving.

Makes 16 servings

Per serving: *199 calories, 2 g protein, 25 g carbohydrate, 11 g fat, 0 mg cholesterol, 181 mg sodium, 3 g fiber*

Diet Exchanges: *0 milk, 0 vegetable, 1 fruit, ½ bread, 0 meat, 2 fat*

2 Carb Choices

301 Calories

Raspberry Cheese Pie

—Anita Durst, Jacksonville, Florida

"When dieting, this dessert satisfies that haunting craving for something sweet and at the same time has calmed that constant yearning for a dessert consistency that completely satisfies my palate."

Prep time: 10 minutes
Chill time: 2 hours

P I E

2 packages (8 ounces each) fat-free cream cheese (softened)

½ cup sugar or Splenda

1 package (1.1 ounces; 4 servings) sugar-free cheesecake pudding mix

½ teaspoon raspberry or lemon extract

1 container (8 ounces) frozen fat-free nondairy whipped topping, thawed

1 reduced-fat graham cracker pie crust (9" diameter)

S A U C E

1 tablespoon cornstarch

¼ cup water

1 package (16 ounces) frozen loose-pack raspberries, thawed

1 teaspoon almond extract

To prepare the pie: In the bowl of an electric mixer, combine the cream cheese and the sugar or Splenda on medium speed for 2 minutes, or until well blended. Gradually add the pudding mix, beating after each addition. Add the raspberry or lemon extract. Beat briefly to blend. By hand, fold in the whipped topping. Spoon the mixture into the crust. Cover and refrigerate for about 2 hours, or until firm.

To prepare the sauce: Meanwhile, in a saucepan, whisk the cornstarch and water until smooth. Add the raspberries. Cook, stirring constantly, over medium-high heat for about 4 minutes, or until bubbling and thickened. Remove from the heat and stir in the extract. With the back of a large spoon, press through a fine sieve to remove the seeds. Let stand until cool. Cover and refrigerate until serving time.

Cut the pie into wedges. Spoon 1 tablespoon of sauce over each piece.

Makes 8 servings

Per serving: *301 calories, 10 g protein, 53 g carbohydrate, 3.5 g fat, 10 mg cholesterol, 532 mg sodium, 2 g fiber*

Diet Exchanges: *0 milk, 0 vegetable, ½ fruit, 1 bread, 1 meat, 0 fat*

3½ Carb Choices

210
Calories

Secret-Weapon Chocolate Brownies

—Tracy Hunold, Lincoln, California

These moist bars are much lower in fat and calories than traditional brownies, but no one will know if you don't tell!

Prep time: 5 minutes
Baking time: 25 to 30 minutes
Cool time: 1 hour

1 box (21 ounces) brownie mix
1 cup canned pumpkin
2 large eggs, beaten
¼ cup canola oil
   Cocoa powder or confectioners' sugar
   (optional)

Preheat the oven to 350°F. Coat an 8" × 8" baking pan with cooking spray.

In a mixing bowl, combine the brownie mix, pumpkin, eggs, and oil. Stir until completely mixed. Pour into the prepared pan.

Bake for 25 to 30 minutes, or until a wooden pick inserted in the center comes out clean. Cool in a pan on a rack for 1 hour. Cut into bars. Dust lightly with cocoa powder or confectioners' sugar, if desired.

Makes 16 servings

Per serving: *210 calories, 2 g protein, 30 g carbohydrate, 10 g fat, 26 mg cholesterol, 125 mg sodium, 2 g fiber*

Diet Exchanges: *0 milk, 0 vegetable, 0 fruit, 2 bread, 0 meat, 1½ fat*

2 Carb Choices

180 Calories

Juicy Apple Pie

—Lisa Mishaga, South Euclid, Ohio

*Using apple juice concentrate not only cuts the need for added sugar,
it intensifies the fruit flavor of this fabulous pie.*

Prep time: 20 minutes
Bake time: 30 to 35 minutes
Cool time: several hours

⅓ cup frozen apple juice concentrate, thawed

2 tablespoons cornstarch

2 tablespoons water

1 tablespoon trans-free margarine

1 teaspoon ground cinnamon

Pinch of salt (optional)

5–6 large Red Delicious apples, peeled and sliced thin

1 frozen pie crust (9" diameter)

¼ cup crushed gingersnaps (about 4 cookies)

Preheat the oven to 375°F.

In a large saucepan, combine 2 tablespoons of the concentrate with the cornstarch and water. Whisk until smooth. Gradually add the remaining concentrate, whisking constantly until blended. Cook over medium heat, stirring constantly, for 2 to 3 minutes, or until thickened. Remove from the heat. Stir in the margarine, cinnamon, and salt, if using. Add the apples. Toss gently to coat. Spread the mixture into the crust. Sprinkle with the crushed gingersnaps.

Bake for 30 to 35 minutes, or until the filling is bubbling. Transfer to a rack until cool after several hours.

Makes 8 servings

Per serving: *180 calories, 1 g protein, 30 g carbohydrate, 7 g fat, 0 mg cholesterol, 106 mg sodium, 1 g fiber*

Diet Exchanges: *0 milk, 0 vegetable, 1 fruit, 1 bread, 0 meat, 1 fat*

2 Carb Choices

188 Calories

Pear-Cranberry Crisp

—Judi Burnison, Michigan City, Indiana

For additional fiber, you can scrub the pears very well but leave the peel on.

Prep time: 15 minutes
Bake time: 40 minutes

- 4 ripe pears, sliced
- ¼ cup brown sugar
- ⅛ teaspoon ground cinnamon
  Pinch of ground allspice
- ¾ cup rolled oats
- 1 tablespoon cold butter or trans-free margarine, cut into small pieces
- ¼ cup dried cranberries
- 2 tablespoons chopped walnuts

Preheat the oven to 350°F. Coat an 8" × 8" baking dish with cooking spray.

Spread the pear slices over the bottom of the dish. In a small bowl, stir together the sugar, cinnamon, and allspice. Sprinkle the mixture over the pear. In a small bowl, combine the oats and butter or margarine. With a fork, cut the butter or margarine into very fine pieces. Add the cranberries and walnuts. Toss to mix. Sprinkle evenly over the pears.

Bake for about 40 minutes, or until bubbling.

Makes 6 servings

Per serving: *188 calories, 3 g protein, 37 g carbohydrate, 4 g fat, 5 mg cholesterol, 180 mg sodium, 5 g fiber*

Diet Exchanges: *0 milk, 0 vegetable, 1½ fruit, 1 bread, 0 meat, 1 fat*

3½ Carb Choices

165 Calories

Chocolate PB Pie

—Tracy Thompson, West Blocton, Alabama

"I love my chocolate and wanted to find ways that I can cheat, so to speak, and not really be falling off the wagon. This recipe is great."

Prep time: 10 minutes
Chilling time: 2 hours

 2 **cups 1% milk**
 1 **box (1.4 ounces; 4 servings) sugar-free chocolate fudge pudding mix**
 2 **tablespoons reduced-fat peanut butter**
 1 **ready-made sugar-free graham cracker piecrust**
   Fat-free aerosol whipped cream
 1 **tablespoon finely chopped roasted peanuts**

In a large bowl, combine the milk and pudding mix. Beat on low speed with an electric mixer until smooth. In a microwaveable bowl, heat the peanut butter on medium for about 30 seconds or until soft. Spread on the bottom of the piecrust. Top with the pudding. Refrigerate for 2 hours, or until set.

   Top each slice with 1 tablespoon whipped cream and sprinkle with the peanuts.

Makes 8 servings

Per serving: *165 calories, 4 g protein, 18 g carbohydrate, 8.5 g fat, 4 mg cholesterol, 115 mg sodium, 0 g fiber*

Diet Exchanges: *½ milk, 0 vegetable, 0 fruit, ½ bread, 0 meat, ½ fat*

1 Carb Choice

SHOPPING SAVVY

The Right Slice

FIFTY 50 Foods, which contributes half of its profits to diabetes research, has added ready-to-use Sugar Free Graham Cracker Pie Crust to its line of reduced-calorie, sugar-free, and whole grain food products. The low-glycemic crumb crust contains NutraSweet and can be used in place of regular graham cracker crusts in any recipe that calls for a crumb crust. Try filling the shell with fresh fruit or drained canned-in-juice fruit folded into sugar-free pudding or sugar-free ice cream. One serving of crust contains 110 calories and 6 grams of fat. Company cofounder and president Gary Russell has had type 1 diabetes for over 30 years. Vice president Pat Gawdun, RD, is past chairman of the New Jersey Affiliate of the American Diabetes Association. To date, contributions to diabetes research have exceeded $10 million. Look for Fifty 50 Foods products in supermarkets, or visit the Web site at www.fifty50foods.com.

360
Calories

Milk Chocolate Pie

—Pam Freeburn, Punta Gorda, Florida

"This is a reduced-fat and reduced-calorie dessert that is rich and delicious!"

Prep time: 15 minutes
Cook time: 5 to 7 minutes
Chill time: 1 to 2 hours

   3 cups cold fat-free milk
   ¾ cup unsweetened cocoa powder
   ⅔ cup sugar or Splenda
   ¼ cup + 2 tablespoons cornstarch
   ⅛ teaspoon salt
   2 large eggs, beaten
   1 cup milk chocolate chips
   2 teaspoons pure vanilla extract
   1 ready-made piecrust (9" diameter),
      baked and cooled
      Nondairy light whipped topping

Heat 1½ cups of the milk in a heavy sauce-pan over medium heat. Meanwhile, in a mixing bowl, whisk together the cocoa, sugar or Splenda, cornstarch, and salt. While whisking, gradually add the remaining 1½ cups of cold milk and the eggs. Mix until smooth. When the milk in the saucepan is warm, add to the cocoa mixture. Whisk to combine. Pour the mixture into the saucepan. Cook over medium heat, stirring constantly, for 5 to 7 minutes, or until thickened. Remove from the heat.

Add the chocolate chips. Stir until the chocolate melts. Add the vanilla extract and mix. Pour into the piecrust. Cover and refrigerate for 1 to 2 hours, or until set.

Serve garnished with a dollop of topping.

Makes 8 servings

Per serving: *360 calories, 9 g protein, 54 g carbohydrate, 13 g fat, 60 mg cholesterol, 181 mg sodium, 3 g fiber*

Diet Exchanges: *½ milk, 0 vegetable, 0 fruit, 2 bread, 0 meat, 1½ fat*

3½ Carb Choices

Apple Pie Pita

—Lisa Boyd, Greenwood, Arizona

"It's extremely low-fat, and it really satisfies my craving for a sweet comfort food."

Prep time: 6 minutes
Microwave time: 3 to 4 minutes

  1 **apple, sliced**
  1 **teaspoon finely chopped pecans**
  1 **teaspoon brown sugar or Splenda**
 ¼ **teaspoon ground cinnamon**
    Pinch of ground nutmeg
 ½ **small pita bread**
  2 **tablespoons light whipped cream**

Place the apple slices on a microwaveable plate. Coat lightly with butter-flavored cooking spray. Sprinkle on the pecans, sugar or Splenda, cinnamon, and nutmeg. Microwave on high power for about 3 to 4 minutes, tossing occasionally, or until soft.

Toast the pita. Spoon the apple mixture onto the pita and top with a dollop of the whipped cream.

Makes 1 serving

Per serving: *212 calories, 3 g protein, 42 g carbohydrate, 5 g fat, 0 mg cholesterol, 152 mg sodium, 6 g fiber*

Diet Exchanges: *0 milk, 0 vegetable, 1 fruit, 1 bread, 0 meat, ½ fat*

3 Carb Choices

212 Calories

218 Calories

Chocolate Truffle Tartlets

—Joyce Tenerowicz, West Brookfield, Massachusetts

"It satisfies chocolate cravings in a huge way. It seems rich and indulgent, but it's healthier than any restaurant dessert."

Prep time: 20 minutes
Chill time: 2 hours
Bake time: 5 to 7 minutes

- 1 **cup semisweet or bittersweet chocolate chips**
- 1 **package (10½ ounces) light silken tofu, drained**
- 1 **teaspoon orange extract**
- 4 **sheets frozen phyllo dough (14" × 8"), thawed**
  Reduced-fat aerosol whipped cream
  Orange peel curls (optional)

Place the chocolate chips in a microwaveable bowl. Microwave on high power for 90 seconds, or until the chips start to lose their shape. Stir to melt completely. If necessary, microwave for 30 more seconds.

Place the tofu in a food processor fitted with a metal blade or a blender. Process until smooth. Add the chocolate and orange extract. Process until smooth. Cover and chill for at least 2 hours, or until set.

Meanwhile, preheat the oven to 375°F.

Set six 3½"-wide fluted removeable-bottom tart pans on a baking sheet. Coat the pans with butter-flavored cooking spray.

Lay 1 phyllo sheet on a work surface. Coat lightly with cooking spray. Cut into 6 rectangles (approximately 3½" × 4" each). One at a time, lay each rectangle into one of the tart pans, so part of it covers the bottom and the other part forms a pointed side. Place the next rectangle to the right of the first. Continue rotating the rectangles until a tart shell is formed. Continue with the remaining 5 sheets of phyllo to make 5 more shells. Coat the shells lightly with spray.

Bake for 5 to 7 minutes, or until golden and crisp. Transfer to a rack to cool.

To serve, remove the shells from the pans and place on plates. Spoon the chocolate truffle mixture into the tart shells. Just before serving, top with whipped cream and garnish with orange curls, if desired.

Makes 6 servings

Per serving: *218 calories, 6 g protein, 28 g carbohydrate, 10.5 g fat, 0 mg cholesterol, 118 mg sodium, 1 g fiber*

Diet Exchanges: *0 milk, 0 vegetable, 0 fruit, 2 bread, ½ meat, 1 fat*

2 Carb Choices

Kitchen Tip

Both the truffle filling and the tart shells may be prepared 24 hours in advance of serving. Refrigerate the filling. Store the shells in an airtight container.

Pure vanilla extract may be used instead of the orange extract, if desired.

The shells may be baked in a muffin pan, if desired.

Warm Dried-Plum Snack Cake

—Joy Austin, St. Petersburg, Florida

If you can afford the extra calories, ¼ cup chopped walnuts is a healthy-fat addition to the batter.

Prep time: 15 minutes
Bake time: 25 to 30 minutes
Cool time: 10 minutes

1 cup all-purpose flour
1 teaspoon baking powder
½ teaspoon baking soda
½ teaspoon ground cinnamon
   Pinch of salt
½ cup fat-free plain yogurt
¼ cup canola oil
2 large eggs
½ cup brown sugar
1 teaspoon lemon extract
½ cup dried plums, finely chopped
   Confectioners' sugar

Preheat the oven to 350°F. Coat a 9" round cake pan with cooking spray. Set aside.

In a large bowl, combine the flour, baking powder, baking soda, cinnamon, and salt. In a large bowl, beat the yogurt, oil, and eggs with a fork until blended. Add the sugar and lemon extract. Beat until smooth. Stir in the dry ingredients until just blended. Add the dried plums and stir to mix. Pour the batter into the prepared pan.

Bake 25 to 30 minutes, or until browned and the cake springs back when lightly pressed. Let cool on a rack for about 10 minutes. Dust lightly with confectioners' sugar. Serve warm.

Makes 8 servings

Per serving: 213 calories, 4 g protein, 31 g carbohydrate, 8.5 g fat, 53 mg cholesterol, 179 mg sodium, 1 g fiber

Diet Exchanges: *0 milk, 0 vegetable, ½ fruit, 1½ bread, 0 meat, 1½ fat*

2 Carb Choices

Kitchen Tip

To keep the dried plum pieces from sticking together during chopping, sprinkle them with 1 tablespoon of flour from the recipe. If desired, use dried plums with lemon essence.

214 Calories

Pineapple Marshmallow Pie

—Miryam Travis, Brooklyn, New York

"This pie helped me to calm that craving by having a little piece each day."

Prep time: 5 minutes
Freeze time: 4 hours

1 **can (20 ounces) crushed pineapple packed in juice, drained**
1 **cup marshmallow fluff**
1 **cup sugar-free nondairy whipped topping, thawed**
2 **tablespoons nondairy creamer or milk**
1 **reduced-fat graham cracker piecrust (9" diameter)**
2 **tablespoons finely chopped pecans (optional)**

In a mixing bowl, combine the pineapple, marshmallow, whipped topping, and non-dairy creamer or milk. Stir to mix. Spread the mixture into the piecrust. Sprinkle with the pecans, if desired. Cover and place in the freezer for 4 hours, or until frozen.

Makes 8 servings

Per serving: *214 calories, 1 g protein, 41 g carbohydrate, 4 g fat, 0 mg cholesterol, 100 mg sodium, 1 g fiber*

Diet Exchanges: *0 milk, 0 vegetable, ½ fruit, ½ bread, 0 meat, 0 fat*

3 Carb Choices

275 Calories

Chocolate Dream Pie

—Carla Richard, Port Barre, Louisiana

"It makes me feel like I'm indulging in something really rich and tasty, but it's not high in calories. My whole family likes it."

Prep time: 10 minutes
Bake time: 12 minutes
Cool time: 15 minutes
Chill time: 2 hours

1 cup flour
¼ cup butter or trans-free margarine, melted
8 ounces reduced-fat cream cheese, softened
¾ cup confectioners' sugar
2 packages (1.4 ounces each; 4 servings) sugar-free instant chocolate pudding mix
1 cup 2% milk
1 container (8 ounces) frozen nondairy whipped topping, thawed

Preheat the oven to 350°F.

In a 9" glass pie dish, combine the flour and butter or margarine with a fork until crumbs hold together. Pat out into a crust. Bake for 12 minutes, or until lightly browned. Cool on a rack.

Meanwhile, in a mixing bowl, combine the cream cheese and confectioners' sugar. Beat until smooth. Spread evenly on the reserved crust.

In the same bowl, combine the pudding mix and milk. Beat until smooth. Spread over the cream cheese. Spread the topping on the cream cheese mixture.

Refrigerate for 2 hours, or until set.

Makes 8 servings

Per serving: *275 calories, 5 g protein, 36 g carbohydrate, 11 g fat, 31 mg cholesterol, 205 mg sodium, 2 g fiber*

Diet Exchanges: *0 milk, 0 vegetable, 0 fruit, 1½ bread, ½ meat, 2 fat*

2½ Carb Choices

Lemon Pie

—Frances Perry, Jupiter, Florida

*Vibrantly flavored citrus juices are fabulous weight-loss foods
because they contain virtually no calories.*

**Prep time: 5 minutes
Chill time: 1 hour**

1 can (14 ounces) fat-free sweetened
condensed milk

½ cup lemon juice (2 to 3 large lemons),
preferably freshly squeezed

2 teaspoons grated lemon peel

1 container (8 ounces) frozen nondairy
whipped topping, thawed

1 sugar-free graham cracker piecrust
(9" in diameter)

Lemon peel, mint leaves, fresh
raspberries (optional)

In the bowl of an electric mixer, combine the
milk, lemon juice, and lemon peel. Beat on
high speed for 1 minute, or until thickened.
Add the whipped topping. Mix on low speed
until just combined. Mound the mixture into
the piecrust.

Refrigerate for 1 hour, or until set. Cut
into wedges. Garnish with lemon curls, mint
leaves, or raspberries, if desired.

Makes 8 servings

Per serving: *334 calories, 5 g protein, 51 g
carbohydrate, 11 g fat, 6 mg cholesterol, 116 mg
sodium, 0 g fiber*

Diet Exchanges: *0 milk, 0 vegetable, 0 fruit,
2 bread, 0 meat, 0 fat*

3½ Carb Choices

Kitchen Tip

Sugar-free graham cracker piecrusts are available
in some supermarkets. If unavailable, replace with
a regular crust and factor in the extra calories. You
can also make the pie filling as a dessert by itself.

Banana Loaf

—Beckey Langille, Truro, Nova Scotia, Canada

This recipe is moist and full of fiber. It makes a popular family dessert or sweet teatime snack topped with a teaspoon of softened reduced-fat cream cheese.

Prep time: 10 minutes
Bake time: 50 minutes
Cool time: several hours

1½ **cups whole wheat pastry flour**
1½ **teaspoons baking powder**
½ **teaspoon baking soda**
 Pinch of salt
½ **cup sugar**
¼ **cup ground flaxseed**
2 **large eggs, beaten**
1½ **cups mashed ripe bananas**
 (2 to 3 bananas)
¼ **cup canola oil**
¼ **cup fat-free milk**
¾ **teaspoon pure vanilla extract**

Preheat the oven to 350°F. Coat a 9" × 5" × 3" loaf pan with cooking spray.

In a bowl, combine the flour, baking powder, baking soda, and salt. Stir with a fork to mix.

In another bowl, combine the sugar, flaxseed, and eggs. Stir to mix. Add the bananas, oil, milk, and vanilla extract. Stir to mix. Add the flour mixture. Stir just until all the flour mixture is absorbed. Pour the batter into the prepared pan.

Bake for about 50 minutes, or until a wooden pick inserted in the center of the loaf comes out clean. Transfer to a rack to cool for 10 minutes. Remove from the pan and cool completely.

Makes 12 servings (½" slice per serving)

Per serving: 182 calories, 4 g protein, 27 g carbohydrate, 7 g fat, 35 mg cholesterol, 129 mg sodium, 3 g fiber

Diet Exchanges: *0 milk, 0 vegetable, ½ fruit, ½ bread, 0 meat, 1 fat*

2 Carb Choices

— *Kitchen Tip* —

Overly ripe bananas make the sweetest bread and can be frozen for later use when you have them on hand. Freeze bananas by placing the banana into a resealable plastic storage bag and mashing the bag gently with the palm of your hand to flatten the fruit. Expel the air before sealing. Place in the freezer for up to 3 months. To use, gently break apart the frozen banana by manipulating the unopened bag. Remove the amount you need, reseal, and refreeze.

Menus for
Special Times

Watching your weight does not mean the end of enjoying yourself with special-occasion meals. The key to success is a bit of advance planning. Whether you're having a family supper or a casual party for friends, turn to the following menus made up of delectable *Eat Up Slim Down Annual Recipes 2008* dishes. Whether it's a Springtime Dinner, a Tuscan Grill, or Time to Tailgate, no one but you will guess that you're watching your calories and portions. They'll be too busy asking you to share the recipes.

Try these menus as they are, or pick and choose dishes from several different menus to create a whole new meal. Each menu includes a one-serving nutritional analysis, and sometimes recommended nonrecipe sides, so you can easily factor them into your daily eating plan. The portion size for all the recipes listed is one serving.

So, what are you waiting for? Let's get this party started.

Springtime Dinner

Roasted Orange Tilapia and
Asparagus, page 173

Tasty & Colorful Quinoa, page 150

Raspberry Cheese Pie, page 261

Per serving: 733 calories, 42 g
protein, 95 g carbohydrate, 19 g fat,
67 mg cholesterol, 1,425 mg sodium,
8 g fiber

Diet Exchanges: 0 milk, 1½ vegetable,
0 fruit, 3½ bread, 4½ meat, 2 fat

6 Carb Choices

Weekend Breakfast

Orange-pineapple juice

Apple Pancakes, page 224

Turkey breakfast sausage

Coffee, tea, or hot chocolate

Per serving: 404 calories, 18 g
protein, 56 g carbohydrate, 12 g fat,
46 mg cholesterol, 916 mg sodium,
2 g fiber

Diet Exchanges: ½ milk, 0 vegetable,
0 fruit, 3½ bread, 2 meat, 1 fat

4 Carb Choices

Friday Night Pizza

Guilt-Free Alfredo Pizza, page 132

Citrus-Avocado Salad, page 58

Apple Paradisio, page 60

> **Per serving:** 580 calories, 23 g protein, 59 g carbohydrate, 31 g fat, 40 mg cholesterol, 907 mg sodium, 13 g fiber
>
> **Diet Exchanges:** 0 milk, 1 vegetable, 2 fruit, ½ bread, 2 meat, 4½ fat
>
> **4 Carb Choices**

Chilling by the Pool

Strawberry Mock Daiquiri, page 248

Skinny Crab Dip, page 104

Vegetable Fajitas, page 167

Pineapple Fluff, page 253

> **Per serving:** 54 calories, 18 g protein, 69 g carbohydrate, 19 g fat, 45 mg cholesterol, 778 mg sodium, 11 g fiber
>
> **Diet Exchanges:** 0 milk, 2 vegetable, 2 fruit, 0 bread, 0 meat, 3 fat
>
> **5 Carb Choices**

A Tuscan Grill

Pork Kebabs Italiano, page 215

Gianna's Grilled Stuffed Eggplant, page 138

Double Dark Chocolate Biscotti, page 256, with ½ cup lemon sorbet

Per serving: 719 calories, 30 g protein, 101 g carbohydrate, 24 g fat, 72 mg cholesterol, 1,283 mg sodium, 12 g fiber

Diet Exchanges: 0 milk, 5 vegetable, 0 fruit, 4 bread, 3 meat, 4 fat

7 Carb Choices

Neptune's Bounty

Orange Coconut Shrimp, page 170

Grilled Mixed Vegetables, page 136

Lemon Pie, page 276

Per serving: 773 calories, 29 g protein, 84 g carbohydrate, 34 g fat, 157 mg cholesterol, 669 mg sodium, 5 g fiber

Diet Exchanges: 0 milk, 2 vegetable, 0 fruit, 3 bread, 3 meat, 4 fat

6 Carb Choices

Salad Daze

Black-Eyed Pea Salad, page 68

Ted's Fresh Mozzarella Salad, page 70

Chicken Caesar Salad, page 79

Pineapple-and-Strawberry Soy Shake, page 239 (partially frozen, half serving for dessert)

Per serving: 590 calories, 31 g protein, 37 g carbohydrate, 35 g fat, 71 mg cholesterol, 921 mg sodium, 7 g fiber

Diet Exchanges: 0 milk, 2 vegetable, ½ fruit, 1½ bread, 1½ meat, 3½ fat

2½ Carb Choices

Time to Tailgate

Chicken, Corn, & Tomatillo Chili, page 190

Crusty multigrain bread

Pear-Cranberry Crisp, page 265

Per serving: 448 calories, 22 g protein, 75 g carbohydrate, 8½ g fat, 30 mg cholesterol, 715 mg sodium, 11 g fiber

Diet Exchanges: 0 milk, 1 vegetable, 1½ fruit, 3 bread, 1½ meat, 1 fat

5 Carb Choices

Southern-Style Supper

Pork Chops and Sweet Potatoes, page 218

Kale with Pumpkin Seeds, page 146

Chocolate PB Pie, page 266

Per serving: 527 calories, 27 g protein, 53 g carbohydrate, 25 g fat, 48 mg cholesterol, 955 mg sodium, 6 g fiber

Diet Exchanges: 0 milk, 3 vegetable, 0 fruit, 1 bread, 3 meat, 2 fat

4 Carb Choices

Souper Buffet

Cream of Broccoli Soup, page 82

Manhattan Clam Chowder, page 91

Gianna's Lentil Soup, page 84

Multigrain bread

Swedish Nuts, page 97

Per serving: 780 calories, 48 g protein, 83 g carbohydrate, 30 g fat, 47 mg cholesterol, 2,325 mg sodium, 23 g fiber

Diet Exchanges: ½ milk, 4 vegetable, 0 fruit, 2 bread, 3½ meat, 5 fat

5½ Carb Choices

Holiday Open House

Pomegranate Salsa, page 102, with Belgian endive

Glazed Ham with Mandarin Oranges, page 212

Broccoli Salad, page 63

Gianna's Garlic Lemon Potatoes, page 148

Eggnog Pudding, page 254, topped with 1 teaspoon cherry jam

Per serving: 432 calories, 28 g protein, 62 g carbohydrate, 7 g fat, 37 mg cholesterol, 2,327 mg sodium, 5 g fiber

Diet Exchanges: ½ milk, 1 vegetable, ½ fruit, 1½ bread, 3 meat, 1 fat

4 Carb Choices

Pacific Rim Repast

Easy Chinese Vegetable Soup, page 85

Black-Bean Vegetable Noodle Stir-Fry, page 156

Easy Tropical Fruit Salad, page 56

Per serving: 271 calories, 10 g protein, 45 g carbohydrate, 8 g fat, 1 mg cholesterol, 1,334 mg sodium, 10 g fiber

Diet Exchanges: 0 milk, 3 vegetable, 0 fruit, 1 bread, 1 meat, 1½ fat

3 Carb Choices

Come In from the Cold

Chicken, Corn, & Tomatillo Chili, page 190

Whole wheat tortilla

Simple Slaw, page 61

Juicy Apple Pie, page 263

Per serving: 502 calories, 19 g protein, 72 g carbohydrate, 16 g fat, 25 mg cholesterol, 968 mg sodium, 10 g fiber

Diet Exchanges: 0 milk, 2 vegetable, 1 fruit, 2½ bread, 1½ meat, 2 fat

5 Carb Choices

Hungarian Rhapsody

Goodness Goulash, page 207

Green Beans with Dill, page 141

Warm Dried-Plum Snack Cake, page 273, with ½ cup reduced-fat vanilla ice cream

Per serving: 695 calories, 43 g protein, 65 g carbohydrate, 29 g fat, 124 mg cholesterol, 747 mg sodium, 8 g fiber

Diet Exchanges: 0 milk, 2 vegetable, 0 fruit, 3 bread, 5 meat, 5 fat

4 Carb Choices

Happy Birthday to You

Cajun Chicken Fingers with Cool Cuke Dip, page 107

Bow Tie Pasta with Spinach, Tomato, and Olives, page 159

Chocolate Cupcakes with Butterscotch Frosting, page 258

Per serving: 710 calories, 43 g protein, 95 g carbohydrate, 19 g fat, 93 mg cholesterol, 1,082 mg sodium, 5 g fiber

Diet Exchanges: 0 milk, 1 vegetable, 0 fruit, 4½ bread, 3 meat, 3 fat

6 Carb Choices

Brunch Is Served

Omelet Italian-Style, page 229

Mixed Fruit Parfait, page 232

Banana Loaf, page 279, with reduced-fat cream cheese

Per serving: 518 calories, 25 g protein, 54 g carbohydrate, 24 g fat, 254 mg cholesterol, 406 mg sodium, 7 g fiber

Diet Exchanges: ½ milk, ½ vegetable, 1½ fruit, 1 bread, 3 meat, 4 fat

4 Carb Choices

CALORIE AND NUTRIENTS CHART OF COMMON FOODS

BEANS AND LEGUMES

Food Item	Serving Size	Calories	Protein (g)	Carb (g)
Baked beans	⅓ c	126	5	18
Baked beans, vegetarian	⅓ c	79	4	18
Bean sprouts (mung beans)	½ c	13	1	3
Black beans, cooked with salt	½ c	114	8	20
Black beans, dry	¼ c	165	10	30
Black-eyed peas (cowpeas), cooked with salt	½ c	99	6.6	18
Black-eyed peas, fresh	¼ c	33	1	7
Butter beans (lima), canned	½ c	95	6	18
Butter beans (lima), cooked with salt	½ c	105	6	20
Butter beans (lima), cooked without salt	½ c	105	6	20
Butter beans (lima), raw	½ c	88	5	16
Cannellini beans, cooked without salt	½ c	100	6	17
Cannellini beans, dry	¼ c	153	11	28
Chickpeas (garbanzo beans), cooked with salt	½ c	134	7	22
Chickpeas (garbanzo beans), cooked without salt	½ c	134	7	22
Edamame (immature green soybeans), frozen, prepared	½ c	95	8	8
Edamame, out of shell, cooked without salt	½ c	100	10	9
Falafel, cooked	2.25 in patty	57	2	5
Falafel, dry	¼ c	120	7	21
French beans, cooked with salt	½ c	114	6	21
French beans, cooked without salt	½ c	114	6	21

Fiber (g)	Sugar (g)	Fat (g)	Sat Fat (g)	Sodium (mg)
5	0	4	2	352
3	7	1	0	288
1	2	0	0	6
8	0	1	0	204
7	1	0	0	2
6	3	½	0	205
2	1	0	0	1
6	1	0	0	405
5	1	0	0	215
5	1	0	0	14
4	1	1	0	6
5	1	1	0	40
11	1	0	0	11
6	4	2	0	199
6	4	2	0	6
4	2	4	0	5
1	2	2.5	0	70
0	0	3	0	50
6	3	2	0	370
8	0	1	0	214
8	0	1	0	5

Food Item	Serving Size	Calories	Protein (g)	Carb (g)
French beans, raw	3 oz	30	2	6
Hummus	⅛ c	54	1	6
Kidney beans, red, cooked with salt	½ c	112	8	20
Kidney beans, red, cooked without salt	½ c	112	8	20
Lentils, brown, cooked with salt	½ c	115	9	20
Lentils, brown, cooked without salt	½ c	115	9	20
Navy beans, cooked with salt	½ c	127	7	24
Navy beans, cooked without salt	½ c	127	7	24
Pinto beans, cooked with salt	½ c	122	8	22
Pinto beans, cooked without salt	½ c	122	8	22
Refried beans, canned	½ c	118	7	20
Refried beans, fat-free	½ c	130	6	18
Refried beans, vegetarian	½ c	100	6	17
Soybeans, cooked	½ c	148	14	8
Soybeans, dry-roasted, salted	¼ c	194	17	14
Soybeans, dry-roasted, unsalted	¼ c	194	17	14
Soybeans, green, boiled without salt	½ c	127	11	10
White beans, small, cooked with salt	½ c	127	8	23

BEVERAGES

Food Item	Serving Size	Calories	Protein (g)	Carb (g)
Alcohol				
Beer, lager	12 fl oz	172	17	1
Beer, light	12 fl oz	103	6	0
Beer, nonalcoholic, O'Doul's	12 fl oz	70	15	n/a
Bloody Mary	8 fl oz	50	8	1
Coffee and cream liqueur	1.5 fl oz	153	10	0
Gin and tonic cocktail	6 fl oz	117	6	0
Highball cocktail	6 fl oz	111	0	0
Long Island iced tea	6 fl oz	142	11	0

Fiber (g)	Sugar (g)	Fat (g)	Sat Fat (g)	Sodium (mg)
2	0	0	0	0
1	0	3	0	74
7	0	0	0	211
7	0	0	0	2
8	2	0	0	236
8	2	0	0	2
10	0	1	0	216
10	0	1	0	0
8	0	1	0	203
8	0	1	0	1
7	0	2	1	379
6	1	0	0	580
6	2	1	0	560
5	3	7	1	1
4	0	9	1	70
4	0	9	1	1
4	0	6	1	13
9	0	1	0	213

Fiber (g)	Sugar (g)	Fat (g)	Sat Fat (g)	Sodium (mg)
17	0	0	0	9
6	0	0	0	14
15	n/a	0	0	9
8	5	0	0	605
10	9	7	5	43
6	6	0	0	5
0	0	0	0	27
11	n/a	0	0	7

Food Item	Serving Size	Calories	Protein (g)	Carb (g)
Margarita	1.5 fl oz	94	6	0
Martini	1.5 fl oz	103	1	0
Piña colada	1.5 fl oz	82	11	0
Sangria	98	0	13	0
Screwdriver	6 fl oz	145	15	0
Wine cooler	5 fl oz	71	8	0
Wine, light	5 fl oz	74	2	0
Wine, red, Merlot	5 fl oz	123	4	0
Wine, white, Pinot Grigio	5 fl oz	123	3	n/a
Wine, white, Sauvignon Blanc	5 fl oz	121	3	n
Wine spritzer	5 fl oz	59	1	0
Coffee and Tea				
Cappuccino, with 1% milk	8 fl oz	73	7	0
Chai, Celestial Seasonings, original	8 fl oz	0	0	0
Coffee, brewed	8 fl oz	2	0	0
Coffee, decaf, brewed	8 fl oz	0	0	0
Coffee, iced latte, with 1% milk	8 fl oz	60	7	0
Coffee, instant	1 Tbsp	7	1	0
Coffee, instant, decaf	1 Tbsp	12	2	0
Coffee, instant, 50% less caffeine	1 Tbsp	9	2	0
Coffee, latte, with 1% milk	8 fl oz	60	7	0
Coffee, mocha, with 1% milk	8 fl oz	200	22	1
Espresso	4 fl oz	11	2	0
Tea, black, decaf	8 fl oz	0	0	0
Tea, black, iced, unsweetened	8 fl oz	0	0	0
Juice				
Apple juice, unsweetened, bottled or canned	4 fl oz	58	14	0
Apple juice, unsweetened, frozen, prepared	4 fl oz	56	14	0
Apple-cranberry juice	4 fl oz	77	19	0

Fiber (g)	Sugar (g)	Fat (g)	Sat Fat (g)	Sodium (mg)
6	6	0	0	2
1	0	0	0	1
0	11	1	1	3
0	n/a	0	0	10
0	15	0	0	2
0	n/a	0	0	12
0	2	0	0	10
0	1	0	0	6
n/a	n/a	0	0	n/a
n/a	n/a	0	0	n/a
0	n/a	0	0	19
0	7	2	2	73
0	0	0	0	0
0	0	0	0	5
0	0	0	0	5
0	6	2	1	67
0	0	0	0	1
0	0	0	0	1
0	0	0	0	1
0	6	2	1	67
0	19	10	6	107
0	2	0	0	17
0	0	0	0	0
0	0	0	0	0
0	14	0	0	4
0	13	0	0	8
0	18	0	0	2

Food Item	Serving Size	Calories	Protein (g)	Carb (g)
Cranberry juice, unsweetened	4 fl oz	58	15	0
Cranberry juice cocktail	4 fl oz	68	17	0
Cranberry juice cocktail, low-calorie	4 fl oz	22	5	0
Grape juice, unsweetened	4 fl oz	77	19	0
Grape juice drink	4 fl oz	71	18	0
Grapefruit juice, unsweetened, canned, white	4 fl oz	47	11	0
Grapefruit juice white, unsweetened, frozen, from concentrate, prepared	4 fl oz	50	12	0
Grapefruit juice, white, raw	4 fl oz	48	11	0
Lemon juice, raw	4 fl oz	30	10	0
Lime juice, raw	4 fl oz	31	10	0
Orange juice, raw	4 fl oz	56	13	0
Orange juice, frozen, from concentrate, unsweetened, prepared	4 fl oz	56	13	0
Tomato juice, canned	4 fl oz	20	5	1
Tomato juice, canned, unsalted	4 fl oz	21	5	0
Tomato-vegetable juice, low-sodium	4 fl oz	27	6	1
Vegetable juice, V8	4 fl oz	25	5	1
Vegetable juice, V8, Picante	4 fl oz	25	5	1
Vegetable juice, V8, Spicy Hot	4 fl oz	25	5	1
Milk and Nondairy				
Half-and-half, fat-free	1 fl oz	18	3	0
Milk, fat-free, with added nonmilk fat solids	1 c	91	12	0
Milk, low-fat 1 %	1 c	118	14	0
Milk, reduced-fat 2%	1 c	122	11	0
Milk, whole	1 c	146	11	0
Soy milk	1 c	127	12	3

Fiber (g)	Sugar (g)	Fat (g)	Sat Fat (g)	Sodium (mg)
0	15	0	0	3
0	15	0	0	3
0	5	0	0	4
0	19	0	0	4
0	18	0	0	11
0	11	0	0	1
0	12	0	0	1
0	11	0	0	1
0	3	0	0	1
0	2	0	0	2
0	10	0	0	1
0	10	0	0	1
1	4	0	0	323
0	4	0	0	12
1	5	0	0	85
1	4	0	0	240
1	4	0	0	295
1	4	0	0	355
0	1.5	.5	0	43
0	12	0	0	130
0	11	3	2	143
0	12	5	3	100
0	13	8	5	98
3	1	5	1	135

BREADS AND CRACKERS

Food Item	Serving Size	Calories	Protein (g)	Carb (g)
Bagel, cinnamon-raisin	1 oz	77	3	16
Bagel, egg	1 oz	79	3	15
Bagel, onion	1 oz	78	3	15
Bagel, plain	1 oz	78	3	15
Bagel, poppy seed	1 oz	78	3	15
Bagel, whole grain	1 oz	57	2	12
Biscuit, buttermilk or plain, prepared from recipe	½ of 2.5 in biscuit	106	2	13
Biscuit, plain or buttermilk, commercially baked	½ of 2.5 in biscuit	64	1	8
Bread, banana	½ slice (1 oz)	98	1	16
Bread, Ezekiel 4:9 Sprouted Grain	1 slice (34 g)	80	4	15
Bread, French	1 slice (1 oz)	82	3	16
Bread, pita, white	½ of 6.5 in pita (1 oz)	82	3	17
Bread, pita, whole wheat	½ of 6.5 in pita (1 oz)	85	3	18
Bread, pumpernickel	1 slice (1 oz)	71	2	13
Bread, raisin	1 slice (approx. 1 oz)	71	2	14
Bread, rye	1 slice (approx. 1 oz)	83	3	15
Bread, seven-grain	1 slice (approx. 1 oz)	65	3	12
Bread, white	1 slice (approx. 1 oz)	66	2	13
Bread, white, reduced-calorie	2 slices (2 oz)	95	4	20
Bread, wholegrain	1 slice (approx. 1 oz)	65	3	12
Bread, whole wheat	1 slice (approx. 1 oz)	69	4	12
Bread crumbs, dry	1 oz	112	4	20
Cornbread	1 oz	89	2	14

Fiber (g)	Sugar (g)	Fat (g)	Sat Fat (g)	Sodium (mg)
1	2	0	0	91
1	n/a	1	0	143
1	n/a	0	0	151
1	n/a	0	0	151
1	n/a	0	0	151
2	1	1	0	67
1	1	5	1	174
0	1	3	0	184
0	n/a	3	1	91
3	n/a	1	0	75
1	1	1	0	184
1	0	0	0	161
2	0	1	0	170
2	0	1	0	190
1	1	1	0	101
2	1	1	0	211
2	3	1	0	127
1	1	1	0	170
4	2	1	0	208
2	3	1	0	127
2	2	1	0	132
1	2	2	0	208
1	n/a	3	1	221

Food Item	Serving Size	Calories	Protein (g)	Carb (g)
Cracker, graham	0.75 oz	90	1	16
Cracker, melba toast, plain	0.75 oz	83	3	16
Cracker, melba toast, rye	0.75 oz	83	2	16
Cracker, melba toast, wheat	0.75 oz	80	3	16
Cracker, saltine	0.75 oz	91	2	15
Cracker, saltine, fat-free	0.75 oz	84	2	18
Cracker, Wheat Thins	31 g	147	3	20
Croissant	½ medium	116	2	13
Croissant, cheese	½ medium	118	3	13
English muffin	½ (1 oz)	67	2	13
English muffin, cinnamon-raisin	½ (1 oz)	68	2	14
English muffin, whole wheat	½ (1 oz)	67	3	13
French toast	½ slice (1 oz)	74	3	8
Muffin, blueberry	½ (1 oz)	111	2	14
Muffin, bran	½ (1 oz)	77	2	14
Muffin, plain, low-fat	½ (1 oz)	84	2	12
Muffin, wheat bran	½ (1 oz)	53	1	10
Pancake, blueberry	½ of 6 in pancake (1 oz)	85	2	11
Pancake, buckwheat	½ of 5 in pancake (1 oz)	57	2	11
Pancake, buttermilk	1 (4 in) pancake (1 oz)	64	2	11
Pancake, plain	1 (4 in) pancake (1 oz)	64	2	18
Pancake, whole wheat	½ of 5 in pancake (1 oz)	53	2	10
Roll, dinner, plain	1 (1 oz)	87	3	15

Fiber (g)	Sugar (g)	Fat (g)	Sat Fat (g)	Sodium (mg)
1	7	2	0	129
1	0	1	0	177
2	n/a	1	0	191
2	n/a	0	0	178
1	0	2	0	228
1	0	0	0	135
1	4	6	1.5	246
1	3	6	3	212
1	3	6	3	158
1	1	1	0	132
1	4	1	0	95
2	3	1	0	156
0	n/a	4	1	156
1	8	5	1	89
1	3	2	0	111
1	11	3	1	133
1	3	2	0	89
0	n/a	4	1	159
1	1	1	0	168
1	3	1.5	0	143
0	n/a	3	1	124
1	1	.5	0	113
1	2	2	0	150

Food Item	Serving Size	Calories	Protein (g)	Carb (g)
Roll, dinner, whole wheat	1 (1 oz)	74	2	14
Roll, French	1 (over 1 oz)	105	3	19
Roll, hamburger bun	½ (less than 1 oz)	60	2	11
Roll, hot dog bun	½ (1 oz)	60	2	11
Roll, kaiser	½ (less than 1 oz)	84	3	15
Taco shell, baked	1 (0.5 oz)	59	1	8
Tortilla, flour	1 (10 in)	225	6	37
Tortilla, wheat	1 (11 in)	207	8	56
Waffle, plain	½ (1 oz)	82	2	9

CEREALS

Food Item	Serving Size	Calories	Protein (g)	Carb (g)
All-Bran	½ c	80	4	23
Basic 4	¼ c	52	1	11
Cheerios	½ c	55	2	11
Cheerios, Honey Nut	½ c	56	1	12
Cheerios, MultiGrain	½ c	57	1	13
Cornflakes	½ c	50	1	12
Cracklin' Oat Bran	¼ c	67	1	12
Cream of Rice, cooked	½ c	63	1	14
Cream of Rice, uncooked	2 Tbsp	75	1	17
Fiber One	½ c	60	2	25
Granola, homemade	¼ c	149	5	16
Grape-Nuts	¼ c	104	3	24
Grape-Nuts Flakes	½ c	70	2	16
Kashi 7 Whole Grain Nuggets	½ c	210	7	47
Kashi 7 Whole Grain Puffs	1 c	70	2	15
Kashi GOLEAN	½ c	70	7	15
Muesli, dried fruit and nuts	¼ c	72	2	17

Fiber (g)	Sugar (g)	Fat (g)	Sat Fat (g)	Sodium (mg)
2	2	1	0	134
1	0	2	0	231
1	1	1	0	103
1	1	1	0	103
1	1	1	0	155
1	0	3	1	49
2	1	6	1	458
5	n/a	1	0	485
1	1	4	1	145

Fiber (g)	Sugar (g)	Fat (g)	Sat Fat (g)	Sodium (mg)
10	6	1	0	80
1	4	1	0	80
1	1	1	0	105
1	5	1	0	135
1	3	1	0	104
1	1	0	0	133
2	5	2	1	50
0	0	0	0	211
0	0	0	0	1
14	0	1	0	105
3	6	7	1	8
3	3	1	0	177
2	3	1	0	92
7	3	2	0	260
1	0	1	0	0
5	3	1	0	43
2	7	1	0	49

Food Item	Serving Size	Calories	Protein (g)	Carb (g)
Multigrain hot cereal	½ c	101	3	20
Multigrain oatmeal	½ c	71	2	16
Oat bran	¼ c	58	4	16
Oat bran flakes	⅓ c	47	2	8
Oatmeal Crisp, Hearty Raisin	⅓ c	69	2	15
100% Bran	⅓ c	83	4	23
Raisin bran	⅓ c	63	2	15
Post Raisin Bran	⅓ c	62	2	15
Raisin Bran Crunch	⅓ c	63	1	15
Rice Krispies	½ c	54	1	12
Shredded wheat cereal	1 single-serve box (1 oz)	96	3	22
Special K	½ c	60	4	11
Steel-cut oats, organic, uncooked	2 Tbsp	74	3	14
Total	½ c	66	1	15
Total Raisin Bran	⅓ c	57	1	14
Wheaties	½ c	55	2	12

CHEESE

Food Item	Serving Size	Calories	Protein (g)	Carb (g)
American, pasteurized process, fat-free	1 in cube	24	4	2
American, pasteurized process, low-fat	1 in cube	32	4	1
American, pasteurized process, low-sodium	1 in cube	68	4	0
American cheese food	1 oz	93	6	2
American cheese food, low-fat	1 in cube	32	4	1
Blue, crumbled	1 Tbsp	30	2	0
Brie	1 in cube	57	4	0
Cheddar	1 in cube	69	4	0
Cheddar, fat-free	1 in cube	40	8	1
Cheddar, low-fat	1 in cube	30	4	0

Fiber (g)	Sugar (g)	Fat (g)	Sat Fat (g)	Sodium (mg)
2	1	1	0	1
3	0	1	0	4
4	0	2	0	1
1	1	1	0	27
1	6	1	0	73
8	7	1	0	121
2	6	0	0	117
2	5	0	0	95
1	7	0	0	70
0	1	0	0	133
3	0	.5	0	2
0	2	0	0	110
2	0	1	0	1
2	3	0	0	125
2	6	0	0	80
2	2	0	0	105

Fiber (g)	Sugar (g)	Fat (g)	Sat Fat (g)	Sodium (mg)
0	2	0	0	244
0	0	1	1	257
0	0	6	4	1
0	2	7	4	452
0	0	1	1	257
0	0	2.5	1.5	118
0	0	5	3	107
0	0	6	4	106
0	1	0	0	220
0	0	1	1	106

Food Item	Serving Size	Calories	Protein (g)	Carb (g)
Cottage cheese, low-fat 1%	4 oz	81	14	3
Cottage cheese, fat-free, large curd, dry	½ c	96	20	2
Cottage cheese, low-fat 2%	¼ c	51	8	2
Cream cheese	2 Tbsp	101	2	1
Cream cheese, fat-free	2 Tbsp	28	4	2
Cream cheese, low-fat	2 Tbsp	69	3	2
Feta	1 in cube	45	2	1
Gouda	1 oz	101	7	1
Monterey Jack, fat-free	1 in cube	40	8	1
Monterey Jack, low-fat	1 in cube	53	5	0
Mozzarella, fat-free, shredded	¼ oz	42	9	1
Mozzarella, low-sodium	1 in cube	50	5	1
Mozzarella, part-skim, low moisture	1 oz	86	7	1
Mozzarella, string	1 (1 oz)	80	8	1
Muenster	1 in cube	66	4	0
Muenster, low-fat	1 in cube	49	4	1
Parmesan, grated	2 Tbsp	43	4	0
Parmesan, hard	1 in cube	40	4	0
Provolone	1 in cube	60	4	0
Ricotta	¼ c	107	7	2
Ricotta, low-fat	¼ c	85	7	3
Swiss	1 in cube	57	4	1
Swiss, low-fat	1 in cube	27	4	1
Swiss, low-fat, singles	1 slice	50	8	1

Fiber (g)	Sugar (g)	Fat (g)	Sat Fat (g)	Sodium (mg)
0	3	1	1	459
0	2	0	0	15
0	0	1	1	229
0	0	10	6	86
0	0	0	0	158
0	0	5	3	89
0	1	4	3	190
0	1	8	5	232
0	1	0	0	220
0	0	4	2	96
1	0	0	0	210
0	0	3	2	3
0	0	6	4	150
0	0	6	3	240
0	0	5	3	113
0	1	3	2	108
0	0	3	2	153
0	0	3	2	165
0	0	5	3	149
0	0	8	5	52
0	0	5	3	77
0	0	4	3	29
0	0	1	1	39
0	0	1	1	73

CONDIMENTS, DRESSINGS, MARINADES, AND SPREADS

Food Item	Serving Size	Calories	Protein (g)	Carb (g)
Barbecue sauce	1 Tbsp	26	0	6
Cocktail sauce, Steel's Gourmet, no sugar added	4 Tbsp	30	2	5
Dressing, bacon and tomato	1 Tbsp	49	0	0
Dressing, balsamic vinegar	1 Tbsp	14	0	3
Dressing, blue cheese	1 Tbsp	76	1	1
Dressing, blue cheese, fat-free	1 Tbsp	20	0	4
Dressing, blue cheese, low-calorie	1 Tbsp	15	1	0
Dressing, Caesar	1 Tbsp	78	0	0
Dressing, Caesar, low-fat	1 Tbsp	16	0	3
Dressing, Catalina, fat-free	1 Tbsp	18	0	4
Dressing, creamy Italian, fat-free	1 Tbsp	25	0	6
Dressing, French	1 Tbsp	73	0	2
Dressing, French, fat-free	1 Tbsp	21	0	5
Dressing, French, reduced-calorie	1 Tbsp	32	0	4
Dressing, honey Dijon, low-fat	1 Tbsp	18	0	2
Dressing, honey mustard	1 Tbsp	51	0	7
Dressing, Italian, reduced-fat, without salt	1 Tbsp	11	0	1
Dressing, Italian, fat-free	1 Tbsp	7	0	1
Dressing, Italian, Kraft Light Done Right!	1 Tbsp	26	0	1
Dressing, Italian, reduced-calorie	1 Tbsp	28	0	1
Dressing, ranch	1 Tbsp	73	0	1
Dressing, ranch, fat-free	1 Tbsp	17	0	4
Dressing, ranch, low-fat	1 Tbsp	23	0	4
Dressing, ranch, reduced-fat	1 Tbsp	33	0	2
Dressing, red wine vinaigrette, fat-free	1 Tbsp	8	0	2
Dressing, Russian, low-calorie	1 Tbsp	23	0	4
Dressing, Thousand Island	1 Tbsp	59	0	2

Fiber (g)	Sugar (g)	Fat (g)	Sat Fat (g)	Sodium (mg)
0	5	0	0	196
0	3	0	0	220
0	0	5	1	163
0	2	0	0	4
0	1	8	1	164
1	2	0	0	136
0	0	1	0	180
0	0	8	1	158
0	2	1	0	162
1	4	0	0	160
0	3	0	0	165
0	3	7	1	134
0	3	0	0	128
0	4	2	0	160
0	2	1	0	100
0	7	3	0	37
0	1	1	0	4
0	1	0	0	158
0	1	2	0	114
0	0	3	0	199
0	0	8	n/a	122
0	1	0	0	107
0	2	1	0	165
0	0	3	0	140
0	2	0	0	200
0	4	1	0	139
0	2	6	1	138

Food Item	Serving Size	Calories	Protein (g)	Carb (g)
Dressing, Thousand Island, fat-free	1 Tbsp	21	0	5
Dressing, Thousand Island, reduced-fat	1 Tbsp	31	0	3
Horseradish	1 Tbsp	7	0	2
Horseradish sauce	1 Tbsp	30	0	1
Ketchup	1 Tbsp	15	0	4
Mustard	1 Tbsp	10	1	1
Olives	5 small	18	0	1
Olives	5 large	25	0	1
Olives	5 jumbo	34	0	2
Olives	5 super colossal	62	1	4
Pickle, dill	1 small	4	0	1
Pickle, dill	1 medium	8	0	2
Pickle, dill	1 large	16	1	4
Salsa	1 Tbsp	4	0	1
Soy sauce	1 Tbsp	11	2	1
Soy sauce, low-sodium	1 Tbsp	10	1	2
Tabasco sauce	1 Tbsp	2	0	0
Tahini	1 Tbsp	89	3	3
Vinaigrette, balsamic	1 Tbsp	45	0	2
Vinaigrette, red wine	1 Tbsp	45	0	1
Wasabi	1 Tbsp	9	0	2
Worcestershire sauce	1 Tbsp	11	0	3

DAIRY PRODUCTS (*ALSO SEE* CHEESE)

Food Item	Serving Size	Calories	Protein (g)	Carb (g)
Milk, fat-free	1 c	86	8	12
Milk, 1%	1 c	102	8	12
Milk, 2%	1 c	122	8	11
Milk, whole	1 c	146	8	11

Fiber (g)	Sugar (g)	Fat (g)	Sat Fat (g)	Sodium (mg)
1	3	0	0	117
0	3	2	0	125
0	1	0	0	47
0	n/a	3	2	10
0	3	0	0	167
1	0	1	0	170
1	0	2	0	140
1	0	2	0	192
1	0	3	0	373
2	0	5	1	682
0	0	0	0	324
1	1	0	0	569
2	2	0	0	1,181
0	0	0	0	96
0	0	0	0	1,005
0	0	0	0	533
0	n/a	0	0	89
1	n/a	8	1	5
0	2	4	1.5	150
0	12	5	0	240
1	0	0	0	1
0	2	0	0	167

Fiber (g)	Sugar (g)	Fat (g)	Sat Fat (g)	Sodium (mg)
0	12	0	0	127
0	13	2	2	107
0	12	5	3	100
0	12	8	5	98

Food Item	Serving Size	Calories	Protein (g)	Carb (g)
Sour cream	1 Tbsp	31	0	1
Yogurt, banana, low-fat	4 oz	120	5	21
Yogurt, blueberry–French vanilla, low-fat	4 oz	120	5	24
Yogurt, coffee, fat-free	4 oz	103	6	20
Yogurt, plain, fat-free	4 oz	63	6	9
Yogurt, plain, low-fat	4 oz	71	6	8
Yogurt, plain, whole milk	4 oz	69	4	5
Yogurt, strawberry, fat-free, Breyer's	4 oz	62	4	11
Yogurt, strawberry, low-fat, Breyer's	4 oz	109	4	21
Yogurt, vanilla, low-fat	4 oz	96	6	16

DESSERTS AND SWEET TREATS

Food Item	Serving Size	Calories	Protein (g)	Carb (g)
Brownie, prepared from recipe	2 in square	112	1	12
Cake, German chocolate	1 slice (2¾ oz)	280	3	35
Cake, yellow, with chocolate frosting	1 piece (⅛ of 18 oz cake)	243	2	35
Candy, Almond Joy	1 fun size	95	1	12
Candy, chocolate bar with almonds	1 fun size (nugget)	60	1	5
Candy, chocolate-covered almond	1 (½ oz)	100	2	9
Candy, hard, sugar-free	1 piece	11	0	3
Candy, M&M'S Peanut	1 fun size	93	2	11
Candy, M&M'S Plain	1 fun size	89	1	13
Candy, milk chocolate bar	1 mini bar (0.25 oz)	37	1	4
Candy, Tootsie Pop	1	26	0	6
Candy, Twix	1 oz	143	1	19

Fiber (g)	Sugar (g)	Fat (g)	Sat Fat (g)	Sodium (mg)
0	0	3	2	8
0	18	2	2	60
0	21	1	0	70
0	20	0	0	78
0	9	0	0	87
0	8	2	1	79
0	5	4	2	52
0	9	0	0	51
0	20	1	1	59
0	16	1	1	75

Fiber (g)	Sugar (g)	Fat (g)	Sat Fat (g)	Sodium (mg)
n/a	n/a	7	2	82
0	24	15	5	300
1	n/a	11	3	216
1	10	5	3	218
0	4	4	2	5
0	7	6	3	10
0	0	0	0	0
1	9	5	2	9
1	11	4	2	11
0	4	2	1	6
0	4	0	0	3
0	14	7	5	56

Food Item	Serving Size	Calories	Protein (g)	Carb (g)
Cheesecake	1 piece (¹⁄₁₂ of 9 in cake)	271	5	35
Cookie, butter, commercially baked	0.5 oz	66	1	10
Cookie, chocolate chip	0.5 oz	70	1	10
Cookie, fig bar	1	56	1	11
Cookie, fortune	1	30	0	7
Cookie, fudge and caramel	1 small	80	1	10
Cookie, oatmeal	1	81	2	12
Cookie, oatmeal raisin	1	65	1	11
Cookie, sugar	1	72	1	10
Doughnut, cake, chocolate	1 (3 in dia)	175	2	24
Doughnut, cake, plain	1 (3¼ in dia)	226	3	25
Doughnut hole, cake, plain	1	59	1	6
Frozen yogurt, chocolate	½ c	110	3	19
Frozen yogurt, chocolate, fat-free	½ c	100	4	18
Frozen yogurt, coffee	½ c	110	3	19
Frozen yogurt, vanilla, soft-serve	½ c	117	3	17
Frozen yogurt, vanilla, low-fat	½ c	160	7	33
Gum, chewing, regular	1 stick	7	0	2
Ice cream, chocolate	½ c	142	3	19
Ice cream, chocolate, 98% fat-free, Breyer's	½ c	92	3	21
Ice cream, chocolate, sugar-free	½ c	109	3	18
Ice cream, vanilla	½ c	145	3	17
Ice cream, vanilla, low-fat, Breyer's All Natural Light	½ c	110	3	17
Ice cream, vanilla, sugar-free, Breyer's	½ c	99	3	15
Ice cream sandwich	1	144	3	22
Pie, apple	1 piece (¹⁄₆ of 8 in pie)	277	2	40

Fiber (g)	Sugar (g)	Fat (g)	Sat Fat (g)	Sodium (mg)
2	21	13	7	376
0	3	3	2	5
0	n/a	3	1	33
1	7	1	0	56
0	4	0	0	22
0	7	4	3	15
1	4	3	1	69
1	9	2	0	81
0	6	3	1	54
1	13	8	2	143
1	9	3	2	143
0	2	3	1	78
1	19	3	2	55
1	12	1	0	75
0	19	3	2	55
0	17	4	2	63
0	19	0	0	51
0	2	0	0	0
1	17	7	4	50
4	14	1	1	51
1	4	4	3	54
1	15	8	5	58
0	15	3	2	48
0	4	4	3	46
1	15	6	3	36
2	18	13	4	311

Food Item	Serving Size	Calories	Protein (g)	Carb (g)
Pie, banana cream	1 piece (⅛ of 9 in pie)	387	6	47
Pie, blueberry	1 piece (⅙ of 8 in pie)	271	2	41
Pie, Boston cream	1 piece (⅙ of 8 in pie)	232	2	39
Pie, cherry	1 piece (⅙ of 8 in pie)	304	2	47
Pie, pecan, prepared from recipe	1 piece (⅛ of 9 in pie)	503	6	64
Pie, pumpkin	1 piece	316	7	41
Sherbet, orange	½ c	107	1	23

EGGS

Food Item	Serving Size	Calories	Protein (g)	Carb (g)
Egg, hard-cooked	1 large	78	6	1
Egg, poached	1 large	71	6	0
Egg, scrambled	1 large	102	7	1
Egg white, cooked	1 large	17	4	0
Egg white, Egg Beaters	¼ c	30	6	1

ENTRÉES AND SIDE DISHES

Food Item	Serving Size	Calories	Protein (g)	Carb (g)
Breakfast burrito, ham and cheese	4 oz	210	9	30
Burrito, bean	1 piece	224	7	36
Burrito, cheese and bean	1 piece	189	8	27

Fiber (g)	Sugar (g)	Fat (g)	Sat Fat (g)	Sodium (mg)
1	17	20	5	346
1	12	12	2	380
1	33	8	2	132
1	17	13	3	288
n/a	n/a	27	5	320
n/a	n/a	14	5	349
2	18	1	1	34

Fiber (g)	Sugar (g)	Fat (g)	Sat Fat (g)	Sodium (mg)
0	1	5	2	62
0	0	5	2	147
0	1	7	2	171
0	0	0	0	55
0	0	0	0	115

Fiber (g)	Sugar (g)	Fat (g)	Sat Fat (g)	Sodium (mg)
0	2	6	2	500
n/a	n/a	7	3	493
n/a	n/a	6	3	583

Food Item	Serving Size	Calories	Protein (g)	Carb (g)
Burrito, chicken	8 oz (1 piece)	207	11	30
Burrito, meat and bean	1 piece	254	11	33
Chicken, barbecued, breast	3 oz	162	20	2
Chicken, barbecued, drumstick	1 (2½ oz)	129	16	2
Chicken, buffalo wing, spicy	5 pieces	246	21	0
Chicken fajita	8 oz (1 piece)	363	20	44
Chicken Parmesan	4 oz	199	18	10
Chicken potpie, frozen	1 serving	484	13	43
Chili, vegetarian, with beans, canned, Hormel	1 c	205	12	38
Chili, with beans, canned	1 c	287	15	30
Chili, with beans and turkey, canned, Hormel	1 c	203	19	26
Chili, without beans, Hormel	1 c	194	17	18
Chili con carne, with beans, canned	½ c	149	9	14
Crab cake	1	160	11	5
Egg roll	1	107	3	18
Enchilada, cheese	1	319	10	29
Enchilada, chicken (low-calorie)	7 oz	356	26	29
Fettuccine Alfredo	8 oz	280	13	40
Lasagna, with meat and sauce, low-fat frozen entrée	5 oz	143	10	19
Pizza, cheese	1 slice (14" in pie)	272	12	34
Pizza, pepperoni and cheese	1 slice (14" in pie)	298	13	34
Sandwich, chicken salad, on whole wheat bread	1	398	31	5
Sandwich, turkey, on whole wheat	1	360	27	29
Shrimp cocktail	3 oz	81	10	8

Fiber (g)	Sugar (g)	Fat (g)	Sat Fat (g)	Sodium (mg)
2	n/a	5	1	1,756
n/a	n/a	9	4	668
0	n/a	8	2	181
0	n/a	6	2	145
0	0	17	5	64
5	n/a	12	2	343
1	6	10	3	399
2	8	29	10	857
10	6	1	0	778
11	3	14	6	1,336
6	6	3	1	1,198
3	3	7	2	970
5	n/a	6	2	522
0	n/a	10	2	491
1	2	2	1	191
n/a	n/a	19	11	784
2	n/a	15	9	1,018
2	7	7	4	690
2	n/a	3	1	257
2	4	10	4	551
2	4	12	5	683
3	3	26	3	527
4	3	16	2.5	1,733
2	4	1	0	417

Food Item	Serving Size	Calories	Protein (g)	Carb (g)
Spaghetti and meatballs, canned	½ c	136	5	14
Taco, chicken, soft, prepared from recipe	1 (2½ oz)	175	15	9

FATS AND OILS

Food Item	Serving Size	Calories	Protein (g)	Carb (g)
Butter, with salt	1 tsp	34	0	0
Butter, without salt	1 tsp	34	0	0
Butter-margarine blend, stick, without salt	1 tsp	33	0	0
Flaxseed oil	1 tsp	40	0	0
Margarine, hard, corn and soybean oils	1 tsp	33	0	0
Margarine, hard, corn oil	1 tsp	34	0	0
Margarine, hard, soybean oil	1 tsp	34	0	0
Margarine, regular, with salt	1 tsp	34	0	0
Margarine, regular, without salt	1 tsp	34	0	0
Oil, canola	1 tsp	40	0	0
Oil, olive	1 tsp	40	0	0
Oil, safflower	1 tsp	40	0	0
Oil, sesame	1 tsp	40	0	0
Oil, walnut	1 tsp	40	0	0

FISH

Food Item	Serving Size	Calories	Protein (g)	Carb (g)
Cod, Atlantic, baked	3 oz	89	19	0
Flounder, baked	3 oz	99	21	0
Grouper, baked	3 oz	100	21	0
Halibut, Atlantic and Pacific, baked	3 oz	119	23	0
Mahi mahi, baked	3 oz	93	20	0

Fiber (g)	Sugar (g)	Fat (g)	Sat Fat (g)	Sodium (mg)
n/a	4	7	3	518
1	.5	8.5	3	134

Fiber (g)	Sugar (g)	Fat (g)	Sat Fat (g)	Sodium (mg)
0	0	4	2	27
0	0	4	2	1
0	0	4	1	1
0	0	5	0	0
0	0	4	1	30
0	0	4	1	44
0	0	4	1	44
0	0	4	1	44
0	0	4	1	0
0	0	5	0	0
0	0	5	1	0
0	0	5	0	0
0	0	5	1	0
0	0	5	0	0

Fiber (g)	Sugar (g)	Fat (g)	Sat Fat (g)	Sodium (mg)
0	0	1	0	66
0	0	1	0	89
0	0	1	0	45
0	0	3	0	59
0	0	1	0	96

Food Item	Serving Size	Calories	Protein (g)	Carb (g)
Salmon, Alaskan chinook, smoked, canned	3 oz	128	20	1
Salmon, pink, canned, drained	3 oz	116	20	0
Swordfish, baked	3 oz	132	22	0
Tilapia, baked or broiled	3 oz	109	22	0
Tuna, bluefin, baked	3 oz	156	25	0
Tuna, StarKist Chunk Light, canned in water, drained	2 oz	70	15	0
Tuna, white, canned in water, drained	3 oz	109	20	0
Tuna, yellowfin, baked	3 oz	118	25	0

FRUIT

Food Item	Serving Size	Calories	Protein (g)	Carb (g)
Apple	1 medium (2¾ in. dia)	72	0	19
Apricot	1	17	0	4
Avocado	¼ c	58	1	3
Banana	1 large (8 in)	121	1	31
Banana	1 extra large (9 in)	135	2	35
Blackberries	1 c	62	2	14
Blueberries	½ c	42	1	11
Cantaloupe, wedged	⅛ small	19	0	4
Cantaloupe, wedged	⅛ medium	23	1	6
Cantaloupe, wedged	⅛ large	35	1	8
Cranberries	1 c	44	0	12
Grapefruit, pink, red, white	½ small	32	1	8
Grapefruit, pink, red, white	½ medium	41	1	10
Grapefruit, pink, red, white	½ large	53	1	13
Grapes, green	½ c	52	1	14
Grapes, red	½ c	52	1	14

Fiber (g)	Sugar (g)	Fat (g)	Sat Fat (g)	Sodium (mg)
0	0	5	n/a	n/a
0	0	4	1	339
0	0	4	1	98
0	0	2	1	48
0	0	5	1	42
0	0	0	0	230
0	0	3	1	320
0	0	1	0	40

Fiber (g)	Sugar (g)	Fat (g)	Sat Fat (g)	Sodium (mg)
3	14	0	0	1
1	3	0	0	0
2	0	5	1	3
4	17	0	0	1
4	19	1	0	2
8	7	1	0	1
2	7	0	0	1
1	4	0	0	9
1	5	0	0	11
1	8	0	0	16
4	4	0	0	2
1	7	0	0	0
1	9	0	0	0
2	12	0	0	0
1	12	0	0	2
1	12	0	0	2

Food Item	Serving Size	Calories	Protein (g)	Carb (g)
Lemon	1 medium (2⅛ in)	17	1	5
Nectarine	1 medium (2¾ in)	69	2	16
Orange	1 small (2⅜ in)	45	1	11
Orange	1 large (3 1/16 in)	86	2	22
Peach	1 medium	58	1	14
Pear	½ medium	52	0	14
Pineapple	¼	57	1	15
Plum	1 (2⅛ in)	30	0	8
Raspberries, red	¾ c	48	1	11
Strawberry	1 medium	4	0	1
Watermelon, sliced	1 wedge (1/16 of melon)	86	2	22

GRAINS AND RICES

Food Item	Serving Size	Calories	Protein (g)	Carb (g)
Couscous, cooked	⅓ c	59	2	12
Oat bran, cooked	⅓ c	29	2	8
Oats, rolled, dry	2 Tbsp	37	1	7
Quinoa, dry	2 Tbsp	79	3	15
Rice, brown, long-grain, cooked	¼ c	54	1	11
Rice, brown, medium-grain, cooked	¼ c	55	1	11
Rice, brown, short-grain, dry	1½ Tbsp	66	1	15
Rice, whole grain, brown, Uncle Ben's 10-minute, dry	¼ c	170	1	35
Rice, white, long-grain, cooked	¼ c	51	1	11
Rice, wild, cooked	⅓ c	55	2	12

Fiber (g)	Sugar (g)	Fat (g)	Sat Fat (g)	Sodium (mg)
2	1	0	0	1
3	12	1	0	0
2	9	0	0	0
4	17	0	0	0
2	13	0	0	0
3	9	0	0	1
2	11	0	0	1
1	7	0	0	0
6	4	1	0	1
0	1	0	0	2
1	18	0	0	3

Fiber (g)	Sugar (g)	Fat (g)	Sat Fat (g)	Sodium (mg)
1	0	0	0	3
2	n/a	1	0	1
1	0	1	0	0
1	n/a	1	0	4
1	0	0	0	2
1	n/a	0	0	0
1	0	1	0	2
2	0	1.5	0	0
0	0	0	0	0
1	0	0	0	2

MEATS

Food Item	Serving Size	Calories	Protein (g)	Carb (g)
Beef				
Bottom round, all lean, grilled	3 oz	155	23	0
Bottom round, all lean, roasted, boneless	3 oz	144	24	0
Bottom round, trimmed, boneless, braised	3 oz	190	28	0
Corned beef, cooked	3 oz	213	15	0
Corned beef lunchmeat, sliced	3 oz	85	13	0
Filet mignon, lean, broiled	3 oz	164	24	0
Flank steak, lean, braised	3 oz	201	24	0
Flank steak, lean, raw	4 oz	169	25	0
Ground patty, 10% fat, raw	4 oz	199	23	0
Ground, 20% fat, pan-broiled	3 oz	209	20	0
Ground, 20% fat, raw	4 oz	287	19	0
Ground patty, 30% fat, pan-broiled	3 oz	202	19	0
Ground, 30% fat, raw	4 oz	375	16	0
Ground, extra lean, raw (5% fat)	4 oz	155	24	0
Hot dog, beef, fat-free	1 frank	62	7	3
Roast beef, lunchmeat, medium-rare	1 oz	30	6	1
Salami, beef, beerwurst	1 oz	78	4	1
Salami, beef, cooked	1 oz	74	4	1
Sausage, beef, precooked	25 g	101	4	0
Steak, top sirloin, lean, broiled	3 oz	160	26	0
Steak, top sirloin, 1/8 trim, broiled	3 oz	207	23	0
Steak, top sirloin, 1/8 trim, raw	4 oz	228	23	0
T-bone, lean, broiled	3 oz	161	22	0
T-bone, raw (trimmed to 1/4 in fat)	4 oz	240	22	0
Tenderloin, lean, boneless, raw	4 oz	136	24	0
Tenderloin, select lean, boneless, roasted	3 oz	139	24	0

Fiber (g)	Sugar (g)	Fat (g)	Sat Fat (g)	Sodium (mg)
0	0	6	2	49
0	0	5	2	32
0	0	8	3	37
0	0	16	5	964
0	0	4	2	982
0	0	7	3	50
0	0	11	5	61
0	0	7	3	65
0	0	11	5	75
0	0	14	5	71
0	0	23	9	76
0	0	13	5	78
0	0	34	13	76
0	0	6	3	75
0	0	1	0	455
0	1	1	1	235
0	0	6	2	205
0	0	6	3	323
0	0	19	4	228
0	0	6	2	54
0	0	12	5	48
0	0	14	6	59
0	0	7	3	60
0	0	16	6	61
0	0	4	1	57
0	0	4	1	48

Food Item	Serving Size	Calories	Protein (g)	Carb (g)
Pork				
Bacon, medium slice, cooked (fried or roasted)	1 slice	43	3	0
Bacon, medium slice, raw	1 slice	157	11	0
Canadian bacon, grilled	1 slice	43	6	0
Chop, center lean, with bone, braised	3 oz	172	25	0
Chop, with barbecue sauce	4 oz	209	23	3
Chop sirloin, lean, raw, boneless	1 chop	129	21	0
Chop sirloin, lean, with bone, braised	1 chop	142	19	0
Ground, cooked	3 oz	252	22	0
Ground, raw	4 oz	297	19	0
Ham, low-sodium, 96% fat-free, roasted, boneless	1 oz	47	6	0
Ham, rump, lean, raw	4 oz	155	24	0
Hot dog, pork	1 frank	204	10	0
Hotdog, pork, beef, and turkey, fat-free	1 frank	50	6	6
Meatballs	1 oz (1 meatball)	60	5	2
Ribs, country-style, lean, braised	3 oz	199	22	0
Ribs, country-style, lean, raw	4 oz	178	22	0
Sausage, pork, cooked	1 oz (1 each)	82	4	0
Tenderloin, raw, lean	4 oz	136	24	0
Tenderloin, roasted, lean	3 oz	139	24	0
Tenderloin, teriyaki, Hormel Always Tender	4 oz	133	20	5
Tenderloin, lean, broiled	3 oz	159	26	0
Veal				
Breast, braised, boneless, lean	3 oz	185	26	0
Ground, broiled	3 oz	146	21	0
Loin, roasted, lean	3 oz	149	22	0

Fiber (g)	Sugar (g)	Fat (g)	Sat Fat (g)	Sodium (mg)
0	0	3	1	185
0	0	12	4	670
0	0	2	1	363
0	0	7	3	53
0	0	11	4	860
0	0	4	1	52
0	0	6	2	38
0	0	18	7	62
0	0	24	9	63
0	0	2	1	275
0	0	6	2	78
0	0	18	7	620
0	2	0	0	490
0	0	3.5	1	35
0	0	12	4	54
0	0	9	3	76
0	0	7.5	3	200
0	0	4	1	57
0	0	4	1	48
n/a	4	3	1	463
0	n/a	5	2	55
n/a	n/a	8	3	58
0	0	6	3	71
0	0	6	2	82

NUTS, SEEDS, AND BUTTERS

Food Item	Serving Size	Calories	Protein (g)	Carb (g)
Almond butter, plain, with salt	1 Tbsp	101	2	3
Almond butter, plain, without salt	1 Tbsp	101	2	3
Almonds, blanched	1 Tbsp	53	2	2
Almonds, dry-roasted, blanched	1 Tbsp (¼ oz)	52	2	1
Almonds, dry-roasted, with salt	½ oz (11 nuts)	85	3	3
Almonds, dry-roasted, without salt	½ oz	85	3	3
Almonds, honey-roasted	½ oz	84	3	4
Almonds, natural, sliced	½ oz	82	3	3
Almonds, oil-roasted, with salt	½ oz	86	3	3
Almonds, oil-roasted, without salt	½ oz	86	3	3
Brazil nuts, dried	1 nut	33	1	1
Brazil nuts, dried	½ oz (3 nuts)	93	2	2
Cashew butter, plain, with salt	1 Tbsp	94	3	4
Cashew butter, plain, without salt	1 Tbsp	94	3	4
Cashew nuts, dry-roasted, with salt	½ oz	81	2	5
Cashew nuts, dry-roasted, without salt	1 Tbsp	49	1	3
Cashew nuts, raw	½ oz	78	3	4
Flaxseed, ground	1 Tbsp	37	1	2
Macadamia nuts, dry-roasted, with salt	½ oz (5–6 nuts)	101	1	2
Macadamia nuts, dry-roasted, without salt	½ oz	102	1	2
Mixed nuts, dry-roasted, with peanuts, with salt	½ oz	84	2	4
Mixed nuts, dry-roasted, with peanuts, without salt	½ oz	84	2	4
Mixed nuts, oil-roasted, with peanuts, with salt	½ oz	87	2	3

Fiber (g)	Sugar (g)	Fat (g)	Sat Fat (g)	Sodium (mg)
1	1	9	1	72
1	n/a	9	1	2
1	0	5	0	3
1	0	5	.5	0
2	1	7	1	48
2	1	7	1	0
2	n/a	7	1	18
2	1	7	1	0
2	1	8	1	48
2	1	8	1	0
0	0	3	1	0
1	0	9	2	0
0	1	8	2	98
0	1	8	2	2
0	1	7	1	91
0	0	4	1	1
1	1	6	1	2
2	0	3	0	2
1	1	11	2	38
1	1	11	2	1
1	1	7	1	95
1	1	7	1	2
1	1	8	1	59

Food Item	Serving Size	Calories	Protein (g)	Carb (g)
Mixed nuts, oil-roasted, with peanuts, without salt	½ oz	87	2	3
Mixed nuts, oil-roasted, without peanuts, with salt	1 Tbsp	87	2	3
Mixed nuts, oil-roasted, without peanuts, without salt	½ oz	87	2	3
Peanut butter, creamy, with salt	1 Tbsp	94	4	3
Peanut butter, with salt, reduced-fat	1 Tbsp	83	4	6
Peanut butter, crunchy, with salt	1 Tbsp	95	4	3
Peanut butter, natural	1 Tbsp	100	4	4
Peanut butter, reduced-sodium	1 Tbsp	101	4	4
Peanuts, dry-roasted, with salt	½ oz	83	3	3
Peanuts, dry-roasted, without salt	½ oz	83	3	3
Peanuts, shelled, cooked, with salt	1 Tbsp	36	2	2
Pecans, dried, chopped	⅛ c	94	1	2
Pecans, dried, halved	⅛ c	86	1	2
Pecans, dry-roasted, with salt	½ oz	101	1	2
Pecans, dry-roasted, without salt	½ oz	101	1	2
Pecans, oil-roasted, with salt, halved	½ oz	101	1	2
Pecans, oil-roasted, without salt, halved	½ oz	101	1	2
Pistachios, dry-roasted, with salt	½ oz	81	3	4
Pistachios, dry-roasted, without salt	½ oz	81	3	4
Walnuts, dried, black	1 Tbsp	48	2	1
Walnuts, English, ground	⅛ c	65	2	1
Walnuts, dried, halved	½ oz	93	2	2

PASTA

Food Item	Serving Size	Calories	Protein (g)	Carb (g)
Note: For most pasta shapes, 1 ounce of dry pasta makes approximately ½ cup cooked.				
Angel hair, whole wheat, dry, organic	1 oz	106	4	21
Bow ties, semolina, dry	1 oz	103	4	21

Fiber (g)	Sugar (g)	Fat (g)	Sat Fat (g)	Sodium (mg)
1	1	8	1	2
1	1	8	1	43
1	1	8	1	2
1	1	8	2	73
1	1	5	1	86
1	1	8	1	78
1	1	8	1	60
1	1	8	2	32
1	1	7	1	115
1	1	7	1	1
1	0	2.5	.5	84
1	1	10	0	0
1	1	9	1	0
1	1	11	1	54
1	1	11	1	0
1	1	11	1	56
1	1	11	1	0
2	1	7	1	57
2	1	7	1	1
1	0	5	0	0
1	0	7	1	0
1	0	9	0	0

Fiber (g)	Sugar (g)	Fat (g)	Sat Fat (g)	Sodium (mg)
3	1	1	0	5
1	1	0	0	1

Food Item	Serving Size	Calories	Protein (g)	Carb (g)
Fettuccine (tagliatelle), semolina, dry	1 oz	102	4	21
Fettuccine (tagliatelle), spinach, dry	1 oz	98	4	20
Lasagna, semolina, dry	1 oz	102	4	21
Linguine, semolina, dry	1 oz	102	4	21
Penne, semolina, dry	1 oz	106	4	22
Penne, whole wheat, dry, organic	1 oz	106	4	21
Spaghetti, brown rice, dry	1 oz	106	2	21
Spaghetti, corn, dry	1 oz	101	2	22
Spaghetti, semolina, dry, organic	1 oz	102	4	21
Spaghetti, spinach, dry, organic	1 oz	106	4	21
Spaghetti, whole wheat, dry, organic	1 oz	99	4	21

POULTRY

Food Item	Serving Size	Calories	Protein (g)	Carb (g)
Chicken				
Chicken, breast, boneless, without skin, raw	½ breast	128	27	0
Chicken, breast, boneless, without skin, stewed	½ breast	143	23	0
Chicken, breast, oven-roasted, fat-free, sliced, Oscar Mayer	6 slices	66	14	1
Chicken, breast, with bone, with skin, raw	½ breast	249	30	0
Chicken, breast, with bone, with skin, roasted	1 lb	114	17	0
Chicken, drumstick, with skin, cooked	1 drumstick	112	14	0
Chicken, drumstick, with skin, raw	1 drumstick	118	14	0
Chicken, drumstick, without skin, raw	1 drumstick	74	13	0
Chicken, drumstick, without skin, roasted	½ drumstick	76	12	0
Chicken, thigh, boneless, without skin, raw	1 thigh	82	14	0

Fiber (g)	Sugar (g)	Fat (g)	Sat Fat (g)	Sodium (mg)
1	1	1	0	2
1	1	1	0	9
1	1	1	0	1
1	1	1	0	2
1	1	.5	0	3
3	1	1	0	5
1	0	0	0	n/a
3	0	1	0	1
1	1	1	0	3
3	0	.5	0	10
4	1	.5	0	2

Fiber (g)	Sugar (g)	Fat (g)	Sat Fat (g)	Sodium (mg)
0	0	1	0	60
0	0	3	1	77
0	1	0	0	969
0	0	13	4	91
0	0	5	1	41
0	0	6	2	47
0	0	6	2	61
0	0	2	1	55
0	0	2	1	42
0	0	3	1	59

Food Item	Serving Size	Calories	Protein (g)	Carb (g)
Chicken, thigh, boneless, without skin, roasted	1 thigh	109	13	0
Chicken, thigh, with bone, with skin, raw	1 thigh	198	16	0
Chicken, thigh, with bone, with skin, roasted	1 thigh	153	16	0
Chicken frankfurter	1 frank	116	6	3
Chicken lunchmeat, deli	1 oz	23	5	0
Turkey				
Turkey, breast, fat-free, smoked, Oscar Mayer	3 slices	31	6	1
Turkey, breast, with skin, raw	from 1 lb turkey	154	29	0
Turkey, breast, with skin, roasted	from 1 lb turkey	150	28	0
Turkey, dark meat, with skin, roasted	from 1 lb turkey	230	29	0
Turkey, dark meat, without skin, roasted	from 1 lb turkey	147	26	0
Turkey, drumstick, with skin, smoked	3 oz	131	18	0
Turkey, drumstick, without skin, cooked	3 oz	159	24	0
Turkey, ground, cooked	3 oz	145	17	0
Turkey, leg, with skin, raw	from 1 lb turkey	151	21	0
Turkey, leg, with skin, roasted	from 1 lb turkey	148	20	0
Turkey, light meat, with skin, roasted	from 1 lb turkey	134	19	0
Turkey, light meat, with skin, smoked	3 oz	177	24	0
Turkey, light meat, without skin, roasted	from 1 lb turkey	146	31	0
Turkey, light meat, without skin, smoked	2 thick slices	143	25	0

Fiber (g)	Sugar (g)	Fat (g)	Sat Fat (g)	Sodium (mg)
0	0	6	2	46
0	0	14	4	71
0	0	10	3	52
0	0	9	2	616
0	0	0	0	210
0	0	0	0	427
0	0	3	1	59
0	0	3	1	52
0	0	12	4	79
0	0	4	1	72
0	0	6	2	627
0	0	6	2	67
0	0	8	2	66
0	0	7	2	78
0	0	7	2	55
0	0	6	2	43
0	0	8	2	847
0	n/a	1	0	58
0	0	4	0	837

Food Item	Serving Size	Calories	Protein (g)	Carb (g)
Turkey, wing, with skin, smoked	3 oz	131	16	0
Turkey frankfurter	1	102	6	1
Turkey sausage, smoked, hot	1 oz	44	4	1

SEAFOOD

Food Item	Serving Size	Calories	Protein (g)	Carb (g)
Crab, Alaskan, king crab, steamed	3 oz	82	16	0
Crab, baked or broiled	3 oz	117	16	0
Crab, imitation (surimi)	3 oz	81	6	13
Crab, sautéed	3 oz	117	16	0
Lobster, Northernm steamed	3 oz	83	17	1
Shrimp, cooked	3 oz	84	17	0
Shrimp, steamed	1 large	5	1	0

SNACKS

Food Item	Serving Size	Calories	Protein (g)	Carb (g)
Baked! Cheetos Crunchy Cheese Flavored Snacks	1 oz	130	2	19
Baked! Doritos Nacho Cheese	1 oz	120	2	21
Baked! Lay's Cheddar & Sour Cream Flavored Potato Crisps	1 oz	120	2	21
Baked! Lay's Original Potato Crisps	1 oz	110	2	23
Baked! Tostitos Original Bite Size	1 oz	110	3	24
Chex Party Mix	1 oz	120	3	18
Corn chips	1 oz	147	2	18
Granola bar, almond, hard	1	119	2	15
Granola bar, chocolate chip, hard	1	105	2	17
Jerky, beef	1 oz	116	9	3
Popcorn, air-popped	1 c	31	1	6

Fiber (g)	Sugar (g)	Fat (g)	Sat Fat (g)	Sodium (mg)
0	0	7	2	568
0	0	8	3	642
0	1	2	1	260

Fiber (g)	Sugar (g)	Fat (g)	Sat Fat (g)	Sodium (mg)
0	0	1	0	911
0	n/a	5.5	1	270
0	5	0	0	715
0	0	5	1	270
0	0	1	0	323
0	0	1	0	190
0	0	0	0	12

Fiber (g)	Sugar (g)	Fat (g)	Sat Fat (g)	Sodium (mg)
0	1	5	1	240
2	1	4	1	220
2	3	4	1	210
2	2	2	0	150
2	0	1	0	200
2	n/a	5	2	288
0	n/a	8	6	290
1	n/a	6	3	61
1	n/a	4	3	83
1	3	7	3	627
1	0	0	0	1

Food Item	Serving Size	Calories	Protein (g)	Carb (g)
Popcorn, microwaveable, low-fat, low-sodium	0.5 oz	60	2	10
Popcorn, microwaveable, 94% fat-free	0.5 oz	57	1	11
Potato chips, baked	1 c	159	2	24
Potato chips, fat-free	0.5 oz	54	1	12
Potato chips, light	0.5 oz	71	1	9
Potato chips, reduced-fat	0.5 oz	68	1	9
Potato chips, reduced-fat, unsalted	0.5 oz	69	1	9
Pretzel, hard	1	23	1	5
Pretzel, hard, twist, unsalted	1	23	1	5
Pretzel, hard, whole wheat	0.5 oz	51	2	12
Pretzel, soft	1 medium	389	9	80
Tortilla chips, baked, light	10 chips	74	1	12
Tortilla chips, baked, low-fat	0.5 oz	59	2	11
Tortilla chips, baked, without salt	10 chips	66	2	13
Trail mix	0.5 oz	65	2	6

SOUPS, SAUCES, AND GRAVIES

Food Item	Serving Size	Calories	Protein (g)	Carb (g)
Gravy, au jus, canned	2 Tbsp	2	0	1
Gravy, beef, canned	1 Tbsp	8	1	1
Sauce, Alfredo	2 Tbsp	55	1	1
Sauce, barbecue	2 Tbsp	52	0	13
Sauce, enchilada, Ortega	1 Tbsp	8	0	1
Sauce, marinara	1 Tbsp	12	0	2
Sauce, pasta, with meat, Prego	1 Tbsp	18	0	3
Sauce, sweet-and-sour, Nestlé	1 Tbsp	25	0	6
Sauce, taco, red, La Victoria	1 Tbsp	7	0	1
Sauce, tamari	1 Tbsp	11	2	1
Sauce, teriyaki	1 Tbsp	15	1	3

Fiber (g)	Sugar (g)	Fat (g)	Sat Fat (g)	Sodium (mg)
2	0	1	0	69
2	0	1	0	89
2	2	6	1	312
1	1	0	0	91
1	1	4	1	61
1	0	3	1	70
1	0	3	1	1
0	n/a	0	0	81
0	n/a	0	0	17
1	n/a	0	0	29
2	0	4	1	1,615
1	0	2	0	160
1	0	1	0	59
1	0	1	0	67
n/a	n/a	4	1	32

Fiber (g)	Sugar (g)	Fat (g)	Sat Fat (g)	Sodium (mg)
0	n/a	0	0	7
0	0	1	0	82
0	0	5	2	195
0	9	0	0	392
0	0	0	0	39
0	1	0	0	75
0	2	1	0	66
0	4	0	0	115
0	1	0	0	105
0	0	0	0	1,005
0	2	0	0	670

Food Item	Serving Size	Calories	Protein (g)	Carb (g)
Sauce, tomato, with salt	½ c	29	2	7
Sauce, tomato, without salt, canned	½ c	45	2	9
Soup, bean and bacon	1 c	106	5	16
Soup, beef and vegetable	1 c	78	6	10
Soup, black bean	½ c	58	3	10
Soup, chicken noodle	1 c	75	4	9
Soup, chicken noodle, chunky, canned	1 c	175	13	17
Soup, chicken noodle, low-sodium	1 c	76	4	11
Soup, chili, beef	1 c	170	7	21
Soup, clam chowder, Manhattan-style	1 c	78	2	12
Soup, clam chowder, New England–style	1 c	95	5	12
Soup, crab, canned	1 c	76	5	10
Soup, cream of mushroom	1 c	96	2	8
Soup, French onion, Campbell's, prepared	1 c	90	4	12
Soup, gazpacho, canned	1 c	46	7	4
Soup, green pea	1 c	165	9	27
Soup, lentil, fat-free, canned	½ c	55	5	13
Soup, minestrone	1 c	82	4	11
Soup, tomato	1 c	85	2	17
Soup, vegetable	1 c	75	4	9

VEGETABLES

Food Item	Serving Size	Calories	Protein (g)	Carb (g)
Alfalfa sprouts	½ c	4	1	0
Artichoke	1 medium	60	4	13
Asparagus, cooked	8 spears	26	3	5
Bell pepper, chopped	1 c	30	1	7
Bell pepper, boiled	1 c	38	1	9
Broccoli, chopped, boiled	1 c	55	4	11

Fiber (g)	Sugar (g)	Fat (g)	Sat Fat (g)	Sodium (mg)
2	5	0	0	642
2	5	0	0	13
9	1	2	1	928
1	1	2	1	791
2	1	1	0	599
1	0	2	1	1,106
4	2	6	1	850
1	0	2	1	426
10	7	7	3	1,035
2	1	2	0	578
2	0	3	0	915
1	n/a	2	0	1,235
0	2	7	2	731
2	8	3	1	1,800
1	1	0	0	739
5	8	3	1	918
5	4	0	0	225
1	n/a	3	1	911
1	9	2	0	695
1	1	3	1	945

Fiber (g)	Sugar (g)	Fat (g)	Sat Fat (g)	Sodium (mg)
0	0	0	0	1
7	1	0	0	397
2	2	0	0	17
3	4	0	0	4
2	3	0	0	3
5	2	1	0	64

Food Item	Serving Size	Calories	Protein (g)	Carb (g)
Broccoli, florets, fresh	1 c	20	2	4
Brussels sprouts, raw	1 c	38	3	8
Cabbage, raw	1 medium leaf	6	0	1
Carrot	1 medium	25	1	6
Carrot, baby	1 medium	4	0	1
Cauliflower	¼ medium head	36	3	8
Celery	1 medium stalk	6	0	1
Celery, chopped	1 c	16	1	3
Cherry tomatoes, red	1 c	27	1	6
Corn, sweet white	½ c	66	2	15
Corn, sweet white	1 small ear	63	2	14
Corn, sweet white	1 large ear	123	5	27
Corn, sweet yellow	½ c	66	2	15
Corn, sweet yellow	1 small ear	63	2	14
Corn, sweet yellow	1 large ear	123	5	27
Cucumber with peel, raw	1 (8¼ in)	45	2	11
Garlic	1 clove	4	0	1
Green beans, snap, raw	1 c	34	2	8
Green beans, with almonds, frozen, Green Giant	1 c	91	3	8
Lettuce, iceberg	5 large leaves	10	1	2
Lettuce, romaine	4 leaves	19	1	4
Mushrooms, brown Italian	5	27	3	4
Onion, green (scallions), tops and bulbs, chopped	½ c	16	1	4
Onion, red	1 medium	44	1	10
Onion, yellow	1 medium	44	1	10
Peas, green, raw	½ c	59	4	10

Fiber (g)	Sugar (g)	Fat (g)	Sat Fat (g)	Sodium (mg)
2	0	0	0	19
3	2	0	0	22
1	1	0	0	4
2	3	0	0	42
0	0	0	0	8
4	4	0	0	43
1	1	0	0	32
2	2	0	0	81
2	4	0	0	7
2	2	1	0	12
2	2	1	0	11
4	5	2	0	21
2	2	1	0	12
2	2	1	0	11
4	5	2	0	21
2	5	0	0	6
0	0	0	0	1
4	2	0	0	7
3	3	4.5	0	144
1	1	0	0	8
2	1	0	0	9
1	2	0	0	6
1	1	0	0	8
2	5	0	0	4
2	5	0	0	4
4	4	0	0	4

Food Item	Serving Size	Calories	Protein (g)	Carb (g)
Peas, snow, whole, raw	½ c	13	1	2
Potato, baked, with skin, without salt	1 medium	161	4	37
Sauerkraut, canned, low-sodium	1 c	31	1	6
Snap beans, green	1 c	27	1	7
Spinach	3 oz	20	2	3
Spinach, baby, Dole	1 c	10	1	3
Spinach, cooked, with salt	1 c	41	5	7
Spinach, cooked, without salt	1 c	41	5	7
Squash, summer	1 medium	31	2	7
Sweet potato, baked, with skin, without salt	1 small	54	1	12
Sweet potato, baked, without skin, without salt	1 medium	103	2	24
Tomato, red	1 medium	22	1	5
Zucchini, with skin, raw	1 medium	31	2	7

Fiber (g)	Sugar (g)	Fat (g)	Sat Fat (g)	Sodium (mg)
1	1	0	0	1
4	2	0	0	17
4	3	0	0	437
4	3	0	0	0
2	0	0	0	67
1	0	0	0	39
4	1	0	0	551
4	1	0	0	126
2	4	0	0	4
2	4	0	0	22
4	10	0	0	41
1	3	0	0	0
2	3	0	0	20

Photography Credits

Index

Underscored page references indicate boxed text. **Boldfaced** page references indicate photographs.

Conversion Chart

These equivalents have been slightly rounded to make measuring easier.

Volume Measurements

US	Imperial	Metric
¼ tsp	–	1 ml
½ tsp	–	2 ml
1 tsp	–	5 ml
1 Tbsp	–	15 ml
2 Tbsp (1 oz)	1 fl oz	30 ml
¼ cup (2 oz)	2 fl oz	60 ml
⅓ cup (3 oz)	3 fl oz	80 ml
½ cup (4 oz)	4 fl oz	120 ml
⅔ cup (5 oz)	5 fl oz	160 ml
¾ cup (6 oz)	6 fl oz	180 ml
1 cup (8 oz)	8 fl oz	240 ml

Weight Measurements

US	Metric
1 oz	30 g
2 oz	60 g
4 oz (¼ lb)	115 g
5 oz (⅓ lb)	145 g
6 oz	170 g
7 oz	200 g
8 oz (½ lb)	230 g
10 oz	285 g
12 oz (¾ lb)	340 g
14 oz	400 g
16 oz (1 lb)	455 g
2.2 lb	1 kg

Length Measurements

US	Metric
¼"	0.6 cm
½"	1.25 cm
1"	2.5 cm
2"	5 cm
4"	11 cm
6"	15 cm
8"	20 cm
10"	25 cm
12" (1')	30 cm

Pan Sizes

US	Metric
8" cake pan	20 × 4 cm sandwich or cake tin
9" cake pan	23 × 3.5 cm sandwich or cake tin
11" × 7" baking pan	28 × 18 cm baking tin
13" × 9" baking pan	32.5 × 23 cm baking tin
15" × 10" baking pan	38 × 25.5 cm baking tin (Swiss roll tin)
1½ qt baking dish	1.5 liter baking dish
2 qt baking dish	2 liter baking dish
2 qt rectangular baking dish	30 × 19 cm baking dish
9" pie plate	22 × 4 or 23 × 4 cm pie plate
7" or 8" springform pan	18 or 20 cm springform or loose-bottom cake tin
9" × 5" loaf pan	23 × 13 cm or 2 lb narrow loaf tin or pâté tin

Temperatures

Fahrenheit	Centigrade	Gas
140°	60°	–
160°	70°	–
180°	80°	–
225°	105°	¼
250°	120°	½
275°	135°	1
300°	150°	2
325°	160°	3
350°	180°	4
375°	190°	5
400°	200°	6
425°	220°	7
450°	230°	8
475°	245°	9
500°	260°	–